The Search for Order

The

H B

HARPER & BROTHERS
PUBLISHERS   NEW YORK

Search for Order

THE DEVELOPMENT OF THE MAJOR IDEAS IN THE
PHYSICAL SCIENCES FROM THE EARLIEST TIMES TO
THE PRESENT

ILLUSTRATED

by CECIL J. SCHNEER

FOREWORD BY HENRY MARGENAU

To my father

Contents

Foreword

EDUCATORS, especially teachers of science, have long clamored for general or integrated science courses, and there has been much experimentation in this field. Their concern arose because of the fragmentation of our cultural scene which the unsophisticated observer takes to be an unavoidable consequence of scientific specialization. Knowledge is bursting at its seams; facts are discovered at an unprecedented rate, and no memory can hold any sizable portion of them. Men in the same area of research find it difficult to converse on a factual level; the organic chemist no longer understands his colleagues in physical chemistry, the experimental physicist is bewildered by the jargon of the theorist, and the mathematician working in function theory has ceased to follow his colleague's discourse on topology. The age of the encompassing genius, of men like Aristotle, St. Thomas, Newton, Kant and Helmholtz, is passed.

Nearly all agree that fragmentation, specialization and consequent provincialism are unfortunate. Since these are consequences of scientific research, the suggestion is sometimes made that scientific researches be curbed or redirected, that greater emphasis be placed on work in the so-called liberal arts. Quite aside from the detriment to technical progress implicit in that suggestion, its lack of wisdom must be apparent to everyone conversant with research in the liberal arts, where specialization and provincialism are as commonplace as they are in the natural sciences. Redistribution of effort is clearly not a remedy, but it might be that the identification of specialism with fragmentation, of technical research with provincialism is wrong. Perhaps if the specialist saw his work in a larger setting, if technical research were viewed against a background of philosophic and historical meanings, the evils of specialization might be less severe.

Experience has shown that few "general education" courses on the college level have been successful. Their purpose was to expose students to a variety of facts from all fields, including the sciences, and thus insure some understanding of certain parts of the present world. As the statistics relating to these endeavors pour in, it is becoming increasingly clear that eclectic knowledge provides no synthesis, that survey courses do not unify but rather accent fragmentation, that mere sampling makes no pattern—in a word, that facts don't integrate.

Amid this anxiety about general education an extremely strange phenomenon occurs at the frontiers of science. Here people are perplexed because the ordinary approaches to the solution of problems seem to fail, and a great search for new fundamental methods goes on. There is the impressive spectacle of nearly every truly distinguished theoretical physicist and many eminent chemists and biologists writing articles on philosophy! Such a development is not accidental, nor can it be explained by the rather common supposition that the honor guard has suddenly gone senile. I like the suggestion made by one of them, to the effect that these men have been philosophers all their lives and that this inclination had something to do with their successes.

But it is hardly fair and certainly idle to say that these men are just philosophers. They are philosophers of a special kind; they are scientists who felt that important problems lay buried deep within the texture of scientific reasoning; they perceive that two kinds of things deserve principled study: first the facts, and then the way in which the facts are understood. The second is not tantamount to a knowledge of formulas and equations; it culminates in philosophic comprehension of the methods which introduce organization and relatedness in the realm of facts.

Interest in basic method is new in the United States. An all-pervading pragmatic spirit has largely kept its scientists busy with immediately profitable tasks. Interest in philosophy and history on the part of scientists has been frowned upon in view of the patent fact that it has kept some of them from doing their best work. Results had to be achieved and the less said about the way in which they were attained the better. Is it not true that a bird can fly without knowing the principles of aerodynamics? If a bumblebee studied the design of aircraft he would never entrust himself to the air, for he would know that his ratio of wing surface to body weight is far too small to make flight possible.

All this is true, and it is good advice for birds and bumblebees. But suppose the art of flying is to be transferred from birds to men. Watching the birds is not sufficient for this task. A conscious effort is required to study the phenomenon of flight and to formulate the laws which regulate it. All this is well known within the physical sciences. But the tremendous task facing the present and coming generations is to understand human behavior in society, and the best promise of success in that undertaking must lie where past endeavors have been most fruitful in yielding understanding, that is to say, within the natural sciences. Now it is clear that the facts and the detailed laws of physics and chemistry cannot be applied directly to the social realm; yet there is a rising hope among thoughtful students that there may be relevance in their basic methodological approach with its peculiar interplay of inductive and deductive procedures, with its equal reliance on historic fact and elegant conjecture. *Social* man must learn of *natural* science. More must be known of these methods than their limited use in the physical sciences demands. And this knowledge must be conveyed to students.

It is commonly supposed that discussion of *method* makes the teaching of science more difficult. I doubt if this is true, but if it is, a compensating emphasis will make it easy. This is the accent on *history* of science, a discipline which adds perspective to the succession of facts as well as methods. History introduces automatically a unifying feature into science, for it exposes the existential bond which holds scientific thought together. Historical incidents furthermore enliven the teaching of science in an anecdotal way, and liveliness is surely needed in our elementary science courses.

When I read the manuscript of Professor Schneer, whom I have never met, I felt it to be a remarkable attempt to utilize such insights as I have vaguely sketched, and I developed a strong desire to see this sort of treatment in the hands of my physics and of my philosophy students. The amount of historical and philosophic information that shines through the treatment of the physical sciences in the pages of this book is amazing, and its style is unusually attractive. For all these reasons, I wish it well.

HENRY MARGENAU
Professor of Physics and Natural Philosophy,
Yale University

Preface

THIS BOOK is the outgrowth of a series of lectures delivered for students of liberal arts at the University of New Hampshire. The objective of the book is to introduce the physical sciences. It is primarily designed as a book about science, rather than, as most scientific books are designed, as a book about the world. The author holds with Einstein who maintained that he never kept in his head such information as could be looked up in tables, and therefore there is a minimum of such material in the text.

While I am most concerned with scientific method, I cannot define it in so many words or even in so many volumes. The scientific method is the method of Pythagoras and Plato, of Copernicus and Kepler, of Planck and Einstein. The scientific method has evidently as much in common with the astrology of Kepler and his mystic preoccupation with the Platonic solids as it does with the mechanism of Helmholtz. To study the scientific method in the abstract and hope in this manner to understand science is like studying a book on how to write a novel in order to understand literature. The arts are grasped through the experiencing. An understanding of science as an exercise of the creative imagination can be grasped in the study of the achievements of science, and these are to be measured as ideas.

Accordingly this volume deals with some few of the major scientific ideas of our world. Some of these were once burning issues. The scientific ideas of the present which will force their way into the history of civilization are the successors to the Copernican doctrine and the theory of evolution. There can be a sense of excitement and compulsion to science. Two centuries ago at the dawning, we could say with Pope:

> Nature and nature's law lay hid in night.
> God said, "Let Newton be," and all was light.

If the confidence of the enlightenment in man's powers and and man's future cannot be restored intact, it is at least my hope that the reasons for that confidence and its substance can be conveyed.

The scientific ideas discussed are presented in historical order for two reasons. First, the earliest ideas tend to be the most direct and therefore the most easily grasped. The later developments of theoretical physics are the furthest from common experience and offer the most difficulty. By employing the bridge of history, a progression in understanding can be achieved from the direct constructions of Aristotle to the abstractions of Einstein. Second, it is the aim of this work to show science as one aspect of our common culture inseparably bound to the intellectual evolution of society. Scientists do not exist in an ivory laboratory. They are participating members of their world, both influencing and being influenced by our common humanity. It is impossible to think of Galileo apart from the Renaissance of Leonardo. It is impossible to conceive of Newton apart from the England of the Restoration, or of Darwinian evolution apart from the nineteenth-century concept of progress.

Although Newton and his contemporaries regarded themselves as philosophers and called their studies natural philosophy, it is common today to describe philosophy and science as antithetical. Too frequently, science is said to be concerned with things and philosophy with ideas. This book does not intend in any sense to present a philosophy of science; but philosophy has been defined as thought about thought, and this book is concerned with thought about science. I hope to demonstrate that science itself is at least as theoretical as it is practical, and thought about science must inevitably run the risk of the label of philosophy. I am here in good company. Since the advent of modern science an increasing self-consciousness has prompted scientists from Duhem to Schrödinger to an examination of the logical foundations of their work.

This volume attempts to treat the science of mathematics and its interrelationships with the physical sciences as an indispensable ingredient for the understanding of the development of science. The physical sciences should not be treated as operating upon a static scientific universe. The development of geological science, as a *historical* science within the larger framework of the growth of natural philosophy, has a special importance that can be compared only with the development of astronomy as a descriptive science. In this book, there is no attempt to survey the sciences or to include even passing references either to all the fields of science or to all the topics of any one science. I have treated here those major examples of scientific ideas which in my opinion have had the greatest influence on the evolution of civilization. Without a preconceived standard of the method of science, I have allowed the method to take form in the examples of these topics: cosmology, mechanism, evolution, field theory, relativity, and quantum mechanics.

If there is any one single concept underlying the whole of this book, it is the theme of the creative imagination. Certain dualisms such as continuity and atomism, determinism and chance, and order and disorder, have influenced science throughout its history, and these have proved convenient touchstones for the elucidation of theory.

In preparing this material, I have constantly had in mind an explanation of science that would lead to an understanding of the role of science in our lives. I do not mean by that, an understanding or appreciation of the wonders of science, the toothpaste, the plastic, the television, the miracle drugs. The intelligent student can take little more interest in these than in a telephone book or a table of logarithms. The role that science plays in our lives is more significant than hydrogen bombs and synthetic rubber. Science consistently influences our lives and our culture by providing the framework of ideas and beliefs within which man's concept of his world, of his fellows, and of his self, must take shape. It is on this interaction of science and civilization that this material is focused.

I record with pleasure my gratitude to Henry Guerlac, who introduced me to the school of modern historians of science; to the scholars and scientists whose labors I have tried to describe and whose results I have presented below; to Harry Woolf; and to Henry Margenau, who most kindly consented to introduce this volume. Isobel Korbel supplied the professional leaven which elevated an idea into a book. The bibliography only inadequately reflects the many sources of ideas on which I have drawn. The books by Holton and Roller and also by C. S. Mason have been invaluable. To Edward Blewett and my many colleagues who have encouraged me; to my students whose spirits and intelligence have contributed so much; to my wife Mary Schneer for patient and useful criticism, my warmest thanks.

July, 1959

CECIL J. SCHNEER

1. Science, Magic, and Religion; Science as Control over Man's Environment

AND THE ENDS OF ALL THESE INQUIRIES THEY
INTEND TO BE THE PLEASURE OF CONTEMPLA-
TIVE MINDS BUT ABOVE ALL, THE EASE AND
DISPATCH OF THE LABOURS OF MENS HANDS.

ROBERT HOOKE, 1665

THE PRIMARY importance of science and the characteristic that distinguishes it from other philosophies and arts is its usefulness. Except for this, science would be an elaborate game, replete with formalist rules and constructions. The most remarkable thing about science is the extent to which nature and the world appear to adhere to the rules and constructions of science.

In many cases this is not accidental, since the rules were devised by observing the behavior of nature. But in those cases in which the rules of scientific formalism predict that certain behavior should occur in the natural world, as for example in the prediction of an eclipse from a knowledge of the motions of the earth, moon, and sun, we can only conclude that the universe displays a faithful adherence to the game. A game of this magnitude is no longer a game. Science involves the fundamental beliefs of man, and his attitudes toward his existence. Magic and religion in turn treat of man's life and faith. The history of mankind has been a history of continual preoccupation with magic, religion, and science. Of these, for the control of the natural world, man presently emphasizes science.

Whenever we set out to define or explain just what it is we mean by science we run into the difficulty of making our definition too narrow to include the really great imaginative leaps that have produced the important advances in science, or too broad to exclude human activities that we prefer to classify as art or philosophy. Dictionary and encyclopedia definitions of science fall into the first pitfall and describe science as an organized body of knowledge, or a collection of orderly facts. In this view, scientists are simply nature's bookkeepers and experimenters are like cryptanalysts, busily deciphering a message encoded in the complexity of the natural world. The facts, and their tidiest arrangement, all exist as the complete sum of science and as soon as we have traced their main outlines our task will be essentially complete and this branch, at any rate, of human wisdom will have come to an end. This is a neat if somewhat dull program, and if it fails to excite our admiration or interest we should scarcely be surprised. It leaves unexplained the almost hypnotic fascination that science has exerted throughout time. It leaves unexplained the violent

Fig. 1. *Praying Boy*, 400 B.C.
Symmetry in early Greece.

reactions against scientific advance, such as the condemnation
of Galileo or the Scopes trial, except by the very narrowest of
black and white views of good and evil. If this were all there
was to science, how would we account for the adulation that
has been bestowed upon the scientific thinkers of the past:

Pythagoras, Newton, Einstein? Edmund Halley wrote an ode to Newton, in which he compared the sober Cambridge don to Prometheus and to Moses. Marcellus, the Roman general who captured Syracuse, is said to have considered that the greatest prize within the city was Archimedes, the mathematician.

The assertions of the earth's motion, of the evolution of species, of the relativity of our measurements, and of the formula for the area of a circle have had great significance for mankind and have excited our deepest hopes and fears. These "facts," then, and their orderly classification are part of the fabric of our culture. They relate intimately to our most cherished beliefs. In some fashion which is not obvious, the idea of numbers that cannot be expressed as a whole ratio between two other numbers or the idea of a gravitational force between any two bodies is more potent than, let us say, the fact that the capital of Maine is Augusta, or that the Mexican volcano is spelled Popocatepetl.

MAGIC

The late Sir James Frazer in his work *The Golden Bough* expressed a more meaningful view of science by comparing it with religion and magic. It is possible to pick holes in Frazer's scheme without too much strain, but we are not attempting a rigorous philosophical discussion and Frazer's ideas are an excellent basis on which to begin the primary task, which is an explanation of science. Frazer asserts that science and magic are both attempts at the control of nature; at forcing nature to bend to man's will. Religion on the other hand is a submission to a higher power, the acknowledgment of the existence of a superior will, and the attempts to placate it. In this view, to put lightning rods on a church steeple is blasphemous impiety, and it is interesting to recall that Benjamin Franklin was attacked as an atheist for his invention of the lightning rod.

Frazer describes magic as a system of natural law, consistent in its beliefs and principles, erroneous perhaps, but nevertheless an orderly and systematic attempt to exert control over nature. The laws of magic are chiefly the law of similarity from which stems the system of homeopathic magic, and the law of contact, from which stems the system of contagious magic. For example, thunder commonly accompanies rain and this had led primitive peoples to practice making sounds *similar* to thunder in the hope of inducing rain. A. J. Liebling wrote of a Colonel John Stingo, a rainmaker employed at Belmont Park to work this bit of homeopathic magic in reverse to insure clear weather for the day's racing. Stingo shot off guns every Saturday morning to prevent rain from falling during the afternoon. At the last meet of the season, the grand finale, something went wrong and it started to rain in the midst of the bombardment. By post time, the track was under a foot of water and the Colonel had taken to the hills. In our own time, professional rainmakers have been dropping certain salts of silver on clouds to induce them to precipitate. This is partly based on the *similarity* between the atomic structures of the salts and ice, and partly on other, more logical chains of reasoning. Is this homeopathic magic or science?

The famous cave paintings of the Dordogne in France are probably another example of homeopathic magic. The pictures of the animals drawn on the cave walls were *similar* to the real animals over which power was sought. The degree of control over the real animal depended in part on the degree of similarity, and the primitive artists took great pains with line and coloring matter to obtain verisimilitude. It should be pointed out that the pictures themselves were directly under the control of the magician and he could make the animals large and juicy if they were for meat, or meek and cowardly, if they were a threatening species like the cave bear. He could wound the animal in the picture, or snare it, or blind it. To anticipate later scientific developments, the modern theoretical physicist casts his ideas in the form of mathematical equations, which he can manipulate in various ways with the ultimate object of controlling the portion of the natural world which his equations reflect.

An example of the second law of magic, the law of contact, is the use of voodoo dolls. An anthropologist in Peru who had angered a villager discovered a frog under his bed. The frog had been stuck with pins by the angered witch who was employing homeopathic magic, expecting that the similarity between the frog and the human being would ensure the anthropologist's meeting the same fate as the hapless amphibian. To make sure that the one particular human being would meet the desired end, the frog was crudely dressed in the anthropologist's sock, stolen from the line a few days before. In some primitive communities, people are very careful to dispose of nail parings and hair clippings to keep them out of the hands of enemies who might employ them for contagious magic. Part of our own attitudes toward disease is based on a similar fear of contagion. This particular anthropologist suffered a severe attack of jaundice shortly after his discovery of the frog, which prejudiced his standing in the community to a considerable degree.

Dowsing or water witching is still practiced in New England and one dowser is even able to detect water underground by employing his wand over a map of the terrain. The similarity of the map to the terrain represented is sufficient to ensure success. Some dowsers employ the branches of shrubs that grow in wet ground, thus making use of the principle of contagion.

In modern times, we are frequently exposed to a technical variety of magic, and to the two principles of Frazer we can add a third, the principle of pseudo-science: using the materials or equipment of science and technology. One example of this would be the use of mathematical statistics to prove the validity of things like extrasensory perception. A certain astrologer was born in the southern hemisphere, for which no horoscopes are available. The predictions of astrology are based upon the positions of various heavenly bodies relative to the horizon at the time of birth. Since astrology developed in the northern hemisphere, the configurations of the skies for various occasions in the southern hemisphere were neglected. This particular astrologer studied navigation and trigonometry in order to calculate the neglected positions. Because navigation and trigonometry are scientific and exact, this astrologer believes that the same reliability attaches to the astrological assertions about character and the future based on the positions so exactly calculated. Devices employing radio tubes, ultraviolet light, etc., have been used in the past as magical cure-alls.

In all these instances we see examples of the misapplication of the association of ideas. Because things are similar in some respects, we associate similar effects with similar causes. Because things are or were in contact we imagine that control over the one ensures control over the other. The logic is consistent, and against logic we have only the defense of experience. Burning my hair clippings fails to warm me. Because radio tubes, statistics, maps, and trigonometry are part of the successful control of nature and the prediction of the future in many instances does not mean that in every employment of these and similar devices the same successful control can be achieved. In medieval times, devils might be exorcised from the sick by ordering them in good Latin to depart. In modern times we have a tendency to employ sodium-acetyl salicylate or chlorophyll in much the same manner. We replace one charm by another.

We tread here on the borderline between science and magic and it is often difficult to be sure which is which. Broadly speaking, certain characteristics of magic are profoundly antipathetic to science. The first of these is the use of labels or words or charms as if the names of things were the things themselves. The philosophers call this the fallacy of misplaced concreteness. One example would be the case of the patient who is cured as soon as the doctor can diagnose his illness. The second of these is the production of effects out of all proportion to the causes. Some people believe that they can cause dice to turn up on a given side by simply willing it (psychokinesis). The production of effects at great distances through all intervening media and instantaneously falls under this category. Ghosts, for example, pass freely through walls, or company appears after a knife is dropped. A third characteristic of magic is its dependence on the special abilities of a gifted individual, a medium, or one who is psychic. By contrast, a scientific result is one which can be obtained independently by a reasonable investigator duplicating the conditions under which the original result was obtained. In some tests of extrasensory perception, remarkable success at predicting the fall of cards was claimed for certain individuals at certain times.

The three characteristics are not entirely hard and fast. The manipulation of symbols in the form of mathematical equations, while producing no direct effects in the physical world, is still the chief modern tool of theoretical science, and the predictions made by such symbolic methods can often have far-reaching applications. The force of gravity, as Newton originally described it, appeared to act instantaneously at all distances. Newton indeed was attacked for this as having introduced occult ideas into scientific matters. Far from denying the charge, Newton attempted to mitigate the offense by saying that he had not offered any theory of the nature of gravitation, but simply a mathematical scheme describing the planetary motions *as if there were a force between bodies* obeying certain rules. For the third characteristic, it is still true that individuals differ greatly in their abilities. If one man can wiggle his ears and an experimenter cannot, that hardly proves that human ears cannot be wiggled. And some scientific phenomena may be unique and therefore incapable of duplication. A volcanic eruption or an astronomical event might be witnessed by an individual gifted to the extent of being within sight, or at a telescope. The information might be nonetheless of great importance for science.

Somehow, we must be selective. The credulity of past generations with their unicorns, their salamanders passing unharmed through fire, their phoenix rising anew from its funeral pyre, and their less innocent notions such as witchcraft and trial by ordeal, is an offense to the dignity of man. A healthy skepticism goes side by side with an open mind, as a protection from clutter. For the scientist some skepticism is essential, for out of the overwhelming variety of experience he must select only those aspects which can be brought into a meaningful pattern to him and to his work. The completely open mind, the totally unprejudiced mind would have to be a completely empty mind.

RELIGION

Going beyond Frazer's definition of religion as submission to higher powers, it is possible to consider religion as purpose and intent. It is possible to consider religion apart from the dicta of any one creed; not Christianity, not Buddhism, not Mohammedanism, but the impulse from which each of these has developed. Religion in this sense is not a particular body of practices or ritual. Religion in this sense does not rest on one or another scheme of natural history to be overthrown in time by some new Copernicus. Science can deal with what *is*, religion is concerned with what *should* be. If we must rely upon science and not upon scripture for our understanding of the natural world, it is nonetheless true that the impulse driving us toward understanding, the craving for truth and right, is beyond the reach of science. The ends we have in mind, our aims and purposes, these are the province of religion.

SCIENCE VS. RELIGION

This perennial debate never fails to arouse considerable interest. In recent times, it has become increasingly clear that while our civilization has become technically proficient and advanced, our moral and psychic development have not necessarily kept pace. In the eighteenth century it was assumed that man's ills were caused by his material poverty and that with the attainment of decent food, clothing, and housing, cruelty and conflict would largely disappear. But today we acknowledge that the greatest achievements of science and technology may very well be employed for socially undesirable ends. The modern high-powered automobile may kill and maim our citizens by the tens of thousands annually. Television may be used for trivial or even stupid communications. The dreadful devices of modern warfare hang as a continual threat over our citizens. Electricity has brought us not only the dishwasher but the electric chair. The barbed wire that extended our food supply by providing efficient fencing for animals has also been used for the fencing of human beings.

Even more alarming than the antisocial uses to which much of our technology has been put is the threat of what may happen if our social studies are similarly misused. It is not pleasant to realize that the techniques of disease control and eradication can be turned in biological warfare to a most insidious and horrible destruction. It is still more terrifying to realize that the psychiatric methods which are evolving to treat the insane and the mentally disturbed may enable corrupt rulers to manipulate whole nations and to pollute the wellsprings of our society. We are in the position of that long-dead caveman who fashioned the first ax with which to cut trees and hunt, and found his neighbor raising it against himself. Even less directly, our technology has had undesirable side effects. Increased farm production has in part depleted soils, caused erosion, and by its very success depressed farm prices. One man with a tractor or a power saw can often destroy the fertility or forest cover of a large region, permanently depriving himself and all those who come after him of the use of that land. In the cities, technological unemployment, the loss of jobs of men to new machines, has time and again brought distress to numbers of workmen. Overproduction, by glutting the channels of trade, has threatened our economy periodically. Of all these effects we are cognizant. Science, our control over our environment, has made tremendous progress. How we use this control, whether for good or evil, is something else again.

A generation ago we were still optimistic. We believed that the progress of science would be accompanied automatically by the moral progress necessary to control not only our world but ourselves. Now that this is no longer self-evident, there is danger that in our reaction we may blame science for our ills. The late George Sarton warned that science without humanism would bring us to the brink. But equally, humanism without science is intellectual pap. The remedy does not lie in attacking science but rather in understanding science as a part of our civilization. Our lives today are too complex for us to turn back the course of civilization. There are 167 million people in the continental

United States, which in a state of nature supported less than one twentieth of this number. We must keep our science or commit mass suicide. We must control ourselves and the uses to which we put our now enormous powers. We cannot ascribe our moral failures to our scientific successes. Nothing is to be gained by going back down on all fours.

The realm then of morals, of values, of ethics—of all that can be considered under the heading of purpose—is out of the reach of science, although science is not out of its reach. There is an impulse that drives men to discovery. Religion is the traditional guardian of purpose. The impulse toward truth is not scientific but it is nonetheless real. Whitehead defines a religious education as one that inculcates a sense of duty. Where attainable knowledge can conceivably change the course of events, the attainment of that knowledge is duty.

2. Order and Regularity in the Natural World

WHERE WAST THOU WHEN I LAID THE FOUN-
DATIONS OF THE EARTH?
DECLARE, IF THOU HAST UNDERSTANDING.
WHO DETERMINED THE MEASURES THEREOF,
IF THOU KNOWEST,
OR WHO STRETCHED THE LINE UPON IT?
WHEREUPON WERE THE FOUNDATIONS
THEREOF FASTENED?
OR WHO LAID THE CORNER STONE THEREOF;
WHEN THE MORNING STARS SANG TOGETHER,
AND ALL THE SONS OF GOD SHOUTED FOR JOY?

JOB

SCIENCE BEGINS with the concepts of order and regularity and the belief that the universe is not arbitrary but governed.

13

This is the concept of natural law. There is a series of orderly events that impress themselves upon the minds of primitive men. The greatest of these is the recurrent seasons. Whether we live or die, there is an annual return in due time of all things, the hum of the locust in summer, the snows of the winter, the waning of the streams in summer, the quickening of green things in the spring. More sophisticated peoples are able to relate these things to the pattern of the skies. The sky above us forms a great sphere and the stars in the sphere form a fixed pattern swirling around the polestar once each night and, more slowly, once each year. Monthly the moon appears as a sliver waxing to a full orb and then waning to disappear again. With the first snows the constellation Orion, the hunter, is in the ascendant. In the summer's heat when the cicada sings, Sirius the Dog Star rises. It rose in the time of the Egyptians, it rises today, and it will rise forever and ever.*

There is a cyclical regularity to life as well: the miracle of the seed turning into the plant and from the plant the seed; of birth and death. Even the simplest organisms display a fine feeling for order. The bee constructs his cells in perfect hexagonal prisms. The problem of constructing the most storage space with the least wax is not beyond its mathematical powers. The chambered nautilus constructs a perfect logarithmic spiral for its shell, and the lowly starfish a pentagon.

Nonliving things, too, display a fine sense of geometry. Recall the marvelous symmetry of the snowflake or the cold precision of the crystal. These observations of natural history were familiar parts of their lives to our ancestors. They were as much a part of the environment of the Indians who inhabited Pre-Colombian America as electricity and automobiles are a part of

---

* Purists may note that subtle shifts in the fixity of this pattern are a part of modern astronomical thinking.

Fig. 2. *Spiral nebula* (Mt. Wilson and Palomar Observatories) / *Chambered Nautilus* (R. Hooke, 1665)

Fig. 3. *Order in inorganic nature: the snowflake.*

our own lives. They had a faith in the orderliness and reproducibility of nature. The wheels would turn and the cycles would sweep away all things, only to bring them back again.

But side by side with this faith in the orderliness of events was an equal faith in the underlying chaos, the disorderliness of nature. The Greeks expressed this dual attitude in their concept of the Fates. What would happen was already determined. The pattern of events was fixed in a tangled web of cloth woven by three blind crones, and not even the gods could change the pattern by the slightest thread. The three blind hags, deciding irrevocably the fate of all things, were the Greek symbol for the arbitrariness, the meaninglessness, the apparent senselessness of events. The weather, lightning, the wind appeared to primitive man as expressions of the essentially chaotic nature of experience. The sun rises in the east and sets in the west, but the wind bloweth where it listeth.

It should be noted that this feeling for chance, for the random event, is an idea completely foreign to the Hebrew mind. Against the background of the Old Testament it appears as lurid blasphemy. For the trials of Job, like the plagues of Egypt, are a part of the cosmic order as much as the sun and the rains of spring. As for the Greeks, the concept of fate became inextricably bound with the concept of order. The shape of the future was inexorable, but it was a pattern.

Disease strikes mysteriously and suddenly. Even in our civilized society, we have no firm means of predicting the blows of sickness and infirmity. One in ten of us will die of cancer according to the statistics, but which one? The paths taken by streams in flat country twist and turn like the branches of a tree. Death must come to all living things but the how and the when are essentially random. The distribution of the dark grains among the light in a sand, the rough bark of a tree, the clustering of stars in the sky, the drift of fallen leaves are all essentially random. The world of nature and events, the world of experience, appears in many aspects to be formless and aimless, to be chaos. Against this chaos man strives for meaning, for order and regularity. We of the twentieth century have faith in natural law. We accept science and technology to an unprecedented degree. We may be skeptical of the effects of a Hopi Indian rain dance, but when we get into our cars we expect them to run. When we arrive at a station, we expect a train to appear. When we turn the tap, we expect water to flow. If we are disappointed, we look for natural causes of the failure; we send for a mechanic or a plumber. A research scientist confronted with a problem embarks on a program of investigation, confident that a solution can be found. We may doubt the wisdom of solving the problem or fear that the solu-

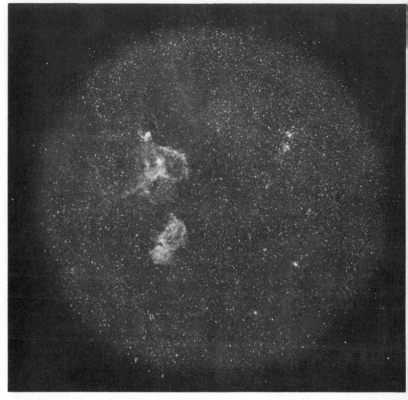

Fig. 4. *The face of chaos: a double cluster of stars in Perseus.* (Yerkes Observatory)

tion may prove dangerous if it is a question of a new kind of bomb, but it never occurs to us to doubt that a solution can ultimately be found: that an orderly explanation will sooner or later be forthcoming.

If we have this faith in a natural law, it is because of our environment and cultural background. Men have not always believed so. Other cultures, other peoples, even today have no such confidence. The development of science has largely taken place in the last three hundred years but civilization itself is at least five thousand years old. Science has developed in the West but the most ancient cultures are those of the East. Eastern peoples are as intelligent as Western. The Chinese, the Indians display today a capacity to learn science and to advance it. In ancient times Eastern peoples were among the most inventive. To China we owe the invention of gunpowder, of printing, of paper, of the magnetic compass. What are the factors that differentiated the West from the East so that it was in the West that science began and that the technological explosion that made the modern world occurred? Alfred North Whitehead in his book *Science and the Modern World* attributes the success of the West to two factors common to our Western heritage but absent in the East. The first was the great religious development that began with Judaic monotheism and led to modern Christianity and Mohammedanism. The belief in a supreme Deity, in one God, the Creator, is a belief that the universe exemplifies purpose and not aimlessness. Natural law governs the world of events because the world of events is the creation of a supreme power. Order, regularity, law, and purpose are attributes of a single Deity. Westerners could search for an explanation of events because their religious heritage had predisposed them to expect that explanations exist.

Our Western culture has its roots not only in the Hebraic vision of a unified world but also in the great Greek civilization that flourished in the Mediterranean region from about 600 B.C. to nearly A.D. 400. Of all the gifts of that civilization, the one that is most pertinent is the Greek emphasis on rationality. Reason, the ordering of our thought processes, the development of logic and philosophy we owe to the Greeks. It is now generally recognized that these two influences were fused in the Western world in the Middle Ages by the theologians who went under the name of scholastics. Of these the best known is St. Thomas Aquinas (1225–1274), who introduced the systematic accumulations of knowledge of the Greeks, chiefly Aristotle, to Christian theology, applying the logical and philosophical techniques of Greek rationality to his faith. Medieval Western culture was common to the Moslem Arabs and to the Jews who had succeeded to the ruins of classical civilization. A similar synthesis of Judaic monotheism and Greek rationality was accomplished for Mohammedanism by a series of scholars, of whom the Spaniard Averroës (1126–1198) was perhaps the most influential. As recently as 1950, a traveler returned from Arabic Egypt reported that the works of Aristotle in ancient Arabic translation still formed a major portion of study at Egyptian schools. The Hebrew physician to the Spanish (Arab) court, Maimonides (1135–1204), laid the foundations of Jewish medieval thought as part of the same process.

While the end product of the work of these and many other scholars was medieval theology, it must be remembered that theology formed the whole of learning in this period, and it was out of this background and on these foundations that science appeared in the time of the Renaissance. During the Middle Ages, the Greek pagan philosophy of Aristotle was Christianized and Aristotelian philosophy was employed to give a systematic structure, logic, order, and rules to the Western religious tradition. It is this aspect of the Western background that provided the impulse to a search for rule and logic and perfection in a world envisioned as the handiwork of a single, perfect Deity.

3. Greek Rationalism and Plato's Problem

YOU HAVE SHOWN ME A STRANGE IMAGE AND
THEY ARE STRANGE PRISONERS.

   LIKE OURSELVES, I REPLIED; AND THEY SEE
ONLY THEIR OWN SHADOWS, OR THE SHAD-
OWS OF ONE ANOTHER, WHICH THE FIRE
THROWS ON THE OPPOSITE WALL OF THE
CAVE.

PLATO, *The Republic*, VII, 514

ANCIENT NUMBER MYSTICISM

VERY FEW avenues of approach to the world and to thought
were not explored by the classical Greeks. In particular, the
concepts of order and regularity, of harmony and perfection

21

were of extreme importance to the ancients. The quasi-legendary Pythagoras of Croton (582 B.C.–500 B.C.) identified perfection with number and form. Even at this early date civilization was thousands of years old, and Pythagoras inherited a world and a culture of considerable sophistication. The origin of the concept of numbers was as little known to Pythagoras as it is to us. Somewhere in prehistory, probably over a great period of time, man had gradually come to the idea of numbers, 1, 2, 3, etc. Numbers are a pure idea. Three apples, or three fish, or three of anything are real and conjure up images in our mind, sense impressions of one sort or another. The first four notes of Beethoven's 5th Symphony, which were used as a symbol of allied victory in World War II, are not perceived as a visual image, but are nonetheless real in our minds. In contrast to four notes, or three apples, or n of any sort of things, are the numbers themselves, 3, 4, . . . n. They remain pure abstractions. We may conceive of a square *field*, or a circular *hoop*, or a triangle drawn on paper, but the circle itself or the other forms are not limited to a hoop or a field or to any *thing*. They are a quality, in short, an idea. A real hoop or a field may be imperfect, but the concept of the circle is perfect, sharing none of the gross attributes of the real. The concept exists in our minds independently of sense impressions. Because numbers and forms appeared to the Greeks as the only ideal and perfect things in a naughty world, they became the focus for a religious mystique. Legend has it that Pythagoras was the founder and leader of a secret society, a religious fraternity, dedicated to the study of the number-universe. To the Pythagoreans numbers and forms were real. Things were only crude approximations of these pure ideas. It was as natural for them to turn their backs on society and the everyday world and to devote themselves to the study of numbers as it was for the theologians of the Middle Ages to immure themselves in the study of scripture and the writings of the Fathers. The motive in both cases was religious.

The Pythagorean studies, though motivated by impulses not subject to the scrutiny of logic, resulted in the founding of mathematics as a branch of learning. The word mathematics originally meant learning, but the Pythagoreans applied it to the study of number, which was for them the only true learning (since number included things which we would divide today among aesthetics, philosophy, science, ethics, law, and religion). To the Pythagoreans, numbers had form. The numbers 1, 1+2, 1+2+3, 1+2+3+4, . . . they visualized as triangles. It was of great significance to them that the sum of any two consecutive triangular numbers was a perfect square. A square partook more of the essence of divine perfection than a triangle. For them, the circle was the most perfect of all plane figures. The sphere was the most perfect of all possible figures. A square was more perfect than a rectangle because it was more orderly, more regular. A rectangle having all its angles equal was more perfect than a parallelogram with only pairs of angles equal. But a circle or sphere, freed of any angles whatsoever, with every point in mystic balance at the same distance from the center as every other point, was perfection itself. The number 10 was the perfect number. The number seven was of special significance. The number thirteen struck the Pythagoreans, as indeed it appears to us, as an ugly number, formless, indivisible, lacking symmetry and proportion. No wonder skyscrapers in Manhattan have been built without thirteenth floors, and apartment houses seldom have an apartment thirteen for rent.

The Pythagorean contributions to mathematics, fundamental as they were, are subordinate to their way of looking at number and the world. Because of the orderliness of number and form, because of the perfection of the numbers, 1, 2, 3,

. . . marching on in regular sequence toward the infinite, each greater than the one before it by 1, each less than the one succeeding it by 1, the Pythagoreans came to identify the whole world with number. For them, numbers were divine, and the ultimate reality. All the world that we consider as real and material the Pythagoreans regarded as an unreal mask or camouflage beneath which was the true reality of the idea: number. The order and regularity that they saw in the natural world served to confirm them in their ideas. The sky was a great sphere. The motions of the stars were circular. The sun and moon were perfect spheres. The world was number and number was the world.

A most curious by-product of this mystique, and one not immediately obvious to a modern, is the idea of atomism. Because the numbers could be visualized as an endless chain of grains of sand, or as forms made up of uniform particles—three to a triangle, four to a square, etc.—the world of number was seen as a world of separate tiny entities: atoms. If you divided up anything, a piece of wood, a bit of fire, a thought, a cry, some ancients thought that in the process of division one must come ultimately to a countable limiting set of particles— the number stuff of which the universe was fashioned. It was, therefore, a considerable shock to the Pythagoreans to discover another set of numbers not to be expressed by any combination of the ordinary numbers. These *irrational* numbers, as they called them in dismay, lie in and among the numbers of the regular series with no regard for orderly arrangement, or form, or decency. And they struck a fundamental blow at the mystic concept of a number-universe. Their discovery came about with the proof of the famous Pythagorean theorem, that is, that the square of the hypotenuse of a right triangle is equal to the sum of the squares of the legs. If a square figure is constructed with side length 1, then the diagonal of the square is the hypotenuse of a right triangle and, by the theorem above, its length must be the square root of 2. Imagine such a square consisting of Greek atoms (round). The diagonal cannot be measured in whole numbers of these atoms. It is longer than one atom and shorter than two. A bit of reflection will show that it is impossible to choose atoms of any size so that both the diagonal and the sides can be expressed as whole numbers of these atoms. The mathematician says that the diagonal and the sides of a square are incommensurable. We express the length of the diagonal today as a decimal, 1.414 . . . , by which we mean that it is greater than 1.4140 and smaller than 1.4150. By considering the diagram with still smaller atoms, it is clear that no matter to how many decimal places we go, the length of the diagonal of the square can never be expressed exactly in terms of the ordinary numbers. It is nevertheless a number, an idea, and if it cannot be expressed by any ratio of the other numbers, we nevertheless represent it exactly by the symbol $\sqrt{2}$. It is an irrational number. The ratio of the circumference of a circle to its diameter is also an irrational number. It is represented by the symbol π. The base of the system of natural logarithms is irrational. It is given the symbol e, with a value in terms of the rational numbers of 2.718. . . . The value of π is 3.141. . . . All multiples of irrational numbers are irrational, as are all fractions of irrational numbers. No such happy relationships exist between e and π and the others as are displayed by the rational numbers. One is not the sum of others and π can be expressed no better with a combination of other irrational numbers than it can with the rational numbers. Like the ordinary numbers, the irrational numbers stretch out to infinity, but while the ordinary numbers can at least be counted in their ranks as they progress, the irrational numbers stretch to an uncountable infinity. Between any two rational numbers there exists an uncountable infinity of irrational numbers. As the Pythagoreans saw their world of order and perfection so rudely shattered by the intrusion of the unregenerate, they chose a dangerous path, that of secrecy. They felt that they themselves could be entrusted with the dreadful knowledge that the answers to the problems of existence and purpose and meaning were not quite complete, but it was better for the common people to think that all was well. They failed in their attempt to keep a scientific secret because it is in the nature of this kind of information that it is discoverable. If one man within the sect could see the significance of a figure like π for their beliefs, other men outside the chosen circle would see it too. The Pythagoreans pursued and murdered the apostate brother who gave their secret away, but just as later men would have to learn to live with the devil, the Pythagoreans kept on with their studies into which the rude and vulgar irrational numbers continued to erupt.

CONTINUITY AND DISCONTINUITY

A sixth-century B.C. skeptic and scoffer, Zeno, who was executed by the state for subversion, pointed out by means of a series of clever paradoxes the simplicity of Pythagorean thinking. Was the world, as Pythagoras asserted, really number, discrete, consisting of separate individual units? Then consider the paradox of the arrow. At any instant of time an arrow must either be in motion or at rest. If the instant is a true point of time having no duration and indivisible, then an arrow could never be in motion. For the arrow to move, the instant would have to be divided (for example into a beginning half and an ending half), which contradicts the original assumption of indivisibility. If the arrow cannot move in any one instant, then it cannot move in time, since time, in a discrete Pythagorean world, would consist of separate instants.

Or is the world then a continuum? Is it made of large-sized continuous bodies which can be cut and divided into smaller bits, as a droplet of water can be shaken from a glass, and the point of a pin can be wet by the droplet? Then consider Zeno's paradox, the Achilles. Let Achilles, the swiftest runner of Greece, be matched against a tortoise with the tortoise given a head start. Then Achilles can never overtake the tortoise no matter how fast he runs, because in the brief time that Achilles requires to overcome the lead of his sluggish adversary, that reptile will nevertheless move some distance forward, so that he will still lead Achilles. However slight the lead, it must still take Achilles some time to overcome it, and this time will permit the tortoise to gain a new lead. Achilles can never overtake the tortoise, confined as he is to a continuous world, capable of indefinite subdivision. In this kind of world, an arrow can never reach its target (the paradox of the dichotomy), for in order to reach its target it must first cover half the distance to the target, and before it can cover the remaining distance, it must first cover half the remaining distance. Since these distances no matter how small can always be halved, there is no end to the process of halving and the arrow can never complete its course.

The Achilles and the dichotomy are paradoxes of a continuously divisible world. The arrow and a fourth paradox, called the Stadium, are the paradoxes of a discrete atomistic world. Actually they tell us nothing whatsoever about our world. They point up instead the inadequacy of Greek mathematics to deal with the world. Pythagoras and Plato believed that numbers were real and absolute, and not creations of the human mind. They believed that one and one must equal two as an absolute truth. But it will make much more sense to conceive of one and one equals two as one of the rules in a human mental process. Zeno had shown that this rational process failed to describe the world of experience in which Achilles does catch the tortoise and in which arrows are in motion. Something more than reasoning will be required to solve the problems of motion. A more complex mathematics than Greek arithmetic will be devised to resolve Zeno's paradoxes. The Greeks were concerned with determining whether the world was a continuity or a discontinuity like the number series. From our point of view, these are mathematical ideas. Continuity and discontinuity are tools for our understanding; the world cannot be one or the other any more than a block of wood can be the saw which operates upon it.

Two principal ideas appear in the very first attempts of man to deal with his world. The first is the idea of order and regularity in contrast to the idea of chaos and chance. Is there a purpose, is there a plan, is there a natural law to the world of events, or is existence haphazard and nature itself a random process? The second is the notion of atomism. Is the world of events made up of small discrete bits or particles, or is it continuous so that one proceeds from *A* to *B* smoothly and not by a series of minuscule jumps? The Pythagoreans made early attempts to place the world of events in a one-to-one correspondence with the world of ideas. The number series led them to preliminary notions of atomism. Their drive toward geometric form led them to important astronomical ideas. Their concentration on orderliness and number led them to the founding of mathematics. Other people before the Greeks had understood arithmetic and surveying. It is obvious that for the Egyptians to build the pyramids required a knowledge of important geometric formulas and surveying methods such as the calculation of areas and volumes of geometric bodies. The Babylonians had divided the circle into 360 degrees and developed a sophisticated solar calendar. But it was apparently the Greeks who first conceived of the study of mathematics for its own sake. The Egyptians discovered formulas for the calculation of volumes. The Greeks proved these formulas and introduced the concept of generality, of an abstract method not restricted to one or another particular case, but to all cases. It was not the discovery of the Pythagorean theorem that was the great advance; it was rather the proof of the theorem that was to mark the beginning of the science of mathematics.

PLATO'S PROBLEM

The philosopher Plato, who systematized the Pythagorean mystique into the formal philosophy of idealism, is responsible for one of the earliest expressions of the scientific aim. Although at first acquaintance idealism and scientific thought would appear to be completely antithetical, it would be difficult to account for the development of science in the West without an understanding of the Platonic ideal. Like Pythagoras, Plato believed that the world around us, the world of sense impressions, the world we see and hear, and touch, and smell, and taste, is unreal and transitory. Only the idea can be real. To illustrate his thought, Plato wrote the parable of the cave. In this parable, a group of men, slaves perhaps, were chained to the wall of a cave. They had been so chained throughout their lives so that the only world they knew was the world of the cave, mean, dark, and squalid. There was only one opening in the cave high above their heads, through which they could catch a glimpse of light. As people in the outside world or animals or branches passed nearby the opening, their shadows were cast on the walls of the cave for the prisoners to see. That was all they knew of the world: their own degradation and the shadowy patches of light on their walls. Then, the story continues, one prisoner by chance was liberated. He emerged from the cave into a world of sunshine and cloud, of trees and fields and mountains and streams. He reveled in his new-found freedom but the remembrance of his comrades still in darkness haunted him, and after a time during which he lived his new life to the fullest he returned to the cave to bring his wonderful discoveries to his fellows. They heard him out in disbelief, and finally, when he persisted in his tale and his belief that it was that other outside world which was real, and their world, the world about them, was a shadow world, a world of illusion and deception, they wrote him off as blind and returned to their life of chains, threatening to kill anyone who would loose another prisoner. Just so, Plato maintained, is our world. We are prisoners in a cave and our sense impressions are but the shadowy illusions of a reality inconceivably more grand and glorious. It was to the study of this ideal world, the reality behind our illusory sense impressions, that Plato dedicated his famous academy, the greatest institution of learning in the history of the world. The Platonic academy lasted until A.D. 529, nearly a thousand years. Over the entrance to the academy Plato had inscribed these words: "Let none who has not learnt mathematics enter here." It was in this academy that Plato propounded his famous problem to his students, the "saving the appearances."

In order to understand Plato's problem, which was originally intended to apply to the apparent motions of the planets but which has become, in part, a motivating problem for all future science, it is necessary to study the appearances of the sky including the sun, the moon, and the pinpoints of light which we call stars. The configurations and motions of the stars, which are practically unknown to us today, were as familiar to our ancestors as the face of a clock or a calendar is to us. Only a few generations ago, most people lived in a much closer rapport with nature than we do today. Their sense of time, of season, and of direction was keyed to the changing face of the sky. Chaucer's pilgrims used the sky to time their tales. New England farmers used their almanacs to tell the phases of the moon, and old Connecticut clocks recorded these as carefully as the time of day. Today, even sailors and pilots who formerly would have steered their way unerringly to a pinpoint of island in the middle of the Pacific rely on radar and Loran and gyro compasses and electronic logs, so that if they chance to glimpse the sky by accident in passing from one cathode-tubed compartment to another it is to them as to children—a meaningless chaos. This unfamiliarity with our world accounts for phenomena like the flying saucer reports, when even honest and technically trained observers found Martians in Canarsie and Nevada. One fighter pilot was killed giving chase to the planet Venus under the impression that it was a hostile saucer.

What then are the appearances of the heavens? They are as available to us as they were to the ancients and they have not changed perceptibly. The sky at night appears to be a huge sphere located at a great distance from us, broken by pinpoints of light. No matter in what direction we go and no matter for how great a distance, the stars appear no nearer and no further. Effectively, since the stars are so far from us, they all appear to be at the same distance. Their locations, therefore, mark the inner surface of an apparent sphere, the celestial sphere. Groups of the stars form recognizable patterns and these are the constellations. The Big Dipper is an obvious example. These patterns and the spaces between them neither shrink nor expand, so that they form a web of points or a total pattern for the whole celestial sphere, more permanent than the configurations of land and sea and mountains and plains that make up the pattern of the surface of the earth. Just as a location on the earth can be specified by its angular distance north or south of the equator (latitude) and its angular distance west of an imaginary line drawn due north and south through Greenwich (longitude), so locations on the celestial sphere can be specified by a similar pair of angles. The celestial sphere is girdled by an imaginary circle corresponding to the circle on the earth called the equator. The celestial equator is a projection of the earth's equator on the celestial sphere. It can be visualized by imagining the earth's equator expanded in such a way that a plane of lines radiating out from the center of the earth through the earth's equator would pass through the celestial equator. Similarly, the celestial poles are projections of the earth's axis. The polestar is located almost exactly on the celestial pole so that to an observer at the North Pole the polestar would always appear to be directly over head. To an observer on the equator, the polestar appears on the horizon. To an observer midway between the equator and the pole (latitude 45°), the polestar appears halfway up the northern sky, or an angular distance of 45° from the point in the sky directly over the observer's head. This point is called the zenith.

Even a few minutes of observation on a clear night will show that the sky is in motion. The pattern of the fixed stars turns steadily and rapidly about the polestar as a pivot. In the course of an hour the entire sky will have rotated 15° counter-clockwise, which is fifteen minutes of arc in every minute of time. During the day, this rotation of the sky carries the sun from east to west just as the fixed stars are visibly carried during the night. The moon too is carried around. Because the sun and moon in their passage blot out the fixed stars, we see that they are closer to the earth than the sphere of the fixed stars. Because the moon has been observed to cast a shadow on the sun, it is clear that the moon's sphere is between the earth and the sun. Five other heavenly bodies are visible in addition to the sun and moon which by this occultation are seen to be

Fig. 5. The camera with open shutter records the counterclockwise turning of the celestial sphere about the celestial pole. The arcs are the trails of the stars. (Yerkes Observatory)

closer than the sphere of the fixed stars. These are the planets Mercury, Venus, Mars, Jupiter, and Saturn. Two of them, Mercury* and Venus, are rarely seen crossing in front of the sun (a transit) and are therefore sometimes between the earth and the sun. Of the two, Mercury is closer to the center than Venus.

Besides the daily (diurnal) rotation of the sphere of the fixed stars, there is an annual rotation as well. Although the polestar will always appear to be in the same position from any spot at one latitude on the earth, and although the other stars will always maintain the same angular distances from the polestar, the times of rising and setting of the stars are progressively later as the season advances. Because of this, the half of the sky which is visible during the winter night is blotted out by the sun in the summer days and, except for the constellations around the Pole, a different part of the sky is visible during different seasons. At the end of each 365¼ days, the cycle is complete and the timing of the celestial patterns repeats. This does not appear as a movement of the celestial sphere but a movement of the sun across the celestial sphere. The half of the sky occupied by the sun will be the daylight half, and the opposite half will be visible at night. By observing the background pattern of stars over the course of a year, it can be seen that the sun does trace a great circle across the sky. In January, the sun is seen against the background pattern of the constellation Capricorn. In February it has moved into Virgo. In March it is in Pisces. If a careful map of the celestial sphere is constructed and the sun's daily positions are marked on it for a year, the 365 points will lie on a circle that divides the sphere into two halves. This arc is called the ecliptic because it is the line against which eclipses are seen. It crosses

---

* The relative distances of the planets from the center of the universe were known to the ancients from their relative speeds.

the great circle arc of the celestial equator in two places, the vernal and autumnal equinoxes, and therefore twice in the year the sun is directly over the equator. The moon and the five planets also travel approximately along the ecliptic. The word "planet" indeed means wanderer, and the Greeks so named these five stars because they alone out of the thousands of stars visible to the naked eye wandered over the celestial sphere. They appear as exceptionally bright stars when they are in position to be observed, and they differ from the other stars in that they do not twinkle. The early Greeks regarded them as divinities. The more sophisticated Greeks of the Pythagorean and Platonic mystique regarded them less as divinities than as expressions of divine perfection.

But the appearances of the planets were erratic in part. Instead of the smooth regular motion of the celestial sphere itself and the sun on its course, the planetary courses, when plotted on a map of the sphere, move forward for a while, then slow down, come to a halt, and then move backward, then slow to a halt and resume a forward motion. Far from a perfect circle, their paths are erratic looped arcs. These in particular were the appearances which Plato saw as a feeble shadow of a concealed perfect ideality.

It is important to emphasize here that the foregoing brief description of the appearances of the skies is almost entirely devoid of interpretation or theory. This is the description that would be obtained from that ideal observer, an automaton equipped with photo-recording eyes and timers. It is the skies as they appeared to the Greeks who had no telescopes and it is the skies as they appear to us today as we observe them and record them with that most versatile of scientific instruments, the human eye. The technology of modern astronomy, the reflecting telescopes, the cameras, the spectrographs have greatly refined these observations without changing the essential out-

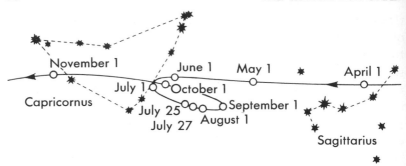

Fig. 6. *The path of Mars: apparent disorderly motion of the planets.* On April 1, Mars was moving east along the ecliptic at a rate which would carry it into the next constellation (Capricornus) in two months. By June 1, the planet was hesitating at the edge of Capricornus and slowing down so noticeably that by July 1 it had come to a standstill. It now began to move again, slowly at first but picking up speed toward the latter part of July, only now it was moving backward, returning to the west toward the constellations through which it had moved early in the spring. On August 1, Mars was again slowing down and by September the planet was at a standstill. As if it had finally made up its mind, it began to move again, this time toward the east with increasing speed, which by November 1 had carried it through Capricornus.

line. The planets still wander erratically along the ecliptic. The constellations sweep nightly about the poles. The sun still traces out its path through the constellations of the zodiac.

Plato's problem was this: to resolve the apparently erratic motions of the planets into that uniform circular motion or combination of circular motions which the Greeks considered as perfect and divine; to reconcile the apparent disorder of the appearances of things to the harmony and simplicity of the ideal. If appearances are chaotic, there is an underlying reality of order and law. The Greek rationality and the Greek aesthetic sense demanded this reconciliation. The Judaeo-Christian faith assures us that it is there to be found. In Whitehead's sense of attainable knowledge, it is our duty to search for solutions to Plato's problem. The original problem, the problem of the motions of the five visible planets, is no longer in the forefront of scientific investigation. Far more complex and absorbing problems present themselves to the science of the twentieth century; the binding forces within the atomic nucleus, the origin of magnetism, the postulates of the theory of relativity and of quantum mechanics. But the fundamental motivation for scientific research is today as it has always been, the seeking out of aesthetically satisfying solutions to Plato's problem, the reduction of the chaos of experience to a meaningful order and harmony. The new military technology, the great advances in nuclear energy, in electronics, in materials, important as they are, remain by-products, secondary and not primary motives. Men pursue this knowledge to lighten the labor of man's hands, but also for its own sake. It may not be generally realized that science cannot be said to have contributed very much to material progress until the nineteenth century. Only a few minor material achievements can even today be attributed to Newton's theory of universal gravitation. Far from the steam engine being the product of the science of thermodynamics, thermodynamics undoubtedly got its start from the study of the steam engine. This is not to suggest that science is not useful, but simply to emphasize that the practical effects of any science cannot be foreseen and that to attribute the pursuit of science to a kind of hard-headed practicality is extremely naïve.

EARLY SOLUTIONS TO PLATO'S PROBLEM

If we study in some detail the earliest Greek attempts at cosmology, our purpose is not purely antiquarian. It is because the traditional cosmology that we have unconsciously absorbed is thrown into sharp relief when studied against the background of the older scheme. If we can demonstrate that the earlier cosmology, far from being a crude expression of primitive naïveté, was actually a subtle and accurately worked out solution to the problem of explaining the astronomical observations of the Greeks, and that the Copernican scheme represents a more advanced solution of the same observations, then we will have made the first step toward acceptance of scientific theories not as absolute truths but for their power in organizing our experience.

The general scheme into which Greek ideas matured in the medieval period was geocentric. Farthest out from the earth was the sphere of the fixed stars. Within it were the successive spheres of the planets, Saturn, Jupiter, Mars, then the sphere of the sun, then Venus, then Mercury, then the moon, and finally the sphere of the earth. Aristotle, the great pupil of Plato, had formalized Greek physics into a scheme which would fit this older cosmology. At the center of the heavy gross earth was the center of the universe. All heavy bodies were imperfect and of the earth. They were drawn to their natural abode. Perfect bodies lacked this grossness and their natural abode was the heavens. So smoke would rise. The planets, including the sun and moon, were perfect and weightless. In Aristotle's physics, force was required to move a body; the heavier the body, the greater the force. Since the planets and the stars moved effortlessly about the earth, they were necessarily weightless. Further, Aristotle taught that for a body to move the force must be applied directly. There could be no force acting at a distance. Since the planets and stars moved continually without being pushed by any visible agent, they were conceived as being embedded in a hard, transparent material like crystal. This too was weightless. Each crystal sphere was rotated in turn by the sphere next beyond it. The outermost sphere of all was turned by the original cause,

called by the Greeks the prime mover,* who became in medieval thought God, operating directly or through an angel. All
this rested on experience and observation. Heavy bodies require a force to maintain them in motion (the effect of a horse
drawing a cart, for example). The earth is solid beneath our
feet, and hardly perfect. Heavy bodies do fall, and light ones
such as smoke rise. The order of the distances from the earth
to the successive heavenly bodies can be observed to be as
Aristotle stated them.

A complication arose, however: the paths of these bodies, except the sun and moon, were not uniform circles with the earth
as center but rather looped arcs. Ptolemy of Alexandria (ca.
A.D. 170) had developed an ingenious and accurate resolution
of these motions into a combination of circular motions. With
the growth of interest in natural philosophy and navigation at
the time of the Renaissance, it was in the highly accurate
Ptolemaic version that the cosmology of the ancients was
adopted. The cruder Aristotelian schemes of the Middle Ages
were dropped.

Ptolemy's scheme was based on three geometric devices employed by earlier Greek scholars. These were the eccentric, the
equant, and the epicycle. In the first device, the planets are
assumed to travel in large circles about a central point located
outside the earth. This point, the eccentric, may in turn travel
in a smaller circle about the earth. As seen from the earth, the
planets then would appear to go now faster, now slower, and
to engage in the apparent disorder of retrograde motion. Yet
by a proper choice of eccentric motion this apparent erraticism
could be resolved into several uniform circular motions (Figure 7).

The device of the epicycle is completely equivalent. Here the

---

* Aristotle himself held that circular motion was "natural" motion, requiring no mover.

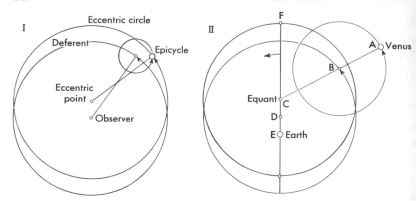

Fig. 7. I. *The equivalence of the eccentric and the epicycle.* The motion of the planet may be considered by the observer as a single circular motion about a point eccentrically displaced from the observer, or else as a slow epicyclic motion about a point moving on a deferent centering on the observer. By having the eccentric in turn rotate about the observer, retrograde loops may also be explained.

II. *The equant* (after Stahlman). Ptolemy accounted for the appearances of Venus by a motion of the planet A about a center B which in turn centered on the point D. D is the center of the deferent. The observer at earth is at the center of the ecliptic (not shown). The motion is uniform about C, the equant. This is expressed by considering the angle BCF as changing by a fixed number of degrees in unit time.

planet travels in a small circle, the epicycle, around a central point that describes a large circle, the deferent, about the earth. This device Ptolemy employed with high success. To resolve completely all his observations into perfect circular motions, he occasionally employed still smaller circles traveling about points that in turn traveled about the epicycle, which in turn traveled about a central point which in turn traveled about the earth. For certain motions of the sun and moon, Ptolemy employed the eccentric. This would account for the fact that the sun appears larger, hence closer in the Northern hemisphere winter, and smaller in the summer. To account for apparent variations in the velocity with which epicyclic motions of certain planets were pursued, Ptolemy introduced still another device, the equant; a point relative to which the angular velocity of the planet was uniform, while at the same time its motion centered on another point.

While Ptolemy was able to refine his scheme to the point where relatively few circles (about forty) and equants described the sum of heavenly motions, by the time of Copernicus other scholars, sometimes less skillful, and sometimes possessed of new observations which had to be reconciled, employed schemes requiring about seventy separate circles and equants. These schemes, by their complexity and their resort to geometric device, were hardly the simple harmonic solution called for by Plato. In particular the device of the equant, by separating the uniformity of the velocity from the circularity of the path, would appear to be not a strict adherence to the Pythagorean concept. There was an appearance of unreality about the whole of the Ptolemaic scheme of which the Alexandrian sophisticates were well aware. For the Renaissance mathematicians and astronomers, the complex interlocking of circle upon circle clearly rendered the reality of the crystalline spheres impossible. The equant could be considered as a mathematical device only and it would be difficult in turn to avoid considering the whole of the Ptolemaic scheme as purely a computational convenience.

THE COPERNICAN SCHEME

Nicholas Copernicus, trained in the science of the sixteenth century, which was chiefly medicine, and a profound scholar of Greek astronomy, was dissatisfied with the complexity of the cosmologic schemes based on Ptolemy's system. The device of the equant appeared to Copernicus as pure sophistry. From his study of the ancients, Copernicus was aware that Aristarchus (310 B.C.–230 B.C.), building on the work of Anaxagoras (488 B.C.–428 B.C.), had proposed a heliocentric scheme. This early idea explained the daily rotation of the celestial sphere as an apparent motion due to the real daily rotation of the earth, and the annual motion of the sun as an apparent motion due to the real annual revolution of the earth. Aristarchus had further arranged the visible planets in orbits around the sun, with Mercury closest in, followed by Venus, next the earth, then Mars, Jupiter, and Saturn. Repelled by the artificiality of the Ptolemaic scheme and the differences among the mathematicians, Copernicus, a medieval mind, looked for the symmetry, the harmony, and the beauty which a true explanation must possess in the discarded scheme of Aristarchus.

The book which set the earth in motion and stopped the sun in the sky was *On the Revolutions of the Celestial Orbs*, published the year of Copernicus' death in 1543. In this work, Copernicus set out to explain the appearances by a set of uniform, circular motions about the sun rather than about the earth. Copernicus developed the mathematics of this scheme in full, no mean task considering the maze of observations on planets, moon, sun, and stars that had to be taken into account. Probably the greatest difficulty arises from the nature of these observations, since all of them are made from necessity on a moving platform, the earth. The earth's motion Copernicus assumed to be compounded of two perfect circular motions, the daily rotation and the annual revolution. He accepted without question the Pythagorean physical principle that a natural motion was uniform and circular. The observed motions of celestial bodies would be compounded of two kinds of motions: those observed motions which were in reality due to the motions of the earth and those motions remaining. Applied to the fixed stars and the sun, only the first kind of motions were observed. The fixed stars and the sun had no motions of their own. Applied to the planets, when those apparent motions due to the motions of the earth were separated out, the remaining motion was for each planet a uniform, circular revolution about the sun. There were some difficulties and Copernicus was obliged to fall back on the battery of Ptolemaic devices, the epicycle and the eccentric. Although he avoided the equant, Copernicus was not able to place the center of his deferents at the center of the sun. The sun was within the innermost sphere, the deferent of Mercury, but not directly at the center of Mercury's orbit. However, he had dispensed with the obnoxious equant, and planetary motions were not only perfectly circular with respect to his center, but uniform as well.

Copernicus actually required thirty-four separate circles as against forty in the refined Ptolemaic version, but the simplicity of the Copernican scheme lay not in the use of half a dozen fewer circles but in accounting for all the stellar motions by the two simple motions of the earth. There is a third motion to the earth, the slow wobble on its axis that produces a shift in the equinoctial point of about 50 seconds of arc per year. This was a well-known additional motion attributed to each of the heavenly bodies separately, which Copernicus had reduced to the single wobble of the earth.

The idea of simplicity, of economy in reasoning, occurs in scientific theory all the way down to the present day. Newton was to advance it as a rule of reasoning. It originally had passed into learning as Ockham's Razor: "It is vain to do with more what can be done with fewer." In our own time, Ernst Mach, brilliant precursor of Einstein, had considered this intellectual economy as the goal and directing principle of science.

In the Copernican scheme, the retrograde motions of the planets are seen as appearances resulting from the real motion of the earth. As an example, consider the appearance of the landscape from the window of a moving train. If the observer

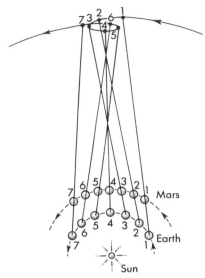

Fig. 8. *Retrograde motion.* Copernicus' explanation of the apparently erratic motions of the planets. As Mars traverses its orbit, the earth moves more rapidly along its orbit about the sun. The projection of Mars against the background of the fixed stars as seen from the earth appears to move in a retrograde loop as the earth overtakes the slower planet. A faster planet as viewed from a slower planet makes a similar retrograde loop.

concentrates on the train, the telephone poles and the immediately adjacent shrubbery appear to rush backward. Such an apparent motion resulting from the real motion of the observer is termed "parallax." The use of parallax to account for the retrograde motion of a planet is shown diagrammatically in Figure 9. All the planets in Copernicus' scheme move from east to west with speeds decreasing as their distance from the sun increases. The sun, of far greater brilliance than any other

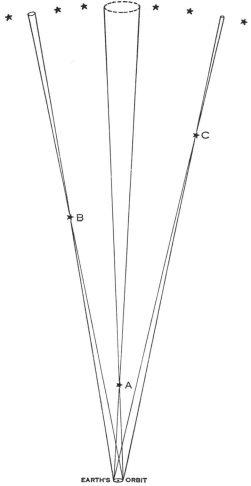

Fig. 9. *Parallax*. A fixed star, viewed from
the moving platform of the earth, appears
to trace a loop against the background of the
celestial sphere, the size of the loop depending on the distance between the star and the
earth's orbit. The inability to detect such
parallactic displacement led Copernicus to
enlarge the size of the sphere of the fixed
stars, but it was a major factor in causing
Brahe to reject the Copernican scheme.
(*Astronomy* by John C. Duncan)

celestial body, is central where in Copernicus' words "It can light up the whole at once."

Analyzing Copernicus' work in contrast to the Ptolemaic scheme, it is clear that the major assumption of both theories is that natural motions are uniform and circular. Given the observations that were available to the naked-eye astronomers, the Ptolemaic solution is as accurate as the Copernican but the Copernican is simpler and more elegant. Examining the situation closely, consider the case of a binary star (one consisting of two stars). Such pairs may be observed from the earth to be revolving about each other. From either star, it would appear that the other was doing the revolving. If the earth and the sun are considered as such a pair and the rest of the universe is ignored, then the Copernican and the Ptolemaic theories correspond.

SUCCESS OF THE COPERNICAN SYSTEM

The same objections were raised to Copernicus' ideas which had been raised to Aristarchus' ideas in ancient times. These were physical and philosophical. The Ptolemaic scheme centered the universe on the earth and on man. All Western religious tradition and speculation agreed with this. In particular a neo-Platonic idea of man as a small centering reproduction of the whole of the universe was widespread. The entire universe of planets and spheres was the great world, the *macrocosm*. Man at the center was the *microcosm*. This idea was at the base of astrology; each of the heavenly bodies was associated with one or more organs of the body. For example, Saturn was associated with the liver. An elaborate medical theory explained personality and character as well as health in terms of various body fluids. Persons born under the influence of Saturn were therefore liver-prominent. The bile secreted by the liver was the dominant fluid in their make-up. This antique theory is preserved for us today in the adjective *saturnine,* which means grave, sullen, or gloomy. Compare the *phlegmatic,* the *mercurial,* the *bilious, sanguine, jovial, martial,* and *choleric* temperaments.

Religious ideas of creation and divine interest in the earth specifically were also thrown into confusion by the heliocentric idea. Giordano Bruno, a monk of Nola in Italy, coming under the subversive influence of Copernicus' book, lectured in London in 1583 at the age of 37. Bruno had already taught at the Universities (all Church institutions) of Lyons, Toulouse, Montpellier, and Paris. His personality and habits had forced him to leave each of these in turn. History records him as penniless, arrogant, and brilliant, a familiar enough figure on the university scene even today.

In heretic England, Bruno's lectures burst all bounds. He later published a book called *On the Infinite Universe and Its Worlds* in which he expressed the ideas of these lectures. He accepted Copernicus' idea that our world was not the center of the universe. If our world was then a planet, the other planets must also be worlds. To Bruno this meant that they must each be like ours with trees, grass, and even men. A devout Christian, Bruno attempted to reconcile his theological with his cosmological ideas. He held that each of the worlds (and here was an infinite number of them) was the scene of the Divine Drama—first the Creation, then the Fall. On each of the worlds, God had sent His Son to suffer Crucifixion. Whatever the logic of Bruno's ideas, his theology was held to be pure heresy. Bruno also saw that the Copernican idea required a universe infinite in time and space. Copernicus had believed that the universe was bounded by the sphere of the fixed stars which, while large, was nevertheless finite. This narrow view of space itself as a set of concentric spheres Bruno shattered

for all time. His third and most important contribution to hi
successors was based on his belief in a single Deity. Since th
universe was the product of one God, it must be permeatec
by a common soul and therefore uniform in all its workings
The physics of the earth had to be the same as the physics o
the heavens, and natural laws discovered on earth had to b
universally applicable. These ideas, which are today completel
devoid of emotional power, were radical enough in the lat
sixteenth century to cause Bruno's arrest. He spent seven year
in the cellars of the Inquisition, where he was persuaded t
recant; but finally, rather than foreswear what he could no
help believing was the truth, he repudiated his recantation
In the savage manner of the times, he was led to a stake pilec
high with faggots and burned alive. The year was 1600. In an
other sixteen years, Galileo would begin the new physics o
Bruno's universe. Before a century had gone by, the ideas tha
he had called for had been adopted by all educated men, an
the names of his tormentors were lost in oblivion.

The physical objections to Copernicus' system appeared a
the time to be insurmountable. Aristotelian physics was bot
natural and easily understood. The earth was heavy, gross, an
corruptible, and the natural home of all heavy bodies. The sk
was light, incorruptible, and the natural abode of all ligh
bodies. So smoke and fire would ascend, while weights woul
fall. The increase in speed of falling bodies Aristotle attribute
to a natural jubilance as they neared their home. Celestial ob
jects such as the moon, sun, and stars had to be weightless i
order to move so rapidly and perfectly. Even in the limitec
closed universe of Aristotle, the diurnal rotation of all celestia
bodies meant that they must travel at fantastic rates of speec
For example, the Greek figure for the distance from the eart
to the sun was about one twentieth of our own figure of ninety
three million miles. For the sun to travel around the eart

once in each day meant that the sun must cover a path of 0.1 × π × 93,000,000 miles in twenty-four hours, or more than a million miles per hour! This could only be encompassed in the Greek mind by assuming that the sun was perfectly weightless. Copernicus' requirement of a daily rotation of the earth involved a velocity at the equator of about a thousand miles per hour. The concept of bodies of the mass of the earth in motions as rapid as this was in direct contradiction to common sense. For common sense demanded (as Aristotle did) that to maintain a state of motion required the constant exertion of a force. Where was the motor that would drive the earth around? Where were the forces to move the planets?

A further serious objection to Copernicus' scheme was the inability of the naked-eye observer to detect parallax (Figure 9). If the earth were to move on an orbit with a radius of ninety-three million miles, then a star viewed as due north in the spring would by fall appear to be displaced to the east. Seen over the course of the year, every star should trace a circle, a replica of the ecliptic, of radius proportional to its distance from the sun, and orientation depending on its direction relative to the solar system. No stellar parallax had ever been detected in the time of Copernicus. Late in the seventeenth century, Robert Hooke may have finally observed this with a carefully constructed telescope, but the earliest generally accepted observation of stellar parallax was not published until 1838 by the German astronomer, Bessel.

Copernicus gave the correct reason for the failure to observe the parallax predicted by his theory. He said that the distance from the sun to the fixed stars was so great that the displacement could not be measured. In this way the Copernican scheme demanded a vast enlargement of the universe. The figure given by Aristarchus for the size of the universe was equivalent to about 10^8 miles in radius, or of the same order of magnitude as the modern figure for the distance to the sun. Copernicus' contemporaries were thinking in terms of ten to twenty times as large a universe. While Copernicus still placed the fixed stars on an outermost sphere bounding the universe, the size of this sphere was indefinitely enlarged. The English astronomer, Thomas Digges, interpreted his own failure to detect parallax somewhat differently. In the first translation of Copernicus to appear in English (1576), Digges placed the fixed stars at varying distances from the sun in an infinite universe. Digges was led to an acceptance of the Copernican scheme by his observation of the nova of 1572. A nova is a sudden flare-up of a star causing it temporarily to outshine major stars like Sirius or even the planets. Because of his failure to detect parallax in the nova of 1572, Digges reasoned correctly that the event had taken place far beyond the sphere of the moon. In Aristotelian cosmology, the universe beyond the moon was perfect and unchangeable and a nova would have had to be confined to the space between the earth and the moon. At such a relatively slight distance, even if the earth were standing still, parallactic displacement of the nova would have to be observed. The moon itself shifts about two degrees in a twelve-hour night.

Observations of the same nova of 1572 led the Danish astronomer, Tycho Brahe, to reject Copernicus' scheme as well as the older Aristotelian cosmology. Not only were the distances involved too vast for Brahe to accept, but the fact that some stars were large enough to appear as discs rather than points and still far enough away to show no parallax with Brahe's very carefully determined data meant that they would have to be larger than the entire solar system out beyond the orbit of Saturn, which by Brahe's time was understood to be on the order of nine hundred million miles in radius. Rather than accept this, Brahe devised his own system in which the planets traveled about the sun, and the sun in turn went around the earth. No parallactic displacements were required for a stationary earth and the vast distances and enormous diameters of stars demanded by the Copernican system were not required. Nor were the physical objections to Brahe's ideas insurmountable.

If the Copernican idea were true and the earth were to rotate with velocities at the surface up to a thousand miles per hour, Copernicus' contemporaries argued that everything loose on the surface of the earth would be left behind and swept away by high winds. A stone dropped from a tower would fall far to the west of the dropping point. Incredible storms would ravage the earth's surface and life would be insupportable. Copernicus' answers to this kind of objection were Aristotelian and must have appeared as weak in the sixteenth century as they do to us today. He argued that it was in the nature of heavy things to partake of the earth's motion, and that the air and winds were heavy enough, at least in part, to share also in this motion.

Copernicus had dethroned the earth as the center of the universe and displaced man from his position as the special charge of God, for whom and around whom the universe had been created. In its stead he placed the sun. He had enlarged the universe but left it finite and bounded by the sphere of the fixed stars. His scheme led to no better calculations than the Ptolemaic universe which it succeeded, both of these being accurate only to within about 1 per cent, but calculations with the Copernican scheme were decidedly simpler. Copernicus had no new observations to maintain his theory. It contradicted the evidence of man's eyes and man's common sense, as well as the physical theory that had been dominant for nearly two thousand years. It did what it had been intended to do, however. It explained the appearances in terms of the perfect circular motions of the Pythagorean mystique, thus satisfactorily providing a solution to Plato's problem. It reduced the complexity and near disorder of the later versions of Ptolemy and substituted instead a harmonious and symmetrical system centered about the uniquely life-giving orb, the sun.

The observations of the nova of 1572 led on the one hand to the acceptance of the Copernican scheme by Digges and the substitution of an infinite universe for the finite universe of Copernicus, followed by the displacement of even the sun from the center of the universe by Bruno. On the other hand, the nova observations led to the rejection of the Copernican scheme by Tycho Brahe, and the construction of still another scheme. All three schemes fitted the observations with about the same precision. The choice between them had to be made on other than strictly logical grounds. It is therefore all the more remarkable that the Copernican scheme was to appeal to many figures of genius; that the Ptolemaic system was to be upheld by authority wedded to prejudice; that the Brahe idea was to be adopted chiefly as a weapon with which to attack and weaken Copernicus' solar system. Many years later, the French mathematician, Poincaré, was to remark that "If a phenomenon is susceptible of one mechanical explanation, it is susceptible of an infinitude of others which would account equally well for all the features revealed by experience."

4. Galilean Science

I, GALILEO, SON OF THE LATE VINCENZO
GALILEI, FLORENTINE, AGED SEVENTY YEARS,
ARRAIGNED PERSONALLY BEFORE THIS TRI-
BUNAL AND KNEELING BEFORE YOU, MOST
EMINENT AND REVEREND LORD CARDINALS
INQUISITORS-GENERAL AGAINST HERETICAL
PRAVITY THROUGHOUT THE ENTIRE CHRIS-
TIAN COMMONWEALTH, HAVING BEFORE MY
EYES AND TOUCHING WITH MY HANDS THE
HOLY GOSPELS, . . . ABJURE, CURSE, AND DE-
TEST . . . THE FALSE OPINION THAT THE
SUN IS THE CENTER OF THE WORLD AND IM-
MOVABLE AND THAT THE EARTH IS NOT THE
CENTER OF THE WORLD AND MOVES. . . .

GALILEO's *abjuration,* 1633
(*after* DE SANTILLANA)

TO THE extent that modern science may be said to have
begun in the seventeenth century, the Italian Galileo Galilei

can be considered as the first modern scientist. Copernicus, with his feeling for the aesthetic quality of the solar system and his veneration of ancient learning, was essentially a man of the Middle Ages. Bruno was a mystic and his concerns were primarily theological. Bruno's reasoning was scholastic, that is, granted certain premises, then the rules of logic and the sense of truth made certain consequences follow directly. The Greeks too had reasoned about the world rather than study it directly. They searched for the world within their minds. The relationship between what they found in their minds and their experience was not always obvious to them. The complexity of experience was too great, the scope of their thinking was too limited. The bridge between idea and experience, the sure foundation for the science of the seventeenth century was provided by Galileo.

Galileo was born in Pisa in 1564, the same year in which Shakespeare was born. He died in 1642, the year of Newton's birth. His lifetime thus encompassed the period which in England was the Elizabethan flowering and on the continent was the time of the Inquisition and religious strife. He began his studies in medicine but his interests drew him to geometry and mathematics. The work of Archimedes had recently become available in Latin translation and this had a profound influence on him.

Archimedes of Syracuse (287–212 B.C.) is best remembered as the prototype of the eccentric scientist. Plutarch tells us that the tyrant, Hiero of Syracuse, had ordered a crown of gold and later, suspecting that silver had been alloyed with the gold, asked Archimedes to determine the true quantity of gold within the crown without destroying it. The story goes that Archimedes hit on the solution in the bath by observing that the lowering of his body into the water displaced a volume of water exactly equal to the volume of his body. On consideration, it would then appear that the water surrounding his body would exert a buoyant force sufficient to counterbalance the weight of the water which had been displaced. Regardless of the composition of the body, whether flesh, gold, silver, or alloy, equal volumes would always suffer the same loss of weight on immersion in water, owing to the buoyant force. One could therefore compare the weights of equal volumes of diverse substances by this immersion procedure. Excited by the discovery, not of a method of satisfying Hiero's suspicions but of the concept of specific gravity, or mass per unit volume, Archimedes ran from the bath to his home shouting "Eureka!" (I have found it!) The scientific preoccupation that afforded the good citizens of Syracuse no little amusement may later have been the cause of Archimedes' death, for according to at least one version, the soldiers of Marcellus came upon him tracing geometric figures in the sand and, ordering him to come with them, killed him when he begged for time enough to complete a proof.

To complete a proof was for Archimedes not a small thing and the occupation which led to his murder in 212 B.C. was the source of Galileo's fascination nineteen hundred years later. Archimedes was never as much concerned with a method or mathematical formula as he was with the proof, with the problem of knowledge. How do we know? How sure is our understanding? With this in mind Archimedes had systematized ancient mechanics. He had developed a complete science of statics in the rigorous, mathematically secure form which the later Greek civilization valued highly. The example of buoyancy and specific gravity belongs to hydrostatics, a subject which Archimedes described in his work *On Floating Bodies.* In similar works, Archimedes presented a science of the first branch of mechanics—statics, a science of machines not in motion. For example, Archimedes developed the law of the lever and the laws governing the behavior of the beam balance. The simplest of these laws asserts that the force on one side of the fulcrum times the length of the lever arm will exactly counterbalance the force on the other lever arm times the length of that lever arm. Such considerations led to the concept of the center of gravity of a body (the single point about which all forces would exactly counterbalance). The idea of equilibrium, of forces exactly in balance, underlay the science of mechanics. Multiplication of motion or of forces, mechanical advantages as by gears or windlass arrangements, or pulleys, cranes, hooks —in fact much of what we now call civil engineering—comes under the heading of statics, and within this area Archimedes has never been corrected and only minor additions have been possible. Archimedes based his work on the model of Euclid's geometry. By assuming only a minimum of general truths which are so obvious as to be universally acceptable and then reasoning logically from these, a cumulative series of general statements or propositions may be derived. The self-evident truths on which Euclid had based his geometry were called axioms or common notions. An example is the statement that the whole is greater than any of its parts. An example of the kind of general proposition which Euclid was able to derive from such simple axioms and a careful definition of his terms, would be the statement that the sum of the angles of a plane triangle is equal to two right angles. Coming after Euclid, Archimedes was able to use the body of Euclidean geometry as an acceptable basis on which to build an even more complicated mathematics. But more than his mathematical achievements, which make him the greatest mathematician of antiquity, the singular accomplishment of Archimedes which interested Galileo was that Archimedes had performed that marriage of geometry and physics which was the science of statics. The levers, gears pulleys, screws, immersed bodies, and fluids of Archimedean statics could be directly compared to levers, gears, etc., in the real world. The mathematical laws which Archimedes had proved in the rigorous Greek fashion described directly the behavior of machines.

By contrast the physics of Aristotle, which was the only science of the period, was unsatisfactory. The mechanics of motion or kinetics of Aristotle was based not on such simple and intuitively obvious axioms as Euclid's, but rather on debatable premises of a philosophic nature; for example, the idea that nature abhorred a vacuum. The physical world for Aristotle was animistic. It had an abundance of these likes and dislikes. Falling bodies increased their speed as they neared the ground because of a natural jubilance on approaching their proper place. A stone in flight proceeded by a process known as antiperistasis. As the stone moved, it would leave a vacuum in the air behind it if it were not for the natural aversion to a vacuum. Air rushing in to prevent the occurrence of a vacuum would push the stone along and the flight would proceed by a continual repetition of this process until the motive force ceased. The speed of the stone would be determined by the force pushing it and by the resistance of the air. The speed of a falling body would also be determined by the motive force, in this case its weight, and would depend in addition on the distance of the falling body from the earth, its natural abode. Aristotle, although a careful observer of the biological world, never looked more than superficially for the physical evidences of his ideas about motion. Statics in the hands of Archimedes had been amenable to this kind of introspection coupled with Euclidean geometry, but kinetics somehow eluded geometry, and the loose, qualitative statements of Aristotle were not tested numerically.

It was Galileo's early ambition to do for kinetics what Archimedes had accomplished for statics; that is, to write the definitive science of motion and to place it in rigorous mathematical form so that there would appear no statement in the work which could not be demonstrated to proceed logically from an earlier and accepted statement. But he was interrupted in this task, seduced by the Copernican theory, then more than a half century old and virtually ignored. Like Copernicus before him, Galileo shared the Pythagorean preoccupation with harmony and simplicity of mathematical form. But the Copernican scheme lacked independent proof and it lacked a consistent physical theory. Galileo was destined to supply both.

In 1609, rumor reached Galileo of a Dutch device for examining distant objects. With his knowledge of Greek optics, a subject which like statics had been readily amenable to the geometric analysis of the later Greeks, Galileo easily constructed such a device for himself. He called it a *perspicillum* and at once turned it on the skies. The Dutch inventors of the telescope had apparently tried to promote it as a kind of military spyglass and by so doing had lost the opportunity, now presented to Galileo, of being the first to advance the science of astronomy through its use. The world that was revealed to Galileo through his *perspicillum* was the universe, and his was a discovery that dwarfed in significance even the discovery of a new world by Columbus.

Galileo turned his telescope on the moon and found that it was by no means as regular and perfect as Aristotle had asserted, but that it had visible craters and mountains just as the earth had. But craters and mountains are the irregular and imperfect phenomena of a heavy body like the earth, and the result of natural processes of change. The moon too would therefore be an imperfect world like the earth and it would share the physics of the earth, and not be weightless and perfect and imbedded in crystal. By turning his telescope on the sun, Galileo discovered that this body as well, shared in the universal corruption of change. He observed the sunspots which had recently been reported. The planet Venus exhibited the waxing and waning phases of our moon and this in itself was a conclusive demonstration of the heliocentric hypothesis. According to Ptolemy, the inner planets Venus and Mercury circling around the earth would always be between the earth

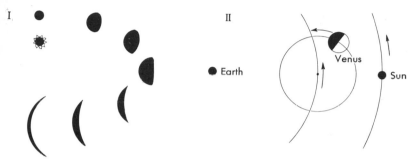

Fig. 10. I. *The phases of Venus.* Sketches from photographs taken at constant magnification. "The mother of Love emulates the figure of Cynthia." Phases more full than the half show that Venus must cross behind the sun from the earth and therefore revolves around the sun rather than the earth.

II. *The motion of Venus according to the Ptolemaic system.* Because Venus is always seen close to the sun, the center of her epicycle was assumed to move with the sun. No phase beyond the half is possible.

and the sun. But by contrast, if a Copernican model were assumed, the inner planets circling around the sun could cross behind the sun, and while in the half of their orbits on the far side of the sun they could exhibit the phases from half illumination to full illumination. If they were confined to narrow epicycles between the earth and the sun, they could never appear more than half-full.

The discovery of the phases of Venus also contradicted Aristotelian physics by demonstrating that the planets were not self-luminous but, like the earth, dark except for the light of the sun. The gross earthy nature of the moon seemed to spread deeper into the heavens with every observation. Even Brahe's apparently insurmountable objection—that the sizes of stars would be too great if they were assumed to lie at distances too far to exhibit parallax—was contradicted. Through the telescope, distant stars appeared as points of light, and their apparent spread over a measurable area was revealed to be an illusion of the naked eye. Galileo first announced his discovery of the phases of Venus in a cautious anagram in Latin, which was translated: the mother of love (Venus) emulates the figure of Cynthia (Moon).

The most spectacular discovery (and it must be recalled that all this befell one man in the space of less than a year) was the discovery that other planets had moons of their own. Galileo found four of the moons of Jupiter, which he promptly named the Medicean planets for his patrons, the ruling house of Tuscany. To this he was later to add two "companions" of Saturn. A solar system in miniature existed around another planet, and therefore the earth was not the only center of motion in the universe (nor the sun either for that matter). Other bodies could be and indeed were the centers of motions. For if the Medicean planets could circle Jupiter, why then could not the sun support satellites, and if a planet carrying moons such as Jupiter could be a satellite of the sun, why not then a planet like the earth?

Somewhat related to his discovery of new planets unknown to the ancients was the Galilean discovery of the multitude of stars. The Greeks had found some thousand stars, the Hebrews some five thousand. Turning his telescope on the Milky Way, Galileo found that the faint milky patches of light resolved themselves into thousands upon thousands of new stars. Literally millions of new stars never before known to man, never before seen or observed, were suddenly admitted to the known universe. Here was the most crushing blow against Aristotle;

the final proof that the ancients and the Church Fathers had not known everything, indeed, that there were other avenues to truth than authority and tradition. However, in all fairness to Aristotle it must be noted that Aristotle, the scientist, had been

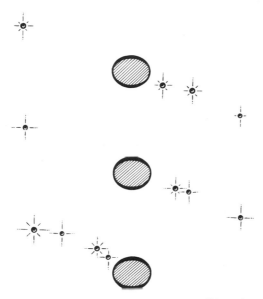

Fig. 11. *The Medicean Planets.* "On the Seventh day of January in this present year 1610 . . . I perceived that beside the planet Jupiter there were three starlets . . . on January eighth—led by what, I do not know —I found a very different arrangement. . . ."

a flexible and keenly alert individual, but Aristotle, the tradition, had become a two-thousand-year-old dogma.

In the scholastic tradition, which was the tradition of the Church and of the thought of Western Europe, a contradiction was settled in a legalistic fashion. The disputants relied for a decision on the intellectual authority of their superiors, and the intellectual world was a portion of an established hierarchy of the higher and more significant world of the spirit. A question was settled by appeal to reason, and a chain of reason rested ultimately on precedent and the authority that had been conceded by precedent, much in the manner of a modern judicial dispute in which attorneys for both sides cite the law and precedents for its interpretation. Galileo challenged both precedent and authority. Against the authority of Plato, Aristotle, Archimedes, Ptolemy, St. Thomas Aquinas, the Inquisition, of Holy Writ, and even of common sense, Galileo placed in the balance his bits of glass and metal. Against the self-evident truths which a careful reasoning from first principles would derive, Galileo placed the new kind of proof—observations. He published his results in 1610 in a brief pamphlet in Latin, the *Message from the Stars.*

"My dear Galileo," wrote Kepler, "I must tell you what occurred the other day. My friend the Baron Wakher von Wachenfels drove up to my door and started shouting excitedly from his carriage: 'Is it true? Is it really true that he has found stars moving around stars?' I told him that it was indeed so, and only then did he step into the house."

But there were others not, like Kepler, convinced Copernicans, who rejected Galileo's work. The Medicean planets, argued Francesco Sizi, a representative scholar of the period, could not exist because the number of the heavenly bodies was seven and furthermore, because to each body there was a corresponding significance in the astrological scheme of things. If the Medicean planets were to exist, they would have no place in astrology, no impact on mankind, hence no existence. Going a bit further, if the Medicean planets cannot be seen by the human eye they cannot have an effect on mankind, and lacking all effect on mankind they must necessarily lack existence. Lest the reader dismiss this reasoning as nonsense, it should be recalled that this is the old argument of the macro-cosm and the microcosm, and to the scholastic mind this kind of accepted framework on which to peg one's concept of the universe took precedence over the new notion of proof through observation. A major idea of modern physics called opera-tionalism is very similar in content. The operationalist defines physical concepts in terms of the methods and measurements by which the concepts are manifest. Immeasurables and un-observables are denied a place in the physical scheme of things. Except that the modern operationalist accepts the validity of instrumental observations, he stands on the same ground as Sizi.

In 1613, Galileo entered an open fight for the Copernican view with his *Letters on the Sun Spots.* He marked his break with scholasticism by writing in Italian instead of Latin. In this he was following the Renaissance tradition begun by Dante and Petrarch. Galileo was going over the heads of authority. The *Letters* spelled out the new astronomical discoveries of the telescope and their significance for the Copernican doctrine. Until these discoveries, the choice between Copernican and Ptolemaic concepts was made on philosophic or theological grounds. Either theory would explain the appearances and solve Plato's problem. But the moons of Jupiter and the phases of Venus were new appearances and could be explained by the heliocentric idea, but not by the geocentric view.

Although he was warned that Copernican ideas were in con-flict with scripture, Galileo continued to hold to them and in 1632 he published a *Dialogue on the Great World Systems,* a charming work in which the cosmological ideas of Galileo and the Aristotelians were set forth in the form of a discussion among friends. In this dialogue Simplicio, the Aristotelian spokesman, was always awarded the final argument and the final victory, but it was always on the basis of an appeal to authority. From the point of view of logic and evidence, Simplicio had not a leg to stand on. The choice of the name of Simplicio for the Aristotelian spokesman was a costly joke for Galileo. He may have felt himself safe because his friend, Cardinal Barberini, a fellow member of the group of distinguished scientists and experimenters who had formed the Accademia dei Lincei, had just become Pope Urban VIII.

Galileo, by this time a man of seventy, was imprisoned in the palace of the Inquisition. His *Dialogue* was banned and all copies of it that could be found were seized and burned. Galileo was condemned and forced to abjure his ideas. Legend has it that as he was led from the hall in which he had just forsworn the Copernican doctrine, he was overheard to mutter, "*Eppur se muove*," (But yet it moves!). Whether the shattered old man really retained this independence in the very moment of his ordeal we cannot know, but the legend of this defiant statement sprang up at once and gained credence all over Europe. Copies of Galileo's *Dialogue* brought large sums on the black market in Italy, and translations appeared immediately in northern Europe. The spectacle of the settlement of a scientific problem by the force of the Church-State did more to publicize and establish the Copernican doctrine than even the discoveries of the telescope. In order to crush Galileo, the full weight of medieval theology and Holy Scripture itself had been thrown into the balance against the bits of glass and tubing of the *perspicillum*.

GALILEAN METHOD

The legend that has Galileo dropping stones from the Leaning Tower of Pisa may be apocryphal and in detail a slight on Galileo's skillful experimental procedures, but it expresses nevertheless the significant break in seventeenth-century science for which Galileo is rightly credited. To the reasons of the learned doctors, to the skillful arguments, the lengthy and exact chains of logic, Galileo opposed the new kind of evidence, the experiment-observation. In this he was following the example of Leonardo da Vinci who had a century before relied on trial and observation. After Galileo, the ultimate proof of a theory would be the evidence of the real world. Even the enemies of Galileo and the opponents of the Copernican scheme were forced back on this ground. It was no longer possible to cite as evidence the words of men or the authority of symbols, however holy. Galileo's trial had proved not that Galileo was heretical, but rather that experiment was the ultimate arbiter of all physical questions and that from the results of experiment the only appeal was to further experiment.

Galileo made a distinction between measurable and im-measurable qualities. The first he called primary qualities, and on these, he said, all reasonable men could agree. Number, weight, length, and geometric form were primary qualities. The secondary qualities were those which exist in the mind of the beholder. Qualities like taste, color, warmth, or coldness he held to be secondary. It was a distinction on which John Locke was to elaborate considerably. Something like taste, Galileo argued, could never be described by number or form but only in terms of another taste. Nor could there be any assur-ance that the impression in one man's mind of the taste of salt would be the same as the impression in another's. The phe-nomenon of color blindness illustrates this nicely. Many peo-ple are color blind in the sense of not being equipped to distin-guish between red and green; they may remain unaware of this until they are formally tested. They may have gone through life referring to the color of grass and leaves as green and that of tomatoes as red in much the same way as most people might discuss a mauve and a lilac shade. Infrared and ultraviolet are examples of sharply distinct "colors" to which we are all blind. And the completely blind may or may not experience the sensation of color, but unless they have previously learned from the experience of sight, there would be no way of comparing their sensations with our own.

This distinction of Galileo's had the effect of diverting experiment toward the measurables on which agreement could be reached and away from areas that were beyond the reach of seventeenth-century instruments and observations. To a certain extent it began the divorce of science from metaphysics, since questions on the ultimate nature of reality were to be excluded in favor of questions on the measurements of reality. Galileo was marking out for natural philosophy—which is science— those areas of philosophy on which agreement can be reached. The Greeks, the Arabs, and the medieval scholastics continually intermixed their primary and secondary qualities and much of their work degenerated into sterile argument. We are told that the science of Aristotle was concerned with causation, that the question for Aristotle was always "Why?" and since behind each cause there lay a deeper cause, the system of Aristotle could be traced cause by cause back to an original cause, just as the motions of the spheres could be traced to the same final cause, the prime mover. For Galileo, the question "Why?" led always to the same result, the final cause. He turned instead to measurement to answer the question, "How?"

The answer was to be found by putting the question to nature, in experiment, in trial, in dirtying one's hands, using one's eyes, in seeing for oneself the stars, the rocks, moving bodies. A century before, Leonardo had strolled about the streets of Florence and Milan observing workmen in construction, in foundries, bridges, mines, boats, and urged his successors to rely upon experience. In Galileo, this tradition was come to fruit.

GALILEAN KINETICS

Although his telescopic observations had already completed the firm establishment of the Copernican theory, one major gap in the system remained. There was still no physical explanation of the motions of the solar system. The problem of moving a heavy body such as the earth, the moon, planets, and their moons was as far from a solution as ever, as was the problem of maintaining these motions of the greatly enlarged solar family, each in its proper position. Aristotelian physics distinguished between celestial and earthly mechanics, and by unwarranted assumptions of weightlessness and celestial perfection provided a physics for the Ptolemaic scheme. But if the Ptolemaic scheme would not explain the new appearances, if the perfection of the celestial world was shown to be myth, if the division between earthly and celestial mechanics was baseless, where was the physics that would account for the Copernican idea? This, too, Galileo was destined to supply. In another volume of dialogue, the *Discourses and Demonstrations Concerning Two New Sciences,* Galileo set out formally the results of a lifetime of thought and experiment that he had begun while still a student. Superimposed over the light tone of the dialogue form, Galileo placed the rigid Euclidean structure of axiom, definition, and derivation.

He first defined his terms. These were uniform motion, accelerated motion, and uniformly accelerated motion. In uniform motion a body must cover equal spaces in equal times. From this definition four axioms follow: simple, incontrovertible statements that nevertheless contain within themselves the implications of the whole new science. The first of the axioms is the statement that in the case of one and the same uniform motion, the distance traversed during a longer interval of time is greater than the distance traversed during a shorter interval of time. It is not necessary to prove this, and it is probably not possible to prove it. The axioms lead to a series of theorems or general statements about particles in uniform motion that will enable Galileo, later in his work, to describe more complicated motions precisely.

Any motion which is not uniform is accelerated motion. Is uniform motion to be found in nature? That is, what is the connection to be made between the mathematical ideas of Galileo and the world of real particles? Galileo was to assert his ideas on uniform motion in the form of what has since become the law of inertia. "Imagine any particle projected along a horizontal plane without friction; then . . . this particle will move along this same plane with a motion which is uniform and perpetual, provided the plane has no limits." Since limitless planes and frictionless motions are ideal situations not realizable in practice, we must recognize that no experiment will exactly justify Galileo's conclusion. On the other hand, by making longer and longer planes and smoother and rounder balls to run across them we will approach closer and closer to Galileo's ideal situation. Galileo was a competent experimentalist, as his construction of the telescope demonstrates, but it may be simpler in this case to consider a more recent experiment.

In 1935, in one of the early examples of a military investigation into the fundamentals of physics, the Army Air Corps dropped a dummy bomb from a moving plane on a carefully marked course with automatic cameras set to record the exact position of the bomb at one-second intervals. A composite diagram (Figure 12) shows the path of the bomb. The table on p. 70 shows the vertical and horizontal displacements of the bomb at successive instants of time. Considering the horizontal motion only, it is clear that this part of the bomb's motion corresponds to Galilean uniform motion, at least up until the sixth second. In each of the first six seconds, the bomb was displaced horizontally by ninety-eight feet. After six seconds, the slight change in horizontal velocity is probably due to friction with the air.

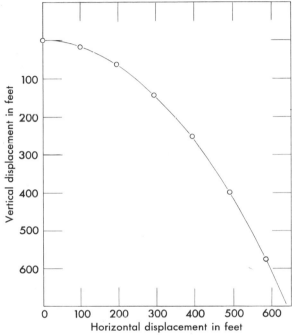

Fig. 12. *Path of a falling bomb.*

By contrast, the vertical displacement is not uniform. The bomb fell sixteen feet in the first second, 64 feet in the first two seconds, and one hundred forty-four feet in the first three seconds. This acceleration of the vertical motion of the bomb is accounted for by the force of gravity. Galileo considered that the motion of a projectile could be broken down into two parts, a uniform motion (horizontal) and an accelerated motion (vertical).

Data for Bomb Dropped from an Airplane

Time t in seconds	Horizontal displacement x in feet at time t	Vertical displacement y in feet at time t
0.000	0	0
1.000	98	16
2.000	196	64
3.000	294	144
4.000	392	256
5.000	490	400
6.000	587	576
7.000	684	782
19.000	1783	5499

From *Mechanics, Molecular Physics, Heat, and Sound*, Millikan, Roller, and Watson. Boston: Ginn and Co., 1937.

INERTIA

Medieval scholars such as William of Ockham and Nicolaus of Cusa, following the sixth-century Alexandrian, John Philoponos, had challenged the more obvious fallacies of Aristotelian kinetics. John Philoponus had proposed that bodies moved by virtue of their possession of *impetus*, a quality which could be transferred on contact, and which, in the case of the planets and heavenly spheres, was nonwasting. Instead of antiperistasis, which would have made motion in a vacuum impossible and so prevented the possibility of a frictionless motion, a body with impetus could traverse a vacuum, and Ockham proposed that impetus rather than the hand of God kept the planets in motion. Inertia, unlike impetus, cannot be imparted to a body nor removed from a body, but like the anti-Aristotelian impetus, Galileo thought of inertia as a quality of the moving body, residing in it and proportionate to the mass of the body. The resistance of the body to acceleration (change of velocity) is its inertia.

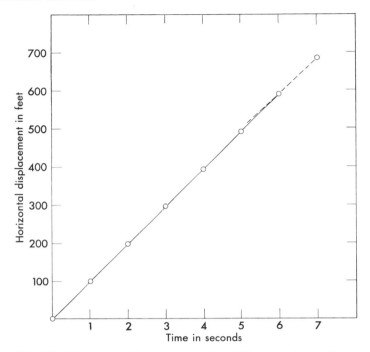

Fig. 13. *Horizontal displacement of a falling bomb vs. time.*

Galileo's great insight into the problem of motion was the realization that a moving body does not require force to maintain its motion as Aristotle had said, but that force is required to change the motion. Motion continuing without change was uniform motion and evidence of the absence of force. This unexpected idea of bodies in motion remaining in uniform motion unless acted upon by an external force is in apparent contradiction to common sense and common experience. We know that a horse pulling a cart over a level track is working, exerting force. We know that it takes fuel to drive a car even at a uniform speed across level plains. Galileo's inertial concept is an ideal one, but not an impractical one. Imagine that a car

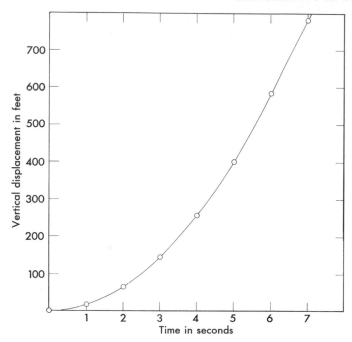

Fig. 14. *Vertical displacement of a falling bomb vs. time.*

is driving across a level plain at the rate of sixty miles per hour and that the engine is disengaged. The car will continue to move. To bring it to a stop or to slow it down, which is to change its velocity, will require the exertion of a considerable force. Of course, left to itself the car will eventually come to a halt, but it is clear that this negative acceleration is due to the friction of the system, including air resistance. If the experiment could be performed in a vacuum with a carefully oiled cart on a carefully smoothed plane, we can conceive of the motion going on indefinitely. In the Army's bomb experiment the air resistance after nineteen seconds had reduced the horizontal velocity of the bomb by 5 per cent.

If we conceive of our idealized cart as coasting down an inclined plane with a hinge in the center so that the lower half of the plane may be inclined at any angle to the upper, then the cart rolling down the first incline will gain speed uniformly; that is, its velocity at the ends of equal intervals of time will be in the proportion of 1:2:3: etc. If the second half of the plane is inclined below the horizontal, the cart on the lower half will continue to accelerate at a new rate depending on the degree of inclination. If, on the other hand, the second half of the plane is inclined upward above the horizontal, the cart will lose velocity at a rate again depending on the degree of inclination. But if it gains or loses velocity, depending on whether the second incline is below or above the horizontal, it is clear that on the horizontal plane the cart can neither gain nor lose velocity. It must therefore continue along the plane in uniform motion with the velocity with which it left the initial incline.

Here is the sought-for mechanism for the universe. The moon in its path about the earth, the planets in their courses, the earth about the sun, the Medicean planets about Jupiter, all move with a natural motion. Force is not required to keep them in motion; on the contrary, force would be required to stop their moving. Planets, moons, the earth, distant pairs of stars rotating one about the other are all kept in motion not by the hand of God or by the exertion of a force, but by their inertia. The motion which St. Thomas Aquinas could explain only by the direct intervention of God turning the outer sphere, which was the sphere of the fixed stars, which would in turn rotate the sphere of Saturn, which would in turn rotate the sphere of Jupiter, and so on down to the heavy and immobile earth, is explained by Galileo as a natural motion requiring no exertion. For Aquinas, the motions of the spheres were the first proof of the existence of God. Galileo, citing Plato, held

that "God, after having created the heavenly bodies, assigned
them the proper and uniform speeds with which they were
forever to revolve."

The idea of separating into two simpler motions the motion
of a projectile, such as the falling bomb in the Army trial
was originally Galileo's. He spoke of a projectile as "a body
whose motion is compounded of two motions, namely one
uniform and one naturally accelerated." A body under the
influence of the force of gravity was a naturally accelerated
body. Such a naturally accelerated body would be uniformly
accelerated, Galileo asserted, because "nature herself, in all
her various other processes [would] employ only those means
which are most common, simple and easy." Galileo had defined
uniform acceleration as the addition of an equal amount of
speed to a body in equal intervals of time. Thus, if a body
starting from rest were to reach a speed of five feet per second
at the end of one second, and ten feet per second at the end
of two seconds, and fifteen feet per second at the end of three
seconds, it would be uniformly accelerated. The increment
in velocity would be five feet per second and the interval of
time would be one second. The body would be accelerated at
the rate of five feet per second per second.

In the *Discorsi* (*Discourses . . . Concerning Two New Sciences*), Sagredo demurred.

"Although I can offer no rational objection to this or indeed
to any other definition, devised by any author whomsoever
since all definitions are arbitrary, I may nevertheless without
offense be allowed to doubt whether such a definition as the
above, established in an abstract manner, corresponds to and
describes that kind of accelerated motion which we meet in
nature in the case of freely falling bodies."

To this, Galileo's spokesman Salviati replied by showing
logically that his was the only possible conclusion. Assume with

Sagredo and Simplicio that the speed of a freely falling body increases proportionately to the distance through which it has fallen rather than, as Galileo asserts, proportionately to the time that it has fallen. Then the velocity with which a body falls eight feet will be just double the velocity with which it falls four feet. In that case, the time that it takes a body to fall eight feet will equal the time that it takes to fall four feet. If it falls the first four feet in this unit of time, then it must fall the second four feet instantaneously or in zero time. To Galileo, instantaneous motion was an impossibility.

". . . so far as I know, no one has yet pointed out that the distances traversed, during equal intervals of time, by a body falling from rest, stand to one another in the same ratio as the odd numbers beginning with unity," Galileo wrote at the beginning of the discussion. As the Pythagoreans before him had fitted the numbers 3, 6, etc., to triangles and 4, 9, etc., to squares, or tried to relate the particles of the world to the units of the number series 1, 2, 3, 4, . . . Galileo had singled out that aspect of freely falling bodies which he could represent by a number series, the odd numbers beginning with one. He was aware that these successive distances traversed in equal time intervals, 1, 3, 5, 7, 9, . . . added to a series of square numbers, $1 = 1, 1 + 3 = 4, 1 + 3 + 5 = 9, 1 + 3 + 5 + 7 = 16$, etc., so that the distances covered by freely falling bodies at the ends of equal intervals of time were proportional to the series of squares: 1, 4, 9, 16, 25, etc.

In the *Discorsi*, it is interesting to note, it is Simplicio, the spokesman of scholasticism, who continued to demur at Galileo's logical structure and demanded experimental verification. "I am convinced that matters are as described, once having accepted the definition of uniformly accelerated motion," Simplicio says, "but as to whether this acceleration is that which one meets in nature in the case of falling bodies, I am still doubtful, and it seems to me, not only for my own sake but also for all those who think as I do, that this would be the proper moment to introduce one of those experiments—and there are many of them I understand—which illustrate in several ways the conclusions reached."

Galileo approached the experimental test of his logically deduced law of motion with a skill and perspicacity worthy of a better memorial than the tale of the Leaning Tower of Pisa. In order to slow down the motion of the falling body, essentially to dilute the force of gravity, Galileo employed an inclined plane, carefully constructed and lined with smoothed parchment to minimize friction. Timing was a more difficult problem. Galileo had employed his pulse beats as a kind of short-interval clock, and by this means he had discovered the isochronism of the pendulum, legend has it, by timing the swings of the chandelier in the cathedral during a dull service. For the accurate demonstration to the Simplicios of his world he used a water clock; a tank of water with a pinhole in it through which a definite amount of water would escape in a definite interval of time. By collecting the water and weighing it carefully, Galileo was able to weigh time, and since the simple balance can be a highly accurate instrument, the water timer was more than accurate enough to demonstrate the one-to-one relationship between the world and his ideas. The amount of water collected while a ball rolled one fourth of the way down the plane was one half the amount collected while the ball rolled all the length of the plane. The amount collected while the ball rolled one ninth of the length of the plane was one third of the final amount. The experiment was not the source of Galileo's ideas; it was its confirmation. It was the stubborn irreducible fact to which Pythagoreanism might be a guide, or logic a clue, but which all the power of human reason could not contravene.

Although Aristotle had been challenged before, it was Galileo, through his work and even more significantly through his life, who worked the great change in Western thought. The *Discorsi* had accomplished Galileo's original purpose, the writing of a kinetics to supplement the statics of Archimedes. With the clean precision of the Alexandrian Greeks, a seventeenth-century Italian had built up a new science, that of motion. The whole of the *Discorsi* was the consistent sum of its parts, so that each statement depended in turn on a previous statement, and no one statement could be challenged without the challenge of the whole. The chain of argument rested firmly on a basis of axiom and postulate so simple and so obviously true as to be readily accepted by all. In place of the ponderous Latin of the scholastics, Galileo had chosen the musical Italian vulgate set in the charming form of a dialogue. But even beyond the reintroduction of the mathematical precision of Archimedes, Galileo, by his skillful employment of experiment, had placed his conclusions beyond contradiction. His trial and condemnation were the acknowledgment of his success. For all argument and demonstration being clearly on the side of the bits of glass and brass, it was necessary to resort to force and the police power of the clerical state to contravene him. Besides his reassertion of the role of experiment in natural philosophy, Galileo had tightened the intellectual processes of science by his distinction between primary and secondary qualities. He had in this way introduced the idea of measurement and quantitative description in opposition to the Aristotelian concern with cause and effect. More than a mere philosopher of science, Galileo's actual discoveries emphasized the importance of his methods. He had established a new physics, first by the law of inertia, which was the law of uniform motion; second, by the law of motion for freely falling bodies and for all uniformly accelerated bodies; third, for the motion

of bodies such as projectiles compounded of the first two kinds
of motion. He had built an important new scientific instrument,
the telescope, and with it he had lifted the problem of cosmology to a new dimension. Until the new discoveries of
the satellites of Jupiter, the sunspots, the Lunar irregularities,
the phases of Venus, and the stellar composition of the Milky
Way, the Copernican construction was an appealing but not a
necessary portrayal of the Universe. By his discovery of the
phases of Venus, Galileo had added new appearances whose
resolution in Plato's sense was possible only by a Copernican
idea. By his discovery of the satellites, he had shown that
other bodies than the earth could be centers of motion. His
discoveries had ended the time-worn distinction between celestial and earth-bound physics, displaced the physics of Aristotle
and provided the basis of the new universal physics which
would explain a Copernican cosmos.

If we have dwelt at length on the persecution of Galileo, it
has been because the ferocity of the attack upon Galileo was
a measure of the significance of his ideas. With these ideas
Galileo was both making the modern world and destroying
himself. "A man who still lived and breathed inside the traditional freedoms of the Renaissance, he could not understand
this first form of the modern state that he collided with, based
like its successors, on propaganda, 'emotional engineering,
and manipulation of public opinion." Formally threatened
with torture, imprisoned and interrogated in the palace of the
Inquisition, finally sentenced to life imprisonment, Galileo
emerged a month after his forced abjuration in the custody of
his friend Archbishop Piccolomini. His sight failing, Galileo
was released to a kind of house arrest on a small farm in Acetri
which was all that remained to him of worldly goods. Here he
lived for eight more years, during which time in a final burst
of vigor he wrote the *Discorsi* and succeeded in smuggling it

out through the French ambassador. Here, too, he was visited by John Milton in 1644 who was himself blind and suspect in a later age and a distant country. In his great plea for freedom of thought, the *Areopagitica,* Milton wrote, "I have sat among their learned men and been counted happy to be born in such a place of philosophic freedom as they supposed England was, while they themselves did nothing but bemoan the servile condition into which learning amongst them was brought; that this was it which had damped the glory of Italian wits, that nothing had been there written now these many years but flattery and fustian. There it was that I found and visited the famous Galileo, grown old, a prisoner of the Inquisition." With the sentence of Galileo, the long night fell over Italy as it had fallen over Spain. The city of Florence where Dante and Petrarch wrought, the city of Machiavelli, of Leonardo, Cardano, and Michaelangelo sank into dusty oblivion. The life of thought and with it civilization moved north to the Dutch Republic and the English Commonwealth. It was in the first freedoms of the Commonwealth after the successful Puritan revolution that Milton flourished and it was in protest against the growing theocracy that he wrote the *Areopagitica.* The fate of Italy is a grim reminder for those who would congeal learning into orthodoxy.

Was Galileo heretical? The most recent of scholarly opinions is that the Church, once having instituted a system of thought control and police powers, was itself victimized by its own agents; for informers, inquisitors, and torturers, once being placed in control of men's beliefs, the prisons would not lack for occupants. Thomas Salusbury, who translated the condemned *Dialogue on the Great World Systems* in 1661, wrote, ". . . Pope Urban VIII taking his honour to be concerned as having in his private capacity been very positive in declaiming against the Pythagorean philosophy, and now (as he sup-

posed) being ill dealt with by Galileo, who had summed up
all his arguments and put them into the mouth of Simplicius.
His Holiness thereupon conceived an implacable displeasure
against our Author. . . ."

In law, Galileo was wrongfully condemned for heresy, for
the Ptolemaic system was not an article of faith and "What a
baker's dozen of cardinals sitting in executive committee may
decide cannot become a matter of faith and salvation." But
beyond the legal right, was Galileo heretical? Not in his own
mind, for even the decree of sentence asserted that he had
answered as a good Catholic. In the dim recesses of their
understanding, though, the men who judged Galileo and the
men who burned Bruno were not wrong in assessing the men-
ace of the new ideas. There was never a revolution in all the
history of the world like the scientific revolution that began in
the seventeenth century and whose end we cannot foresee.
No religious movement, no political movement can compare
in the degree to which it has transformed not only the life of
mankind but even the face of the globe, nor has any philosophical change sunk as deeply or influenced as profoundly the
fundamental beliefs of men. "Where do we come from, what
are we doing here, where are we going?" Gauguin asked.

The certainty with which those questions could have been
answered in the time of Galileo is gone forever. It is perhaps
just as well. For it is strong certainty and monumental faith
that would let us burn a man alive for contradicting it.

5. The End of Plato's Problem

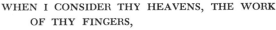

WHEN I CONSIDER THY HEAVENS, THE WORK
  OF THY FINGERS,
THE MOON AND THE STARS, WHICH THOU HAST
  ORDAINED;
OH WHAT IS MAN THAT THOU ART MINDFUL
  OF HIM?

Psalm 8

THE INFLUENCE of Platonic idealism on the development
of science can hardly be exaggerated. In spite of the fact that
science more than any other intellectual discipline externalizes
and concentrates on the world of phenomena as existing outside of and beyond the mind, it is nevertheless by and through
the mind that the external world is apprehended. In particular
the Pythagorean mystique, the world of order, of number and
form, underlies the thinking of the entire scientific movement.
We tend today to think of science apart from the individuals

81

who advance it. We separate the arts and the emotions from
the world of cold-blooded fact. In the flush of the materialism
that demands bigger and better motor cars and more insidious radioactive poisons, we would like to project this materialism into science and in a sense, let Faust make the compact
with the Devil. We imagine that the eternal youth of material
comfort and luxury accrues to us while it is Faust's soul which
is lost. We want the fruits—we shun the responsibilities of freedom of thought. As much as any figure in the history of science,
Johann Kepler, who completed the work of Copernicus, illustrates the fallacy of this dualism—the inseparability of scientific
achievement from the moods and philosophy of the achiever.

Plato's problem, the saving of the appearances, the reconciling of the diverse motions of the planets into a simple circular
scheme, had not been completed entirely by Copernicus. In
detail Copernicus was wrong. The famous simple diagram
showing the planetary orbits concentric about the sun (Figure
15) was not even an accurate representation of Copernicus'
own data, which did not show the sun at the center of the
circles, and made liberal use of the epicycle. In short, Copernicus' data showed that the paths of planets did not conform to
uniform circular motion. Tycho Brahe was able to show the
defects in Copernicus' scheme. It did not conform to observation. The neatness, the simplicity, the harmony of the Copernican heliocentric scheme were as far from the observations of
planetary motions as were the cycles and equants of Ptolemy.
Brahe, working in the latter part of the sixteenth century, was
set up in an observatory, Uraniborg (the castle in the sky), on
the Island of Hveen for Frederick II of Denmark. Brahe built
a quadrant for the accurate measure of planetary angles with
a sighting arm thirty feet in length. His observations were accurate to nearly half a minute of arc, twenty times the accuracy
of Copernicus' observations and very close to the accuracy of

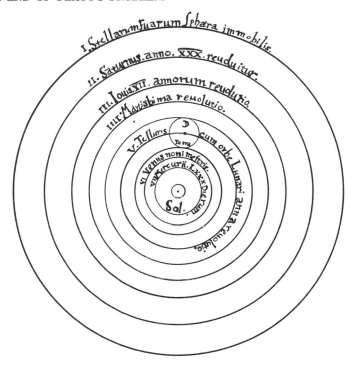

Fig. 15. *The Copernican Universe*. This is actually a simplification by Copernicus. In detail Copernicus too resorted
to epicycle and deferent, which he did not, however, show in
this summary diagram.

modern surveying instruments. Brahe reintroduced the modern
system of locating stars by their positions on the celestial
sphere. The sphere he marked off into a grid system parallel
to the latitude and longitude system of the earth. He was also
the first person to attempt to delimit the positions of the constellations. His instrumental observations and his grid system
raised the observations of astronomy to a new level and Brahe
was able to assert with conviction that Copernicus' scheme was
wrong. It did not fit the appearances.

Towards the end of his life, Brahe was joined for a time by Johann Kepler, a Pythagorean and a mystic who was nevertheless destined to put a final end to Pythagoreanism in the form of Plato's problem. Kepler, a fanatical perfectionist, turned away from the peripatetic philosophy of Aristotle and embraced the purer number-mystique of the Pythagoreans. Aristotle's science was a science of qualities and Kepler envisioned a science of quantities and number. The skill and accuracy of Brahe's work made a deep and lasting impression on the young mystic. Brahe, always methodical, was the first person to compute his personal and instrumental errors so that he could assert with the certainty of knowledge that his observations could not be off by more than one half-minute of arc. On Brahe's death, Kepler continued with the work of resolving the data accumulated in Brahe's lifetime of observation. A confirmed Copernican, his Pythagorean bent would have allowed no other system but Copernicus'. He nevertheless knew better than any one living the accuracy of Brahe's work. A devout Protestant, he maintained the cosmological doctrine that Luther had condemned. Like Plato, like Copernicus before him, Kepler saw that the clue to God's mind as geometric order and numerical relationship was expressed in the system of the world. As Newton was later to put it, it was God's glory to conceal and man's duty to discover the order and regularity of the world. Kepler practiced astrology among other things; he speculated on music, on the composition of the world, on the size of the universe. Everywhere he saw mathematical relationships. The discrepancies, the awkwardness of Copernicus' idea alone would not be resolved.

Brahe had twenty years of observations of the planet Mars and these Kepler attempted to resolve. The problem was to take the enormous number of positions located by Brahe over twenty years and recorded as dates and numbers on Brahe's celestial grid and show that these all lay upon a single circle with the sun at the center rather than the earth. It was also necessary to show that the speed of Mars was uniform in its orbit. After four years of calculations during which Kepler neglected his family and his personal affairs, he found that his best efforts left a discrepancy of eight minutes of arc, or about one part in three thousand. Few modern scientists would fail to accept the result and dismiss the error as trifling. But Kepler asserted with the grandeur of conviction that if God had wished to make a circle, He would have made a perfect circle and not one with eight minutes of arc of discrepancy. Since the path of Mars was not a circle by eight minutes of arc, Copernicus had erred, rather than God, and God had never intended to make a circle.

This inspiration of Kepler led to a magnificent insight: it was not the task of man to constrain God's mind, the world of nature, to any form however perfect it might seem. Rather, perfection would be determined by God expressing Himself in nature. The orbit of Mars, Kepler found, was an ellipse with the sun at one of the two foci. Number and form were to be found in nature and described by man. Kepler, the most determined mystic of all, had solved Plato's problem by discarding it. The appearances were not to be resolved into a combination of perfect circular motions, but rather the simplest mathematical description possible was to be found for the appearances. Kepler's first two laws of planetary motion appeared in 1609, a year before Galileo's telescope. He asserted proudly that the paths of planets are ellipses about the sun as a focus.

In point of time, Kepler had already solved the problem of uniformity of the speed of Mars, with his second law. He thought of the planets as moved in their courses by a motive spirit emanating from the sun in the plane of the planetary orbits. The spirit, like light, weakened with increased distance from the sun because, like light, the same amount of spirit must spread over an increasing area. It would move Mars more rapidly when Mars came closer to the sun (perihelion) and less rapidly when Mars was further from the sun. Kepler's erroneous ideas led him to the second law—the line joining the cen-

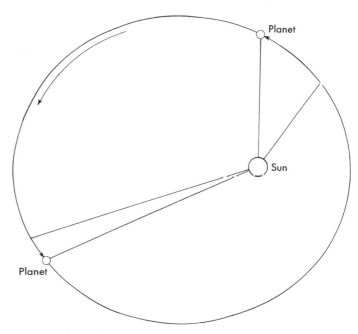

Fig. 16. *Kepler's Second Law.* The line joining the planet to the sun sweeps out equal areas in equal time.

ter of the sun to a moving planet would sweep out equal areas in equal times, a result readily confirmed by Brahe's data.

With these two laws, not only the positions but the velocities of the planets could be computed at all times. Planetary motion could be described completely and accurately and the mathematical description could be fit to Brahe's data with no discrepancy. A perfectly simple heliocentric model of the solar system was now possible, and theoretical astronomy was for the first time in a position to contribute to descriptive astronomy. Kepler's theory was to introduce a new level of accuracy in the calculation of planetary positions for nautical almanacs.

Earlier, as part of his preoccupation with ideal numbers and ideal forms, Kepler had concentrated on Book XIII of Euclid —the unfinished section which raised more questions than it answered. The five perfect solids of Plato were described in Book XIII with the geometric proofs of their perfection (all their sides and all their angles were the same) and also the proof that these were the only perfect or ideal solids. Archimedes had extended the description of regular solids to include subclasses of regularity, but it remained for Kepler to discover additions to the five fundamental solids. By allowing the sides to intersect each other, Kepler determined two more perfectly regular solids (the starred polyhedra). The inner harmony of the cosmos had led the Greeks to identify each of the five Platonic solids with one of the elements, the tetrahedron with

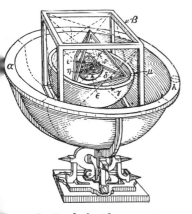
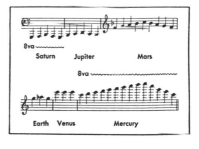

Fig. 17. *Kepler's Platonic Universe and the Harmonies of the Spheres.* (*Astronomy* by John C. Duncan)

fire, the icosahedron with water, the octahedron with air, the cube with earth, and the fifth, the dodecahedron, with the all-pervading stuff of the heavenly spheres, the ether. This harmony led Kepler to place each of the planetary spheres inside one of the Platonic solids—a system of Chinese boxes with the cube inside the sphere of Saturn and the sphere of Jupiter inside the cube; the tetrahedron inside the sphere of Jupiter with the sphere of Mars inscribed just within, and circumscribing the pentagonal dodecahedron which in turn circumscribed the earth. The pentagonal dodecahedron, the regular solid composed of twelve regular pentagons, was of special significance in astrology and the Black Arts of the medieval period.

The strong element of mystery in Kepler's work was of fatal consequence for it turned Galileo away from him, and if Galileo had fully comprehended Kepler's laws, he might have solved the cosmological problem before the birth of Newton. But it is this same mystical turn in Kepler's thought which led him to propose the questions that his laws answered, at a time when the ultimate uses of those laws could not possibly have been foreseen. Galileo was not concerned with the distances of the planets from the sun and if he had thought of the matter at all he would hardly have expected there to be a pattern. He did indeed hint that he had found a pattern in the velocities with which the planets circled the sun, but the fundamental quality of Kepler's thought, the search for harmony and order everywhere, was not shared by the Italian genius. Kepler was convinced that there was an order and a harmony in the positions of the planets and his system of Chinese boxes which related planetary positions to the Platonic solids was an insufficient relationship. For seventeen years he labored over Brahe's data to determine the true distances of the planets from the sun and then suddenly all his results and his years of calculation fell into place and there emerged a single simple law. He called it the Harmonic Law. For all the planets, the period of revolution about the sun squared was proportional to the average radius of the planetary orbit.

$$T^2 = kR^3$$

If the mean radius of the earth's orbit (ninety-three million miles) be taken as 1 astronomical unit and the earth's period of revolution be 1 year, then the value of k is 1. Then from the period (30 years) of Saturn, the mean radius of the Saturnian orbit can be determined.

$$30^2 = 1 \times R^3$$

$$R = \sqrt[3]{900}$$

$$R = 9.7 \text{ Astronomical Units}$$

After a lifetime of privation and heartbreaking labor over the mass of data of Brahe, Kepler had completed his system. He had discovered the three laws of planetary motion which bear his name, three laws describing the mathematical relationships between the motions of the planets with perfect simplicity and complete agreement with Brahe's data. In the *Harmony of the World*, 1619, Kepler published his paean to the unity of nature. The planetary spheres, the elements, the Platonic solids, all testified to an all-pervading harmony, a celestial music, a total perfection which was truly divine.

The mixture of rapture and mathematics, of musical notation and Platonic solids and planetary observations was too rich a diet for 1619. Kepler had found laws which no one wanted. He had put them together in a neo-Platonic system at a time when a newly evolving scientific spirit was in rebellion against mystical and occult theories and an older irrational conservatism was deeply mistrustful of the Pythagorean-Platonic train of thought. As Copernicus' system had waited fifty years for the beginnings of interest, so the kernel of Kepler's work would not be understood for fifty years again. The harmonies between the musical staff and the Platonic solids and the four elements and the planets we know today (as Galileo knew) were illusory. But the harmony of the three laws of Kepler was of vastly greater importance than even Kepler could have conceived. The laws of Kepler are universal physical laws. The naïve universe of a central sun surrounded by musical boxes tinkling hymns to the neo-Platonic Divinity who presided over all is no longer with us. But in the enormous spaces and the vast times of the modern universe the three laws of Kepler hold. They apply as well to distant pairs of stars revolving one about the other as to distant galaxies, island universes in a slow rotation. The electrons about the atom moving at velocities approaching the speed of light in orbits so small that millions of them together cannot be seen under the microscope, these too are governed by Kepler's laws.

In a final work, the *Epitome Astronomiae Copernicanae*, Kepler described our present model of the solar system. He extended his harmonic law to include the satellites of Jupiter and began for the first time to speculate on the forces involved in the motions of the planets. He thought of the planets as being moved about by an *anima motrix*, a radiating magnetic force emanating from the sun. Kepler died in 1630 before the appearance of Galileo's *Discorsi* and the law of inertia. If either Kepler had understood Galileo or Galileo Kepler, the synthesis that was Newton's could have been theirs.

6. The Idea of Mathematics

MATHEMATICS IS THOUGHT MOVING IN THE
SPHERE OF COMPLETE ABSTRACTION FROM
ANY PARTICULAR INSTANCE OF WHAT IT IS
TALKING ABOUT.

WHITEHEAD, 1925

POSITIONS ARE IMMEDIATELY AVAILABLE AT
ALL LEVELS FOR MEN WITH DEGREES IN
MATHEMATICS.

Advt. The New York Times, 1958

WHEN AFTER the death of Isaac Newton his biographers questioned his manservant, Humphrey Newton (no relation), he related that he would many times carry the master's dinner to him on a tray, knock, and leave it outside his door, to return the next morning and find it as he had left it, untouched. The

spectacle of the man too deeply engrossed in thought to heed
the commonalty of human existence—of Archimedes rising
naked from the bath—both touches us and reassures us. We
need this reassurance in an age when few men are for long
out of the hearing of the jets overhead. We are told that this
abstract thought, this manipulation of symbol in some way
enabled Archimedes to destroy the Roman fleet; that our security in some way depends upon the multiplication of x by y,
but at the same time it is reassuring to see the great man walking across the campus with socks that do not match. In all the
years of our youth we have faithfully wrestled with his x and
y, his congruences and his conics. We can see that given
enough time we too could master enough of the formulas to
complete the problems in the back of the book. What we fail
to see is the importance of it all. So Plutarch, to convince us
of the greatness of Archimedes' mind, pays us in the material
coin we understand well. Archimedes' missiles will destroy
more than anyone could ever destroy before. And when our
sense of discomfort at our failure to see the connection grows
unbearable, we will exile Pythagoras to Samos and challenge
young Galois to a duel.

Mathematics is the science of order and relationship. To the
extent that the world is orderly and its parts related, mathematics corresponds and this correspondence is the science of
physics. Even in the concept of accident and chance there is a
possibility of order and correspondence as, for example, in the
average and the mathematics of probability. The mathematician is concerned with the abstract symbol and the orderly
relationships that prevail on the plane of pure abstraction. The
physicist is concerned with the order of the world. By ascrib-
ing the symbols of mathematics α to the phenomena of the
world A, the physicist hopes to find hidden connections within
the world that will parallel the orderly connections on the plane

of symbol. Mathematics is concerned with the orderly relationships that govern the evolution of the symbol α to other symbolic representations β. The physicist is led by the operations of mathematics to β and can search by experiment for the corresponding phenomena B in the world. The process is close to magic. The cavemen of the Dordogne, faced with the problem of the cave bear A, represented it by a symbol, the picture α. As the picture α is under the caveman's control, and he may draw an arrow through its heart, so the equations α are under the control of the physicist. The wounding of the bear in the picture corresponds to the mathematical deductions β by the scientist. Beyond in the forest lies the bear and only trial will tell whether or not it can be wounded.

The relationships between the symbols and operations of mathematics and the phenomena of the real world are part of the problem of the philosophy of mathematics. All mathematicians today are in essential agreement. There is no real connection. The symbols of mathematics, the numbers, the forms, the logic, are part of the human mind. The seventh son of a seventh son has no special attributes. That the sum of the angles of a triangle must equal two right angles is a truth of the same order as the statement that in chess a knight must move one square directly and one obliquely. At the same time, mathematics is more than a game like chess, replete with formal rules. It is more like a code, not of ethics but of practice. The scientist adheres to the code of mathematics like the warrior adhering to the code of the Samurai. It is more than a way of thought, it is a way of life in the sense of coping with the physical world.

But again and again, innovations appear in pure mathematics as well as science, outside of the code, changing it and advancing it. These are at once reconciled to the code, rewritten and related so that even in their presentation they will fit, as if they were parts that had somehow been previously overlooked. This is the central problem of the philosophy of mathematics and on this there is no agreement. What is the origin of innovation in a science of order and relation? The formalists insist that all mathematics treats of entities denoted by words such as seven, circle, integral, etc.; that these entities "do not take for granted any knowledge or intuition whatever," but they presuppose only the validity of certain assumptions. Euclid, it will be recalled, began his *Elements* with definitions, axioms, and postulates. From these he proved his first theorem. John Aubrey wrote that Thomas Hobbes

> . . . was forty years old before he looked on geometry; which appeared accidentally. Being in a gentleman's library, Euclid's *Elements* lay open, and 'twas the 47 Element libri I.[*]
>
> He read the proposition. "By G_____," sayd he, (He would now and then sweare by way of emphasis), "this is impossible!" So he reads the demonstration of it, which referred him back to such a proposition; which proposition he read. That referred him back to another, which he also read. *Et sic deinceps* that at last he was demonstratively convinced of that trueth. This made him in love with geometry.

When Newton in turn wrote the *Principia*, he had no need to prove the geometry which he employed, but only to refer to particular theorems of Euclid. It is in this cumulative effect that the power of mathematics lies. We do not have to start with Euclid, with the assumption that a straight line may be drawn between any two points any more than we would have to start with Faraday and draw our own wires to construct a motor. The accident of birth has made us, to the extent that we can absorb the past, greater mathematicians than Archimedes and greater physicists than Newton. The same culture

[*] The Pythagorean Theorem.

that provides us with ready-made wire and test tubes provides us with a vast scientific heritage. The difference between us and savages is not in the clothes we wear or the size of the car we drive but in the Euclid and the Archimedes that buttress our common thought.

If we now see mathematics as a formal structure, which we can relate back step by step to a limited set of assumptions about completely abstract entities, we are equally sure that this bears little relationship to the origins of mathematics. The Egyptians knew the Pythagorean theorem and a great deal of the geometry which Euclid formally derived from his axioms. What is more, they undoubtedly developed this knowledge in the worst way—that is, out of their experience with the practical problems of surveying and engineering, measuring blocks and laying out angles. At best, the Egyptian Pythagorean theorem would have been an approximation, a simplified average of repeated observations. How much of the rest of mathematics stemmed in this way by fallacious analogy with physical processes or comparison with inapplicable models?

The Italian algebraists of Galileo's day worked on a level of abstraction one degree removed from that of arithmetic. Instead of manipulating numbers, they employed symbols to represent a number not yet known. Their algebra was still rhetorical; the full symbolism of the equation was being developed. The statement of a problem was always in terms of bricks or horses and geese and the first difficulty of the mathematician was to free his mind of the extraneous clutter of information that he held about the particulars of bricks, horses, and geese. In 1637, Descartes introduced the custom of using letters at the end of the alphabet, x, y, and z, for *variables*, that is, entities that may take on any value with defined limits, and a fully symbolic algebra was available for the first time. The symbols of algebraic equations could be manipulated by the ordinary arithmetic operations, multiplication, division, powers, roots, etc., or substituted one for the other, or by numbers, within the restriction that all these operations preserve the balance of the equation.

One of the weaknesses in Euclid and a general characteristic of Greek mathematics was that each successive proof was a new triumph of skill and ingenuity, but there was no general method for the proof of theorems to correspond to the algebraic method for the proof of problems. One could admire the cleverness of Euclid and follow the reasoning, but there was never any evidence of how the proof had been found or of how to determine another. Geometry was not like arithmetic, in which all operations are simply repetitions of the process of counting. Multiplication, for example, is a repetitive addition, and raising to a power is a repetitive multiplication. The modern high-speed computer is limited in its operation to adding one and zero. The machine is capable of detecting whether a current is on or off. But by repeating this many times, the machine can represent any number as a child might count by adding matchsticks, and by repeating the number the machine can multiply. Since all its operations take place with the speed of electricity, the machine can divide a ten-digit number by another ten-digit number and obtain the answer in a time measured in thousandths of a second. The development of the high-speed computer completes the reduction of the operations of arithmetic to a completely automatic process and by removing these mechanical processes from the direct control of the mind to their proper place, the machine, the human mind has been freed. It is a development as significant as the replacement of human labor by machine power. We are beginning to be aware of the problems of a society so organized that a teenager can manipulate 255 horsepower with the snap of a button. We have not yet grasped the potential of a culture that permits the same teenager to operate with a correspondingly multiple intellectual power.

What arithmetic can do with numbers, algebra can do with problems. If Martin has twice as many apples as the days till April's birthday, and he eats one every Tuesday and Sunday, how many will be left? It is a particular problem, a special case of the ancient intercourse between x and y, and we have only to translate the particulars of apples and Tuesdays to the symbols and apply the arithmetic rules to know the answers for any birthday April chooses. The fusion of the direct method of problem solving which was algebra to the reasoning of geometry was the work of René Descartes, 1596–1650.

René Descartes was the son of a Breton Parliamentary counsellor. "The Societie of Jesus glorie in that theyr order had the educating of him," said Aubrey. He began life as a professional soldier, serving indiscriminately in the Dutch, German, and French armies, but the inactivity and the boredom of military life soon led him to the reform of philosophy. It is said that he lay in bed late in the mornings while quartered at Egmont near the Hague and that, watching a fly buzzing around in the corner of his room, he invented the idea of coordinate geometry and the modern graph. The idea of the graph, of representing number by line or picture is older than the Pythagorean Brotherhood. The earliest invention of number must have arisen with the idea of a mechanical or pictorial representation, counting by heaps of pebbles or on fingers and toes. The Egyptians developed geometry out of surveying and the Greeks never questioned the association of geometry with space and form. Descartes' great innovation was to divorce geometry from any a priori concepts of line and form and space and marry it instead to number and algebra. The position of the fly in the corner of the bedroom could be represented by three numbers standing for the distance of the fly down from the ceiling and out from each wall. If three additional numbers were obtained a moment later for a new position, then the differences between the two sets of numbers would be the distances covered by the fly in the time between the two instants. A definite algebraic equation corresponded to the path of the fly. The path was a pictorial representation, a mapping of the equation. Each position of the fly corresponds to a definite set of values for the x, y, and z of the equation— a solution of the equation. Similarly, every possible solution of the equation, every possible set of three values for x, y, and z preserving the balance of the equation, must represent a point of the path of the fly. If instead of representing a path an equation were to represent a velocity or a fluctuation of temperature with time, Descartes realized that it would still bear the same direct correspondence to a spatial representation. Every possible solution of the equation could be represented by a point on a graph. Every possible array of points could be represented by some equation or combination of equations. Equations of the form $y = mx + b$ will be represented by straight lines, equations of the form $x^2 + y^2 = c^2$, by circles. The abstract relationships between Martin's apples and April's birthdays have shape and form. Time and temperature and force and velocity are mappable with length and breadth and width, and the relationships of Galileo take visible and tangible shape. The insights of geometry are at one sweep incorporated into algebraic analysis. For example, if every point on a line is a solution of one equation and if two lines intersect, then the point of intersection must be a solution common to both equations.

Descartes was not primarily concerned with geometry or algebra or even his discovery of analytic geometry. His aim was no less than the complete reform of philosophy. His was an age when it was still possible to conceive of a philosophic system that would encompass the sum of all knowledge, past, present, and future. He looked for a method of truth, as he looked for a method of geometry, in the recesses of his own mind, in the fundamental and obviously incontestable axioms from which all the rest could be derived. He divested himself of all prejudices and preconceptions and so-called knowledge, and searched instead for the absolute truth on which to found a universal system, as Euclid had long before founded a geometry.

His dissection of all knowledge left him with but one certainty, his consciousness of self. "I think, therefore I am." It was not quite enough. To be able to deduce, he was obliged to postulate that every effect must have a proportionate cause, and that the ideas of perfection, space, time, and mass are innate to the mind. In closely reasoned arguments, Descartes arrived at the idea of a distinction between spirit and matter. Man alone was an inhabitant of both spheres. The machine (animal) plus the soul was a man. Since animals were machines lacking souls, they could feel nothing and the squeaks they might emit were like the creaking and groaning of a Flemish mill—mere mechanical camouflage. For a period there were Cartesian philosophers who would vivisect an animal before their classes to marvel at the precise mimicry of suffering that the machine displayed. For if one were not protected by the armor of deductive logic and did not know that the beast lacked a soul, one would have sworn the animal was in pain.

From his ideas on being, causation, and perfection, Descartes arrived at the idea of God and this in turn led to the dualism between spirit and matter. To maintain this dualism it was necessary that God rule by natural law. The universe for Descartes was a machine set in motion at the Creation and maintained, not by the active intervention of the Deity, but by the operation of laws of nature. Out of this method, Descartes emerged with more results than we would have expected. His mechanism set the pattern for scientific explanation for the next two hundred years. He conceived of the universe as an evolving system, a system developing in time with a history and a future, which is a decidedly nonmechanical notion. His development of the idea Leonardo had explored—that the body was a mechanical system—laid the philosophical groundwork for zoology and experimental medicine. From the idea of a fixed creation he derived the idea of a fixed quantity of motion put into the universe at the beginning, which Newton was to express as the law of conservation of momentum.

Descartes wished to enthrone a philosophy of mechanism based on his analytic method of deductive reasoning, but his methods provided magnificent tools for his rivals, the Baconian experimental scientists. His mathematics was only the hand-maiden of his physics, but it was the mathematics that sur-vived to serve a Newtonian master, and Descartes' universal cosmology that proved untenable. He provided the rationale for the mechanism of the age that followed him but his own account of this mechanism as a continuous space of contiguous particles in swirling vortices like ether whirlpools, carrying planets about the sun and moons about the planets, was vague and not susceptible of mathematical analysis. A cautious man, Descartes pointed out the relativity of motion to avoid condemnation on the same grounds as Galileo. From the point of view of an observer on the earth, it was the sun that did the moving. When he learned of Galileo's condemnation in 1633 he withdrew his own manuscript on the system of the world. "In order that I should not remain irresolute in my actions while reason obliged me to be so in my judgements," Descartes wrote, ". . . I formed for myself a code of morals. . . . The first was to obey the laws and customs of my country, adhering constantly to the religion in which by God's grace I had been instructed since my childhood. . . ."

But in 1663 Descartes' works joined those of Galileo on the *Index Expurgatorius*. In an age of thought control, prudence alone was not a safeguard.

The earliest idea, that mathematics is the science of quantity, stems from Aristotle. Auguste Comte identified mathematics with measurement. The idealist philosopher Kant considered mathematics as a reflection of the order inherent in the human mind. Kant did not feel that Euclid's straight line and angle and identity were drawn from experience but rather that these ideas were innate, absolute truths. By the middle of the nineteenth century, however, important branches of mathematics were developed, such as the algebra of logic, which have nothing to do with quantity and measurement. In 1870, the American mathematician Benjamin Peirce could write that "mathematics is the science which draws necessary conclusions." The school of the formalists was founded by Giuseppe Peano, who began by asserting that the elements of geometry were *mere things* without inherent properties such as straightness or extension. Peano's researches led him to a system of postulates to define the integers of arithmetic and thereby the foundations of analysis.

The school loosely termed "intuitionists" deny that the branches of mathematics can be obtained by a straightforward process of deduction from any set of postulates. The French mathematician Henri Poincaré insisted that the systems of axioms were incomplete without induction and that this fundamental leap of the mind was outside logic. Ultimately, mathematical invention rests upon intuition.

"If all the propositions which mathematicians enunciate can be deducted one from the other by the rules of formal logic, why is not mathematics reduced to an immense tautology?

. . . Shall we then admit that the theorems which fill so many volumes are nothing but devious ways of saying that A is A?"

In this challenge to pure formalism we are led inexorably back to Pythagoras and the identification of number with the world. So far, no mathematical development has yet appeared that has not sooner or later found application in the world of phenomena.

7. The Wonderful Machine

THERE IS BUT ONE UNIVERSE . . . IT CAN HAPPEN TO BUT ONE MAN IN THE WORLD'S HISTORY TO BE THE INTERPRETER OF ITS LAWS.

JOSEPH LAGRANGE (1736–1813)

WHEN ROBERT HOOKE succeeded to the post of secretary of the Royal Society, he wrote to Isaac Newton, a young scholar at Cambridge, to invite him to resume his scientific intercourse with the Society. The relationship between the two men was a strained one. Newton had earlier written to the Royal Society to suggest that white light was a mixture of all the colors of the spectrum. He demonstrated this by refracting a beam of sunlight into the colors of the spectrum with a prism and recombining the colors in a second prism to obtain the

103

original beam of white light. Reasoning that this effect made the images obtained through Galilean telescopes varicolored blurs, Newton had fashioned a telescope operating on the principle of reflection. Hooke, whose earlier work on optics had greatly influenced Newton, criticized Newton's paper for completely avoiding a theory of the nature of light. The problem of providing a mechanism, a microscopic description of the light or the glass which would account for this experiment Newton felt was irrelevant. Whatever theory of the nature of light was ultimately adopted, the phenomenon of the colors would still proceed as he had described it, and his reflecting telescope was the direct fruit of this concentration upon the knowable rather than hypotheses on the unprovable.

The Royal Society of London was then just fourteen years in existence. The center of gravity of European thought had shifted after the death of Kepler and the condemnation of Galileo to the English Channel and the three expanding powers of England, France, and the Dutch Republic. The scientific spirit flourished in England in particular. The Puritan tradition of study and labor and the maritime supremacy of the Channel powers combined to produce a latter seventeenth-century flowering that rivaled even the glories of the Elizabethan age. Charles II, shortly after his restoration in 1660, chartered the Royal Society of London in the tradition of Francis Bacon who had prophesied great things from the collection of natural facts. The rival Royal Academy of Paris was founded in 1666. The modern system of cooperative cumulative endeavor in the sciences had begun.

Hooke, who had been the demonstrator for the Royal Society from the beginning, wrote to Newton saying that they had no real quarrel. They had been "put together by the ears," he insisted, by the previous secretary, Henry Oldenburg—Gruber dol—as Hooke referred to him contemptuously. On Oldenburg death, Hooke succeeding temporarily to his duties took the occasion to renew the contact with the touchy mathematician at Cambridge.

In a stiffly courteous reply, Newton suggested a brilliant experiment to prove the motion of the earth. It was another Leaning Tower experiment. Galileo had suggested that no experiment made within a moving system can detect the motion of the system. This Galilean principle of relativity is unfortunate because it suggests that there is no physical test between the heliocentric and geocentric ideas. For Newton, Galileo's principle of relativity did not apply to a circular motion like the rotation of the earth. The top of a tower being further away from the center of the earth than the bottom must move more rapidly, just as the outside of a phonograph record moves more rapidly than the center. A bullet dropped from the top of a tower would therefore, Newton wrote,

> . . . not descend the perpendicular AC, but outrunning the parts of the earth, will shoot forward to the east side of the Perpendicular describing in its fall a spiral line ADEC, quite contrary to the opinion of the vulgar who think that, if the earth moved, heavy bodies in falling would be outrun by its parts and fall on the west side of the perpendicular.

Newton had made two errors and it is a measure of the thoroughness with which the latter seventeenth-century scientists worked that Hooke was immediately aware of these. The first was trivial. Since London was well north of the equator, the bullet drawn to the center of the earth would fall to the southeast, and not the east of the tower. Newton's awareness that the Galilean principle of relativity did not apply to the rotation of the earth and the suggested experiment were deserving of more than the notice of this trivial error. The experiment was performed several times with success, but Newton never for-

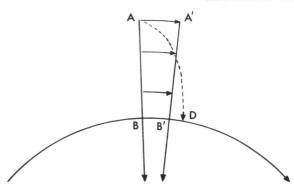

Fig. 18. *Newton's experiment to prove the rotation of the earth.* While the earth's rotation carries the base from B to B', a stone released at A falls to the point D, ahead of B'. This is because the top moving with the velocity of AA' is faster than the bottom by B'D.

gave Hooke for catching him up. The second error was more serious.

> But as to the kind of curue line which you seem to suppose it to Desend by . . . Viz° a kind of spiral which after some few revolutions Leave it in the Center of the Earth my theory of circular motion (compounded by a Direct motion [i.e., a straight, uniform motion] and an attractiue one to a Center) makes me suppose it would be very differing and nothing at all akin to a Spirall but rather a kind Elleptueid.

In asserting that bodies falling toward an attracting center fall in a closed curve, Hooke was pointing out for the first time that planetary and satellite motions are those of free fall. The planets go around in their courses, the moons in theirs, because they are falling perpetually around their centers of attraction.

Newton, who had more than enough of contradiction by Hooke, was furious at having been corrected before the Roya

Society. He wrote back briefly acknowledging that the bullet would fall to the southeast, rather than the east and that

> . . . if its gravity be supposed uniform it will not descend in a spiral to y^e very center but circulate wth an alternate ascent & descent made by its vis centrifuga & gravity alternately overballancing one another. Yet I imagin y^e body will not describe an Ellipsoeid but rather suit a figure as is represented by $A F O G$ . . .

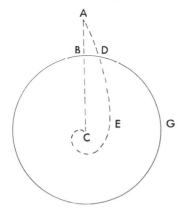

Fig. 19. *Newton's diagram of the path of a falling body* (after Koyré).

Newton had mistaken the problem. His curve was correct *its gravity be supposed uniform,* Hooke wrote, ". . . but my opposition is that the attraction always is in duplicate proportion to the distance from the center reciprocall . . ." or in modern terms, Hooke assumed, $f = \dfrac{k}{r^2}$, where f is the attractive force, k a constant of proportionality, and r the distance to the center. Hooke was using the terrestrial example to solve the cosmological problem and Newton indicated that as of 1675 he had not related the terrestrial force of gravitation to plan-

etary orbits. The inverse square law stems directly from Kepler's Harmonic Law and was therefore clearly understood to
explain the orbital diameters and velocities of the planets in
the group of the Royal Society and its correspondents. What
had not been thought of except by Hooke was the connection
of the inverse square law to terrestrial gravity; nor had the
connection of the inverse square law with the elliptical paths
of the planets been shown. This, in a subsequent letter, Hooke
appealed to Newton to do.

According to Newton, the problem had an entirely different
genesis in his mind. Resting in his mother's garden during the
plague years of 1665–1666, "I was then in the prime of my life
for invention," . . . a falling apple set him off as once the rising bath water had given Archimedes his inspiration. He saw
that the force of gravitation extended beyond the earth to the
tops of the trees and his reasoning was that it must then extend beyond the trees to the moon and that it would therefore
account for the motion of the moon. Newton's full theory, the
Mathematical Principles of Natural Philosophy, was published
in 1687 and its effect on world thought was immediate and
profound.

The universal theory of gravitation propounded by Newton
is the central part of the *Principia*. It asserts that there is a
force of attraction between all particles in the universe.* All
bodies of matter, wherever they may be, are drawn inexorably
toward all other bodies by the attractive force, which depends
solely upon the quantity of matter (mass) of the bodies and
the distances between them. The constant of gravitation, γ, of
Newton's Law is a *universal constant*. It is one of the numbers
built into the frame of the universe. It holds for all time and
all space. There is a limited group of such defining numbers, of

* $f = \gamma \dfrac{m_1 m_2}{r^2}$.

which other examples are the charge on the electron, *e;* the velocity of light, *c;* and Planck's constant *h.* Since these numbers are fundamental to the whole of the physical universe, science, conceived of as a working towards fewer and simpler assumptions, has been described as engaged in finding and measuring the universal constants. Unlike numbers such as π, or the base of natural logarithms, which can be determined a priori, by mathematical reasoning, the universal constants are *empirical.* They must be determined by measurement. The old argument of the idealist, which would hold that the cow in the field has no existence except for the mind of the beholder, so that when you turn your back the cow ceases to exist, may apply to the numbers of mathematics which cannot be said to have existence other than as entities in the human mind. But the nonidealist, like Johnson coming out of Bishop Berkeley's lecture and smartly kicking a stone, "Thus I refute Berkeley!" points to the universal constants as evidence that there is a world external to the mind. For the mind could conceive of other ways to fashion a universe, other velocities at which light could travel, and other proportions between force and matter and distances between bodies, but it is nevertheless true that in this universe, which is the only one we know, those numbers are fixed and their values are c and γ and e and h. There is a view of science that holds that the limiting set of such numbers, that is, the fundamental group, which cannot be derived from others and from which all others can be derived, represents the final least common denominator of science; the unified axiomatic basis from which all the rest can be derived. When all such constants are known and measured, according to this view of the finitude of science, science will be theoretically complete and its task will be over except for the important work of application, invention, refinement, etc. Since few of these fundamental relationships are still unknown, science

would in this view be complete in another hundred years, bar
ring an atomic war. This view of science is best described a
positivistic. Cf. p. 129.

The theory of gravitation is universal. It applies to all bodie
One particular application of the theory is to the solar systen
The force of gravity causes the planets to fall toward the sur
It is exactly counterbalanced by an outward inertial force
called centrifugal force. In Figure 20, the moon is represente

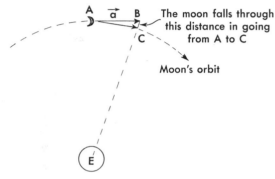

Fig. 20

at the point *A*. At the instant at which the moon is at *A*, it
traveling in the direction indicated by the arrows. If this con
ponent of the motion of the moon is considered by itself, the
at the end of a minute of time the moon would be at the pos
tion *B* instead of *C*, where it is actually found. The line $\overline{BC}$
the change in the velocity. Since a change in a velocity is a
acceleration, and can only be produced by a force acting
the direction of the acceleration, the line $\overline{BC}$ is a vector re
resenting the force deflecting the moon from its inertial m
tion. The force inward, $\overline{BC}$ is exactly equal to and opposite t
centrifugal force outward, $\overline{CB}$.

The value for $\overline{BC}$ is $15\frac{1}{12}$ feet in the units of measure us by Newton called *Paris feet;* it represents the distance fallen by the moon in one minute. Since the moon is located sixty times as far from the center of the earth as the radius of the earth, and

> . . . since that force, in approaching to the earth, increases in the proportion of the inverse square of the distance, and upon that account at the surface of the earth, is $60 \cdot 60$ times greater than at the moon, a body in our regions falling with that force, ought in the space of one minute of time, to describe $60 \cdot 60 \cdot 15\frac{1}{12}$ *Paris* feet; and, in the space of one second of time, to describe $15\frac{1}{12}$ of those feet. . . . And with this very force we actually find that bodies here upon the earth do really descend. . . .

The words are Newton's. The apple fell, the force extended beyond the tops of the trees to the moon, and on trying to compute the forces to see if they were indeed the same, ". . . I found them answer, pretty nearly."

THE MATHEMATICAL PRINCIPLES OF NATURAL PHILOSOPHY, the privilege of designing a system of the world, is reserved for the Deity and the handful of bold thinkers who can comprise in a single human mind the sum of learning. Aristotle's system was such a world-synthesis. The *Summa Theologica* of St. Thomas Aquinas brought together the whole of medieval thought, which was decidedly lean on the scientific side. Now Newton for the last time was to express a complete system of science. As Milton was the last poet in the epic tradition, Newton was the last universal architect. Others would modify the Newtonian edifice, adding rooms and wings and even, like Einstein, changing the foundation and the frame, but creation on a grand scale is no longer possible. Like the epic poem, the *Principia* was limited to the Homeric age. Newton did not modestly entitle his work *Some Mathematical Principles,* but simply *Mathematical Principles*. He meant that there were no others. Nor were these mathematical principles of physics, or of mechanics, or of kinetics, or of these plus astronomy. They were *the* mathematical principles of natural philosophy and Newton was as secure in his work as he was in his beliefs in a Divine Providence and in an absolute space and time.

The *Principia* is cast in the strictly logical form of Euclidean geometry and Archimedean statics. Newton began, as Galileo before him, with the definitions of the terms that he intended to use. These are mass, momentum, force, centripetal force, and several others. They betray the firm faith in the solidity of the physical world and the testimony of common sense which was characteristic of the Puritan world. Newton was by no means naïve in such matters nor was he a metaphysical ignoramus. He followed the definitions by a *scholium,* notes and observations on the definitions in no way central to the argument. In the scholium, Newton met the problem head on. "Absolute, true, and mathematical time, of itself, and from its own nature, flows equably without relation to anything external. . . ." Absolute space, place, and absolute motion exist. The worm of idealism was excluded by this forthright sheathing. For if one is to refuse the definitions, there is no point in reading further, and this edifice at any rate is to rest solidly.

The scholium is followed by a chapter entitled "Axioms, or Laws of Motion." These are the three laws known as Newton's Laws of Motion although they were in part expressed by Galileo. The first law is the law of inertia.

> Every body continues in its state of rest or of uniform motion in a right line, unless it is compelled to change that state by forces impressed upon it. . . .
> Law II. The change of motion is proportional to the motive force impressed; and it is made in the direction of the right line in which that force is impressed. . . .

Law III. To every action there is always opposed an
an equal reaction. . . .

As axioms, these are not susceptible of proof. But they are
plausible and experiments can come close to demonstrating
their validity. Besides the axioms and the closely reasoned
demonstration for each, Newton appended six Corollaries, particular instances or inferences, that follow from the original
laws.

The first portion of the *Principia* is simply an introduction.
Books I, II, and III begin after definitions and axioms have
been established. Book I is entitled *The Motion of Bodies* and
Newton developed the mathematics of motion completely from
first principles, employing Euclidean plane geometry in the
analytic manner of Descartes.

Restricting himself to plane geometry in this way, Newton
was faced with the problem of forcing the straight line of uniform motion into the curved lines of planetary and projectile
paths. Galileo had been content to approximate, but Newton
was after fullest rigor in every proof. Accordingly, he extended
ideas of Archimedes, which in essence treated a curve as a
large number of small straight pieces.

Newton showed that ultimate ratios of the area of a circumscribed polygon, the area of an inscribed polygon, and the area
of the curve approach equality as the number of sides of the
polygon is increased indefinitely.

This is the concept of the limit, and it supplies the mathematics that Zeno lacked. The limit may be defined as the magnitude which can be approached more nearly than any finite
difference ϵ, however small. Zeno asserted that an arrow
would never reach a target because there would always be
half of some small distance left to go. The limit is by definition
the point at which the arrow arrives *after* the halving process.
In his faith in the absolute quality of number, Zeno did not

realize that his dilemma could be resolved by fiat. The ordinary numbers of the number series are ideas insufficient to take us to the end of the path, but the limit is the end of the path by definition.

Using the concept of the limiting ratios of quantities, Newton asserted and proved 98 propositions completely describing the geometrical relationships between moving bodies and the forces acting upon them. He proved these in every case by references to the axioms, to Euclid, and the previous proposition-theorems in the book. The entire work is a completely consistent and logically perfect development. Out of the three laws of motion, Newton constructed step by step the whole elaborate superstructure.

In this way Newton proved "The areas which revolving bodies describe by radii drawn to an immovable center of force . . . are proportional to the times in which they are described." This is the relationship that Kepler found for the planets in the second law.

In a scholium following theorem IV, Newton in the second edition of the *Principia* made partial acknowledgment of his sources: "The case of the sixth Corollary obtains in the celestial bodies (*as* Sir *Christopher Wren*, Dr. *Hooke*, and Dr. *Halley* have severally observed); . . ." The sixth Corollary shows that the inverse square law stems from Kepler's Harmonic Law.

The second book of the *Principia* went on to consider the motion of bodies in resisting media such as air, water, and the mysterious ether that comprised the heavens. Descartes had explained the system of the world by filling the universe with ether in gigantic powerful whirlpools with circular inertial motion. The sun was at the center of a giant vortex in which the planets swirled like chips about an eddy in a stream. But Descartes, with the airy abandon of one who had important philosophy to devise, left the exact workings out of his scheme to others. Now Newton undertook soberly to provide the mathematical physics for such motions and with the inexorable power of his strictest of methods, one by one reduce Descartes' assumptions to rubble.

Book III is entitled *The System of the World*. Books I and II contain all the hypothetical laws of moving bodies—*if* they move in a circle, or if they move through a resistant ether, or if they are drawn by an inverse square force or a direct force. Book III is concerned with our universe as it is. In Book III, the power of the general science of Books I and II is to be applied to the particular case of the world we live in. Before proceeding to his demonstration, Newton laid down his rules of scientific method. Determined to leave not the slightest loophole, the very processes of his reasoning were cast in the form of rules.

> Rule I; *We are to admit no more causes of natural things than such as are both true and sufficient to explain their appearances.*
> To this purpose the philosophers say that Nature does nothing in vain, and more is in vain when less will serve; for Nature is pleased with simplicity, and affects not the pomp of superfluous causes.

There are more direct evidences of Newton's secret adherence to Unitarian belief in an age of legally enforced subservience to the established (Trinitarian) church, but there can be no more revealing expression of the Puritan mental processes than these rules:

> Therefore to the same natural effects we must as far as possible, assign the same causes. . . .
> The qualities of bodies, which admit neither intensification nor remission of degrees, and which are found to belong to all bodies within the reach of our experiments, are to be esteemed the universal qualities of all bodies whatsoever. . . .

> In experimental philosophy we are to look upon propo-
> sitions inferred by general induction from phenomena
> as accurately or very nearly true, notwithstanding any
> contrary hypotheses that may be imagined, till such time
> as other phenomena occur, by which they may either be
> made more accurate or liable to exceptions.

"This rule," Newton explained, "we must follow, that the argument of induction may not be evaded by hypotheses."

Book III proceeds with the *Phenomena,* which are in essence Kepler's laws and observations, by this time greatly refined. The first phenomenon states the data of Kepler's laws for the Medicean planets, the Jovian satellites. Systematically, Kepler's laws are presented for the moons of Saturn, the primary planets, and the Earth's moon. Then follow the propositions. The first proposition asserts that the Medicean planets are drawn to the center of Jupiter by an inverse square law. In proof of this, Newton cited Phenomenon I and the famous sixth Corollary of Proposition IV of Book I. Methodically citing the phenomena and the corollary, Newton demonstrated that each of the bodies of the solar system is drawn to a center of motion by an inverse square law. In the fourth Proposition, Newton showed that the force by which the moon is retained in its orbit becomes at the very surface of the earth equal to the force of gravity (p. 111) and therefore *is* the force of gravity. In proof of which he cited Rules I and II—to the same effects we must assign the same causes, for nature is not vain.

Having extended gravity to the moon, Newton now generalized and asserted that the mysterious force of the inverse square law is gravity. Gravity draws the circumjovial planets to Jupiter and the circumsaturnian planets to Saturn and the primary planets to the sun. From this series of propositions, Newton proceeded to the grand induction of the universal law of gravitation: "That there is a power of gravity pertaining to all bodies. . . ." As a corollary to this universal law, Newton was able to deduce from the phenomena the relative densities of the sun and the various planets. Further, he was able to show "that the motions of the planets in the heavens may subsist . . . for an immense tract of time," and that the center of the world (solar system) is fixed and immovable.

Now Newton reversed his procedure. "We have discoursed above on these motions from the phenomena. Now that we know the principles on which they depend, from those principles we deduce the motions of the heavens a priori." Up to this point, Book III has been an illustration of inductive procedure, perhaps the finest in the history of thought. But having established the fundamental law governing the mechanics of bodies, it should be possible at this point to obtain by strictly deductive procedures not only the original phenomena but new and hitherto unsuspected results. The new law of gravitation has become the axiom, the assumption whose correctness is obvious, and it contains within it, like the pitcher of Baucis, an almost inexhaustible supply of deductions. The operations of mathematics are the tools with which the new results are extracted from the now established law of gravitation.

In rapid succession, Newton was able to derive the original phenomena of Kepler's laws from the law of gravitation, and he then proceeded to new results. Some of these are the statement that the elliptical orbits of the planets are immovable; that the planets are flattened at the poles and hence that the earth is an oblate spheroid some seventeen miles less in polar diameter than equatorial; that the force of gravity must therefore differ as latitude changes; that the inequalities of the motions of the moon follow from the principles already laid down; a theory of the tides; and a theory of cometary motions. In every instance, the deductions are cast in such mathematical form that they may be compared directly with experience, and the pertinent observations are recorded in the discussion. The comet of 1680 was of remarkable size and brilliance and it appeared moreover at the first time in human history that a world-wide nucleus of observers existed, all linked together in a common effort. The year 1680 was rightfully the first geophysical year. Newton was able to record accurate observations made in Saxony, Rome, Avignon, La Fleche, Padua, Venice, Jamaica, Ballasore in the East Indies, Nuremburg, Boston in New England and at the river *Patuxent* near *Hunting Creek*, in *Maryland* in the confines of *Virginia*, by Mr. *Arthur Storer*. The comets move like planets on ellipses with the sun at one focus, but ellipses of such eccentricity that from the vantage point of the solar system the path is close to that of a parabola. Halley had been the first to realize that the comets were recurrent. A remarkable comet had appeared in September after Julius Caesar was killed (the comet mentioned by Shakespeare); another had appeared in A.D. 531, exactly 575 years later, and again in 1106, and finally in 1680. Halley had computed the elliptical orbit in which a comet might revolve in 575 years. Placing the long axis of the ellipse in the position of the axis of the comet of 1680, he found that all observations coincided exactly with the computed path.

As a final triumph of the universal law of gravitation, Newton was able to show that the unequal distribution of matter on a flattened, rotating earth would cause a wobble of the spinning earth on its axis, and this slow wobble, amounting to some 50 seconds per year, was the cause of the long observed and mysterious phenomenon, the slow change that had carried the vernal equinox from its ancient location in Aries to its modern position in Pisces.

In a final scholium, Newton expressed directly the unity of his philosophical (scientific) and his religious thinking. "This most beautiful system of the sun, planets, and comets," he wrote, "could only proceed from the counsel and dominion of an intelligent and powerful Being."

There is a tendency today, in a reaction to economic determinism, to deny the possibility of such a unity, and to assert the complete independence of scientific thought. This move to intellectual fractionation denies Robert Boyle a role in the origins of chemistry because he had written theological tracts, and would make Newton either a hypocritical coward or a kind of amiable idiot whose genius was too lopsided to discriminate in theological matters. But Newton's piety, like Galileo's, was real and unfeigned. The God whose praises he sang on nearly every page, was the Deity of the Puritan movement, jealous, demanding, and perfect in all His contrivance. He was the God of Nature—the laws of the *Principia* were His laws. "The business of true philosophy," wrote Cotes in the preface to the second edition, "is to derive the natures of things from causes truly existent, and to enquire after those laws on which the Great Creator actually chose to found this most beautiful Frame of the World, not those by which he might have done the same, had he so pleased . . . to follow causes proved by phenomena, rather than causes only imagined and not yet proved." The world was a construct, not of man's mind but of God's, and Newton turned the course of science firmly from the path of Descartes back to the method of Bacon.

The old criticism—that here were explanations which were not explanations—had been raised to Newton's early paper on the dispersion of white light into the colors of the spectrum. Now it was raised again. Newton himself had pointed out that Kepler's Laws were only descriptive and offered no explanation, no *causes*. The law of gravitation had simplified and unified the picture. Kepler's three laws were shown as the effects of the single cause, the law of gravitation. At the same time, an explanation, a physics, had been drawn of which

Kepler's laws were a partial description. But what of the mysterious gravity acting at all distances, instantaneously, unchanged by its passage through ether, earth, fire, or water? Newton did indeed speculate on the nature of gravity, the cause of gravity. He thought of it as a pressure transmitted by particles of ether; he denied the possibility of a force acting through a vacuum affecting distant planets with no connecting links between. But this was speculation and had no place in the *Principia*.

> But hitherto I have not been able to discover the cause of those properties of gravity from phenomena, and I frame no hypotheses; for whatever is not deduced from the phenomena is to be called an hypothesis; and hypotheses, whether metaphysical or physical, whether of occult qualities or mechanical, have no place in experimental philosophy. In this philosophy particular propositions are inferred from the phenomena, and afterwards rendered general by induction. . . . And to us it is enough that gravity does really exist, and act according to the laws which we have explained, and abundantly serves to account for all the motions of the celestial bodies, and of our sea.

8. The Triumph of Mechanism

LO, FOR YOUR GAZE, THE PATTERN OF THE
    SKIES!
WHAT BALANCE OF THE MASS, WHAT RECK-
    ONINGS
DIVINE!

                                    HALLEY

THE THEORY of universal gravitation ushered out the seventeenth century. The age, as Whitehead remarked, had begun
with an *auto da fé* and it ended with a minuet. The *Principia*
satisfied its intellectual demands beyond all dreams. Cartesian
mechanism had been vague and uncertain, but it had publicized an idea of mechanism in the universe which it could
not satisfy. Now the *Principia*, rigidly logical, mathematically

tight, designed to forestall all possible criticism, presented the complete mechanism.

There were no immediate practical results of this mechanism. It would be more than a hundred years before anyone would be able to say that the theory of universal gravitation had added as much as one loaf of bread to the tables of the world. But the mathematical system that accounted with such precision for the motions of each of the planets and their satellites, that reconciled the physics of projectile motion with astronomical observations, and accounted for the operations of tides, eclipses, comets, and the timing of pendulum clocks, was acclaimed all over Europe. So neat, so clean, so obviously right was the Newtonian mechanism that even those who could not begin to understand it were to accept it blindly. It appeared to each man as a truth which he had already known in the recesses of his mind but had never heard expressed. The world was a great machine operating according to inexorable laws with a uniform, steady, repetitive motion, a perpetual orderly pulse reflecting, this time with all the purity of numbers themselves, the harmony and rightness of things.

It was impossible to raise a technical objection to the world system of the *Principia*. Every fancied discrepancy led only to a new triumph. When, a century later, William Herschel discovered a new planet, Uranus, beyond Jupiter, and when it was determined that Uranus exhibited departures from Kepler's Laws (perturbations in its orbit), a young English student, J. C. Adams, and the French astronomer Leverrier computed the location of a disturbing mass that would account for this discrepancy and by this means the eighth planet, Neptune, was discovered. The British Astronomer-Royal to whom Adams sent his prediction of the new planet lacked faith in the precision of the Newtonian mechanics over which he presided. He ignored Adams' communication. But Leverrier's prediction went to the German astronomer Galle, who located the new planet in the proper position within the hour. Upon Neptune itself displaying perturbations, the existence of still a ninth planet, Pluto, was predicted, although not actually observed until 1934 by Clyde Tombaugh in California.

Newton's theory provided for a perpetual universe that would never run down. Always cautious, Newton had worded his theorem ". . . that the motions of the planets in the heavens may subsist . . . for an immense tract of time." But the energy of this clockwork system was conserved. The planets and moons in their perpetual fall through frictionless space neither gained nor lost energy. The springs of this mechanism were natural laws and once wound could never unwind. Minor discrepancies appeared to exist, and even Newton found it hard to accept the perfection that his *Principia* made evident. Pierre Simon de Laplace (1749–1827), armed with a calculus that had been a hundred years in developing, wrote a *Celestial Mechanics* that accounted for the minutest departure and demonstrated beyond a doubt the stability of the solar system. Laplace was one of the scientists whom Napoleon took with him on his expedition to Egypt. Napoleon, on being presented with a copy of the *Méchanique Céleste* by Laplace, asked him if it was true that he had nowhere in the work mentioned the Creator. "Sire," Laplace replied, "I had no need of that hypothesis." Lagrange, the greatest mathematician of that period, on hearing the story commented, "Ah, but that is a beautiful hypothesis. It explains so many things." Laplace's Deity, like Kepler's, did not construct circles which were off by eight minutes of arc. The universe of Laplace was infinite and eternal.

The irrefutable logical chain that was the *Principia* could not fail to influence the thinking of the period. John Locke, the English philosopher, set himself the task of translating the mechanism of natural philosophy into general philosophy.

His work was of major importance to the school of the French *philosophes*. Voltaire, exiled to England, was overcome by admiration for English philosophy and Newton's work. He wrote popular explanations of the Newtonian system which enjoyed an enormous circulation. The benevolent despots, Frederick the Great and Catherine of Russia, surrounded themselves in their courts with men of science and men of learning and in imitation of the English court of Charles II and the Court of Louis XIV they founded scientific academies and tried to staff them with hired mathematicians. They spoke of themselves as living in an age of reason and spoke of Newton as a bearer of light.

In the vivid mixture of puritan and classical imagery that so characterized Restoration England, Halley compared Newton to Moses,

> . . . who through the tables of the laws
> Once banished theft and murder, who suppressed
> Adultery and crimes of broken faith . . .

The concept of government was changed as the physical universe was shown to be subject to the absolute rule of natural law. The Divine Right of Kings had no significance in the new world of the eighteenth century. Frederick, Catherine, and Louis XV of France, with their courts full of philosophers and mathematicians, saw society as well as the universe ruled by reason, not by the arbitrary whim of tyrants, whose despotic rages might suit the punitive purposes of a vain and jealous God, but not the calm and unswerving rule of law of the God of the *Principia*.

The mechanism of the *Principia* had restored a sense of identity to man after the long night of the Copernican hypothesis. When Copernicus had displaced man from the center of the universe, the expulsion was not unlike the first expulsion from the Garden of Eden, for it suggested an accidental, a disorderly, a random place for man. He had been the chief concern of his Father, and with the Copernican expulsion he had become the uneasy inhabitant of the third planet in a disturbingly vast and confusing universe. From this night of confusion and doubt, from the conflicts between Copernican and Ptolemaic systems, between Aristotelian assumption and Galilean observation, Newton had extracted a total system with each part in its place, each contributing to the whole, and all working smoothly and effortlessly for eternity. The evidence of reason and design was overwhelming and the educated population of the period responded by a profound religious change. The Deism that they adopted was not a formal theology with church, ministers, and creed. It was rather a *belief* in an age when formal adherence to one or another church was compulsory. "The world embarrasses me," wrote Voltaire, "I cannot conceive of so beautiful a clock without a maker."

God, having designed the clockwork universe, set it going and then stood aside to admire His handiwork. As He was not required to meddle in the works any more than to turn the outermost sphere, so He was not required to meddle in the day-by-day affairs of men. Universal truths of government and human relations existed in the world, just as the natural laws of mechanism were there to be discovered by Newton. The first practical attempt to discover the natural laws of society was the Declaration of Independence where Jefferson expressed Locke's theory of government in axiomatic phrase.

> We hold these truths to be self-evident, that all men are created equal, that they are endowed by their Creator with certain unalienable Rights, that among these are Life, Liberty and the pursuit of Happiness. That to secure these rights, Governments are instituted among Men, deriving their just powers from the consent of the governed.

After the statement of fundamental principles, the Declaration describes the phenomena, the abuses that the colonists had suffered at the hands of George III, and then like its Euclidean model before it, deduces the necessity of independence. It was a compelling argument and perhaps the most effective part of it was that the British Crown and Parliament accepted its basic method and assumptions. The Revolutionary War was fought not so much in demonstration of the theses of the Declaration, for these were accepted by both sides to the conflict, but more to prove that the colonists were in earnest. By 1776, George III of England ruled by the grace of Parliament and his ministers. As far as the dissenting colonists were concerned, far from being God's anointed, he was simply a leading citizen whose leadership had been faulty. They replaced him with a president and formalized their concepts of law in a constitution. The system of checks and balances, the division of the government into three separate and equal bodies, was a mechanical scheme fashioned by men whose idea of a machine was a clockwork, and who were familiar with the statics of Archimedes and the new synthesis of Newton. Franklin had written an essay on the philosophic implications of the *Principia*, "On liberty and necessity; man in the Newtonian universe." Jefferson called himself a scientist and founded the American tradition of governmental encouragement of the sciences. The French Revolution and the Declaration of the Rights of Man were similarly conceived and executed. Eighteenth-century man was confident of his place and his powers. The human reason was supreme and there were no limits to its powers. As proof, one had only to examine the work of Newton. Not since the Age of Pericles had mankind enjoyed so boundless a self-confidence.

The eighteenth-century attitude toward man and his place in the universe was a new and a definite break with the past.

For the peoples of the Book, the cultures which rested their theology on the Old Testament, the world was the stage of the great dramatic tragedy of the conflict between Good and Evil, played out for purposes of the Spirit. The first act was the Creation and the Fall of Adam in the Garden of Eden. The second act was the redemption of man by Christ (Mahomet for Islam and the Messiah for the Jews). The crucifixion was the high point of the sacred drama. Act III was yet to be played. Act III was the second coming of Christ and the Judgment Day like a final curtain on the whole. The medieval world was a tiny nest of spheres, an egg in space and time brought out of nothingness for a moment and due to come to a certain finite end. The first Christians expected the second coming of Christ within their lifetimes, as did the Millerites along the Mohawk Valley in the nineteenth century.

In the eighteenth century, mechanical influences extended into every area of human thought. Descartes' early mechanical ideas of life were given tremendous impetus by the success of Newtonian mechanism. The idea of a living thing as a physical-chemical system became widespread. Illnesses were to be treated as mechanical breakdowns by physical and chemical means. Instead of saying prayers over the sick, veins were opened to bleed them. Patients with chills were given a fiery element like sulphur, and those with hot dry fevers were given mercury to cool them. Transfusions as between animals, between men and animals, and even between men and men were attempted. Plants growing in pots were weighed and the amounts of water given them were measured in the first attempts at arriving at a measure of the plant economy.

The belief that precise, formal rules governed the arts as well as the sciences was characteristic of the whole Renaissance movement. The Italian masters had worked out rules of perspective and thought of themselves as aiming at a literal verisimilitude, an exact mapping of the objects in front of them. Leonardo was the most prominent in the tradition of the artist-engineer, designer of machinery, architect, naturalist, and military engineer. This tradition of the literally absolute character of aesthetics is still popular.

Part of the mechanical idea of the eighteenth century was a recapture of the glories of the classical past. The new American Republic modeled itself on the republics of Greece and Rome. The city of Washington was designed about a hub much as the solar system. Public buildings, Jefferson's Monticello and University of Virginia, were self-conscious reproductions of Greek models. The cities of Greece and ancient Italy lived again along the Mohawk Valley and the Alleghany Trail. Ithaca, Syracuse, Rome, Troy, Carthage, Phoenicia, Illyria, Massena, sprang up as the surplus populations of New London, Ipswich, Roxbury, Charlestown, Raleigh, and Philadelphia moved west. The English writers of the Restoration, Dryden and Pope, and later Addison and Steele, sought models in Cicero and Vergil. Simplicity, directness, clarity of expression were ideals to adhere to. Verbal ornament was vanity, the product of a degenerate age and unworthy of the fellow citizens of Isaac Newton. The French classical stage of Corneille and Racine were similarly oriented toward the direct and the clear cadences of the later Roman models. Even music, formalized in this period into set patterns and restricted modes of expression, reflected a universal belief in the independent existence of absolute canons of taste. The development in this period of mechanical instruments, such as the keyboard group leading up to the piano, reinforced the mechanical tendency in eighteenth-century music. The generic term *classical music* is not a suitable one, since it includes the later music of the nineteenth-century romantics, a music stressing emotion, and mood, and drama.

The attempt to carry over mechanism from the area of physics and cosmology in which it had proved such a conspicuous success into all other fields of science and philosophy led to the idea of a social science. Not only did John Locke's Newtonian ideas of government reflect this attempt, but the beginnings of the study of economics with Adam Smith and the French school known as the *Physiocrats* are traced to this period and the all-pervading mechanistic philosophy. These separate strands of mechanism in human affairs were to culminate a century later in the founding of sociology by Auguste Comte, who was to discover the positive laws governing the development of societies and the evolution of man. In founding definite sciences of man, such as sociology, psychology, and anthropology, Comte provided these with a mechanistic base called *positivism,** which is still dominant in social studies. One may cite the current attempts to mechanize education by applying the efficient methods of advertising or television as an example.

This all-pervading influence of mechanism which Descartes had first expressed and Newton had elevated to a position where it reigned unchallenged was given its final and complete expression by Laplace.

> If an intelligence, for one given instant, recognizes
> all the forces which animate Nature, and the respective

* Originally positivism reflected the ideas of the English philosophers through Hume to Locke. Locke, a friend of Newton, and a classmate of Hooke and Dryden at Dr. Busby's Westminster School, maintained that the empirical tradition of Francis Bacon, the emphasis upon observation and experience of the Royal Society, was the model for all philosophy. Sense experience was the source of all knowledge. Comte assumed that this was the only possible philosophy of science and modeled his newly founded sciences of man on the mechanism of the physical sciences. Modern positivism is no longer linked to mechanism and has redefined its dependency upon sense experience in much more subtle terms. In one extreme version, operationalism, no meaning can be ascribed to any statements beyond measurements and the operations by which the measurements are made.

positions of the things which compose it, and if that intelligence is also sufficiently vast to subject these data to analysis, it will comprehend in one formula the movements of the largest bodies of the universe as well as those of the minutest atom; nothing will be uncertain to it, and the future as well as the past will be present to its vision. The human mind offers in the perfection which it has been able to give to astronomy, a modest example of such an intelligence.

9. The Composition of Things

IT SEEMS NOT IMPROBABLE, BUT THAT BY THESE HELPS THE SUBTILITY OF THE COMPOSITION OF BODIES, THE STRUCTURE OF THEIR PARTS, THE VARIOUS TEXTURE OF THEIR MATTER, THE INSTRUMENTS AND MANNER OF THEIR INWARD MOTIONS, AND ALL OTHER POSSIBLE APPEARANCES OF THINGS, MAY COME TO BE MORE FULLY DISCOVERED . . . THOSE EFFECTS OF BODIES, WHICH HAVE BEEN COMMONLY ATTRIBUTED TO QUALITIES, AND THOSE CONFESSED TO BE OCCULT, ARE PERFORM'D BY THE SMALL MACHINES OF NATURE, . . . SEEMING THE MERE PRODUCTS OF MOTION, FIGURE, AND MAGNITUDE. . . .

ROBERT HOOKE, 1665

ROBERT BOYLE, the seventh and youngest son of the Earl of Cork, was one of the founders and moving spirits of the

131

Royal Society of London. He combined in his person a conscientiousness that continually turned him toward the religious problems of the day, with a Baconian faith in the new philosophy. His contemporaries looked upon him as the first scientist among them. In his early twenties Boyle hired Robert Hooke, who had been highly recommended to him, to build an air pump modeled on the reports of the experiments of von Guericke in Germany. Hooke devised a successful pump, and the two young men proceeded to perform a variety of fundamental experiments on the nature of the air, determining for example, that doubling the pressure of the air would halve the volume (Boyle's Law, $PV = K$); that the sound of a ringing bell could not be heard from an evacuated jar; and that insects could not fly, nor could candles burn or mice or kittens survive in an evacuated jar.

Boyle and Hooke were led by these experiments and by the prevalent Cartesian mechanism of the times, to a revived atomistic theory. In Boyle's book, on what he called the "Spring of the Air," he could account for his observation that the volume of a gas was inversely proportional to the pressure by one of two atomistic hypotheses. Either the air consisted of tiny particles (atoms) that were themselves springs or bundles of fluff, material like wool; or the air consisted of uniform spherical particles that were in rapid random motions and by their collisions resisted compression. The first idea, that the atoms themselves had mechanical properties that could account for the properties of the substances that they composed, was almost universal in the seventeenth century. Hooke had written a careful book, the *Micrographia,* of his observations and discoveries under the microscope. This newly invented instrument revealed to the first investigators a marvelous new world ". . . the Earth itself, which lyes so neer us, under our feet shews quite a new thing to us, and in every little particle of it.

matter, we now behold almost as great a variety of Creatures, as we were able before to reckon up in the whole Universe itself."

To Hooke, who had discovered the myriad perfect hexagonal lenses that made up the compound eye of the fly or the perfect cubes that make up grains of salt, all the properties of matter would be explained by their fine structure. The microscope showed tiny eels or worms in vinegar and the vulgar notion was that these, by biting the tongue, caused the acid taste. Following the lead of Kepler, whose studies of the Platonic solids had led him to conceive of a snowflake as necessarily produced by the packing together of tiny spheres, Hooke considered that the regularities of crystals would be explained by assuming them to be composed of spherical particles packed together. All the properties of matter would ultimately be explained by their fine structure, which would be seen to be mechanical and to follow simple mechanical laws exactly as the great structures of cosmology.

The complexity of the task bothered Boyle. In *The Sceptical Chymist*, 1661, he employed close reasoning based on experiments of his own to found a science of material and composition. He rejected the elements of earth, air, fire, and water along with the principles of mercury and sulphur. The problem for Boyle was not one of qualities such as levity (air) or wetness (water), or of principles, but mechanical. Boyle held that there was but one "Catholick or Universal Matter"—that it was substance, extended, indivisible, and impenetrable. The apparent diversity of bodies must be due to the microscopic local motions of the one matter. From this, Boyle concluded that matter must be divided into parts—primitive fragments with size and shape. The posture and ordering of these fragments or corpuscles gives rise to the *texture* of matter. Color, temperature, taste, etc., are secondary qualities residing in the mind rather than in matter and originating in the figure, size, and disposition of the corpuscles. But Boyle was obliged to distinguish two classes or orders of corpuscle, *minima* or *prima naturalia*, which are particles of the one matter and have their own bulk and shape; and the corpuscles or *primary clusters* of the minima, which would be the smallest units with properties of the elements.

> To prevent mistakes, I must advertise to you, that I now mean by Elements . . . certain primitive and simple, or perfectly unmingled bodies which not being made of any other bodies . . . are the ingredients of which all those called perfectly mixed bodies are immediately compounded, and into which they are ultimately resolved.

The full implications of Boyle's break with the past were not immediately perceived even by their author. In their experimental work, Boyle and Hooke had determined that air contained a vital spirit or essence necessary to support the flame of a candle or the life of an insect, and that this spirit was carried by the blood to support the vital processes of the higher animals. Hooke constructed a jar large enough to contain himself and had the air pumped out of the jar, but beyond a slight ringing in his ears, he could experience no ill effects. This was because of the crudity of the pump. By trying the experiment of burning gunpowder under water, Hooke found that the vital essence of the air was also present in gunpowder. The modern explanation, that air is a mixture of several gases, one of which, oxygen, combines with other elements and gives off heat in the reaction, and that oxygen is contained in gunpowder, was more than a century away. The notion of intermingled gases would wait for the development of the concept of gases, and the idea of chemical reaction would wait until Boyle's idea of chemical elements could spread.

The spread was slow. The burst of Baconian activity that had led to the founding of the Royal Society of London and the triumphs of the Restoration died away after the publication of the *Principia*. The enormous success of Newton, completely overshadowing the labors of Hooke and Boyle and Wren and Huygens put a temporary stop to the Baconian interest in the crafts and experiment. Hooke's *Micrographia* had been the object of derision in a play of Shadwell's in which the leading character was a sot and a coxcomb spending thousands of pounds to look at eels in vinegar, but Newton was elected to Parliament and knighthood. The path of experiment was dark and results were confusing. Even in France where an anti-Newtonian tradition of Cartesian philosophy persisted, the significant strides were in the fields of mathematics and theory.

The German chemists ignored Boyle's work. A theory was evolved and propounded by Becher and Stahl of a mysterious fiery element called *phlogiston,* contained in all combustible bodies. When wood or oil or a thread of metal was burned, phlogiston was released, leaving ash behind. A little equation could be written—ash plus phlogiston equals wood. There was one difficulty. The ash (called calx) of a burned metal weighed more than the original metal. The phlogiston theorists overcame this difficulty by assuming that the phlogiston had levity rather than gravity. It weighed less than nothing. Only a generation of chemists completely divorced from the physical achievements of the previous century could revive Aristotelian qualities in this manner.

The possibility of a substance with levity leads to all sorts of interesting ideas. There is at present a Gravity Research Foundation interested in discovering insulators against the universal force of gravity. By simply collecting a supply of phlogiston as it escapes from the burning metal a useful mate-

rial could be constructed. It has been rumored that the Rus
sians are already in the possession of this gravity insulator in
the form of small plates that are inserted beneath each soldier'
pack to render it weightless. Another application would be to
slide a plate of this insulator under a water fall and in thi
way use the same water over and over again to generate power

The concept of levity in the phlogiston theory involve
reversing the sign of the force term in Newton's equation
$\left(f = \gamma \dfrac{m_1 m_2}{r^2} \right)$. Since this equation is the direct mathematica
consequence of the axioms at the beginning of the *Principia*
the axioms themselves would have to be reversed. The per
petual motion involving the creation of energy out of nothing
would follow from the reversed axiom of conservation—the
whole would no longer equal the sum of the parts.

Experimental advance is often independent of idea. Josep
Black, Henry Cavendish, and Joseph Priestley were inspired
by the phlogiston doctrine late in the eighteenth century to
undertake a series of crucial experiments which laid the founda
tions of modern chemistry, "a web of experiments," Lavoisie
wrote, "almost uninterrupted by any kind of reasoning." Even
Cavendish, whose mechanical skill was equal to the task of
making the first direct measurement of the constant of gravita
tion, could not appreciate the discrepancy between his chem
cal theory and his discoveries.

Joseph Black made the first important discovery. He isolate
and studied the properties of carbon dioxide gas (CO_2), whic
he called fixed air because it would no longer support combus
tion. He found that heating magnesium carbonate ($MgCO_3$
yielded a powdery residue (MgO) and fixed air (CO_2). Dissolv
ing $MgCO_3$ in acid yielded the same amount of fixed air. Fixe
air could also be obtained in this way from other substance
such as soda ($NaHCO_3$) or by adding soda to the solution o

magnesium carbonate in acid, the original magnesium carbonate would precipitate.

Black's experiments opened the way for modern chemistry
by showing how Boyle's ideas of combination and dissolution
could be applied. The idea of air as a mixture of gases followed
the first concept of a gas. In the same series of experiments,
Cavendish isolated and described the properties of hydrogen,
and Priestley followed with a systematic attack on the problem
which led him to the discovery of ammonia, hydrochloric acid,
oxygen, nitrogen, three oxides of nitrogen, carbon monoxide,
and sulphur dioxide.

Joseph Priestley (1733–1804) was typical of the new British
scientists of the eighteenth century. He was a nonconformist
in religion like John Dalton, Michael Faraday, James Watt,
Abraham Darby, Watt's partner Matthew Boulton, and his
associates Roebuck and Wilkinson. Priestley was one of the
first scientific refugees. He fled to America in 1794 after a mob
had burned his house thinking that he with his wife and children were inside. Priestley was a Unitarian minister and one
of the leading spirits in the Lunar Society, a provincial scientific group that met in Birmingham and included Boulton, Watt,
Erasmus Darwin, whose evolutionary theory influenced his
famous grandson, and John Baskerville, the typefounder.

The association of the scientists with nonconformist groups
was a remarkable feature of eighteenth-century English life.
The number of Quakers elected to the Royal Society during
this period was thirty times their proportion of the population.
The scientists were also politically unorthodox. James Watt,
Jr., and a friend were actually elected to the French Revolutionary Assembly. The nonconformists were the heirs to the
Puritan tradition in England. They were largely sober trades-
men and skilled craftsmen and they were concentrated in the
midland villages of England. This was the section of the Eng-

lish coal and iron deposits and the dissenters, with their passion for work and thrift, set up the beginnings of the iron and weaving industries. By the test oaths requiring conformity to the Anglican faith, they were excluded from all public office, including attendance and teaching in the great English universities. Accordingly, they set up their own schools where trade and science could be introduced with nonconformist religion. Priestley for a time was a tutor at such an academy and Dalton was a Quaker schoolmaster.

The Lunar Society at Birmingham was a scientific-political club of this new-rising nonconformist middle class. Some of its members, like Boulton, were to become immensely wealthy iron-masters, the first of the industrial kings of the new age. A similar society in Manchester was the inspiration for a great development of provincial scientific societies. The Philosophical Society of Edinburgh, formed in 1732, included David Hume, Adam Smith, Joseph Black, and James Hutton, the geologist, who made his fortune from the manufacture of bleach. The American Philosophical Society founded in 1743 by Franklin in Quaker Philadelphia was still another of these provincial scientific societies destined to exert an influence out of all proportion to their size.

Antoine Lavoisier, the man ordinarily credited as the father of chemistry, was guillotined by the French in 1794, the same year that Priestley reached the United States. Lavoisier had held government posts under the Old Regime and the revolutionaries never forgave him. The Old Regime also had contributed to the exile of scholars. The Revocation of the Edict of Nantes drove Denis Papin to England with his invention of the pressure cooker, one of the steps on the road to the steam engine.

Lavoisier may have been a conservative in his politics but he called for a revolution in chemistry. He inaugurated his course of lectures by burning the works of Becher and Stahl to signalize the overthrow of the phlogiston theory. Actually it was Madame Lavoisier whose flair for the dramatic prompted this gesture. Lavoisier repeated the experiment of heating tin to obtain a calx but with an important difference. He heated the tin in a sealed flask on a balance and was able to observe that there was no change in the total weight of the system. Then on opening the flask, he observed that air rushed in (to take the place of the oxygen which had been consumed in burning the tin to a calx). The weight of the system was now increased. In 1783, Lavoisier described his new idea of combustion and chemical reaction. A burning or the conversion of a metal to its calx was a combining with oxygen. The changes in weight were always consistent and due to the oxygen gained or the oxide gas lost. This explanation was based on the concept of the conservation of mass. No weightless substances or substances with levity could exist. Progress from this point on was rapid. Priestley exploded hydrogen and oxygen together and obtained water. Not only that, but he found that it took two volumes of hydrogen and one of oxygen to obtain one volume of steam. Lavoisier did not bother to weigh the products on his confirmation of this result. He knew the answer.

"It is no less true in physics than it is in geometry that the whole is equal to the sum of its parts . . . we are right in concluding that the weight of this water was equal to that of the two airs which served to form it."

With this experiment and Lavoisier's understanding of it, the idea of elements combined in compounds and broken back into the original elements was established. In 1789, Lavoisier wrote the first modern chemical textbook in which he was able to list and describe twenty-three elements. That they combined in certain definite proportions was an experimental fact that he knew, but did not think it necessary to verify. The idea of atomism was a hypothesis for Lavoisier, and in the tradition of Newton he rejected all hypotheses. It made no difference in the only thing that was important to him—the actual behavior of the elements in experiment—whether or not they were to be made of mysterious metaphysical particles or continuous stuffs. To Lavoisier, always the Gallic precisionist, goes the credit for establishing a logical, quantitative chemistry free of the mystical preoccupation with pentagons and stars in the ascendant and magic numbers and principles, which had clung to it from its disreputable past. He considered himself, rightly the Newton of chemistry. Preoccupation with numerical regularities and considerations of continuity and discontinuity he dismissed as the rankest metaphysics. Having shown the way to a clear, clean, rational science, this apostle of the Enlightenment could not fathom the motives of men who would have turned back to the occultist past. An aristocrat of the mind as well as by birth, Lavoisier went to the guillotine convinced that in him the Enlightenment had reached full flower. He was beheaded by the newest scientific device in the name of the reason and progress that he had served so faithfully. The chemistry he began was incomplete and it would receive its greatest impetus from the marriage of Lavoisier's idea of reacting elements with the metaphysical concept of atomism which he had disdained.

ATOMISM

The ancient Greek preoccupation with ideas of continuity and discontinuity was primarily philosophical. The Greeks were concerned with problems such as the holes made by the irrational numbers in the otherwise dense line of the rational numbers. Their extension of atomism to the real world was vague. Democritus asserted that nothing existed but atoms and

he void. As an odor would be caused by subtle atoms, thought,
n idea, light, etc., would be constructed of still subtler atoms.
he last great proponent of atomism, Epicurus, fitted it to a
ational materialistic system much like Confucianism, in that
t rejected all mysticism as superstition and presented instead
  secular philosophy as a way of life. In addition, Epicurus
aught that all knowledge came to us through the senses. By
ontrast, the Aristotelian tradition was one of Pythagorean
bsolutes. The mind itself was a source of knowledge. There
ere no atoms, there could be no vacuum in Aristotle's system.
picurean ideas were widespread among the educated classes
f the latter Hellenistic period. Cicero, for example, was an
picurean. At the same time, the mystery rites and cults de-
oted to the worship of Dionysius and Aphrodite and Bacchus
ere spread throughout the Roman Empire. The Judaeo-Chris-
an mystical tradition spreading among the lower classes
mped the whole as pagan abomination. Epicurus the moral-
t, the preacher of moderation and abstinence, of calm and
ontemplation, became the symbol of unbridled sensuality for
e new rising Christianity. The confusion of philosophical
aterialism, a doctrine averring the real existence of the tangi-
e, with moral materialism dates to this age. This is the con-
sion between the idea of the senses as the source of experi-
ce and sensuality as gratification of the senses. It is the same
  the confusion between idealism, the philosophy denying
e existence of anything other than idea, and idealism as a
cial philosophy. Atomism, lust, and atheism were synony-
ous for the pious mobs wrecking the library at Alexandria
d the baths at Caracalla. Not until the Renaissance was it
ssible for even a cautious discussion of atomism to begin
ain.

Descartes was both corpuscularian and plenist. That is, his
stem provided for particles but of infinitely varied shapes and

sizes so that there were no voids between them. The difficulties in applying this mechanism he left to others to resolve. The seventeenth-century revival of atomism was linked to the all-pervading mechanism. The evidence for a particle nature of matter, the regular shapes of crystals, the mixing of liquids and gases, the spring of the air, which led Boyle to place atomism at the core of his chemistry, was not quantitative. The uses of atomism were not apparent to empirical chemists such as Priestley, while Lavoisier was definitely antagonistic. In modern times, the physicist Mach, the physical chemists Duhem and Ostwald—the last until his death in 1932—persisted in their rejection of atomism as hypothesis neither proved nor useful.

John Dalton, a Quaker schoolmaster associated with Priestley in the Lunar Society, revived the idea of atomism in 1802 and tied it to the new chemical discoveries in a rigorous, quantitative fashion. Dalton had the familiarity with gas experiments that can only come from their repetition time and time again before classes of schoolboys. He had many times weighed the products of the reactions between gases and confirmed over and over again that equality which Lavoisier had known without the bother of measurement. The gases combine in equivalent proportions. That is, one gram of hydrogen combines with eight grams of oxygen to form nine grams of water vapor. At the same time, one gram of hydrogen will combine with sixteen grams of sulphur to form seventeen grams of hydrogen sulfide gas and sixteen grams of sulphur will combine with sixteen grams of oxygen to form thirty-two grams of sulphur dioxide. Six grams of carbon would combine with eight grams of oxygen to form the noxious gas, carbon monoxide, or six grams of carbon could combine with sixteen grams of oxygen to form ordinary fixed air, carbon dioxide. This rule of combination always in fixed proportions had been enunciated by a German chemist, Richter, in 1791. The proportions 1:8, 1:16, 16:

2×8), 6:8, and 6:(2×8), etc., were fixed. The concept of
 compound always containing exactly this fixed proportion is
nown as Proust's Law and was formulated in 1797. All water,
/hether as droplets of steam, rivers, or tons of ice must always
ontain hydrogen and oxygen in the ratio 1:8 by weight.

Dalton began by following a suggestion of Newton's—that
ases might consist of atoms which repelled each other with an
iverse square force. He thought that this force must be due
) the presence of the heat substance—caloric. Heating a gas
icreased its pressure in proportion to the degree of heating
the temperature of the gas) and to the quantity of the gas.
i the course of his measurements, he discovered that the effect
n a given quantity of gas was the same whether or not the
as was alone or in a mixture of other gases. If the pressure of
gas was then due, as Dalton believed, to the mutual repulsion
f particles of the gas, it appeared that the particles of a given
as exerted their mutual repulsive forces against each other
it not against the particles of a different gas. The atoms of a
as had some way of distinguishing their own kind and there-
re all atoms of one gas were alike and the atoms of different
ases were distinct. One obvious difference as Dalton saw it
as in the relative weight of each kind of atom, and these
eights were given by the proportions in which the gases
mbined.

Dalton introduced a series of small symbols for the atoms
id was able to explain the laws of fixed proportions by little
odels. Now, not only did the combining weights of the ele-
ents stand in fixed ratio, but the numbers of atoms which
mbined were in simple numerical ratios, 1:1, 1:2, etc. The
eights of the combining ratios were proportional to the
eights of the atoms themselves. Taking the weight of a single
drogen atom as unity, Dalton drew up a table of atomic
eights based on the combining proportions. In this table oxy-

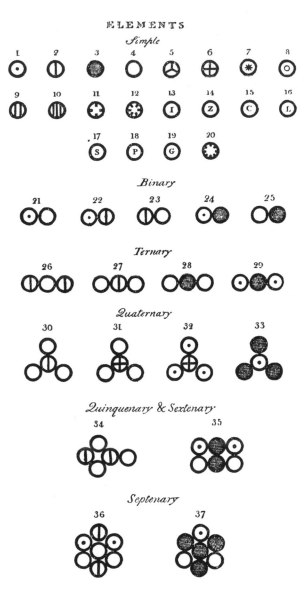

Fig. 21. *Dalton's ideographs as shown in his* New System of Chemic
Philosophy. Each numbered sign is identified in a list (not shown), t
upper three rows representing atoms, the remaining rows representi
"compound atoms" or molecules.

gen weighed 8, sulphur 16, carbon 6, etc. This was the first able of the elements. The visualization of chemical compounds was of enormous influence in the development of chemistry. The Swedish mineralogist and chemist, Berzelius, soon rationalized Dalton's models by introducing the modern system of chemical notation and with it the ability to represent not only compounds but chemical reactions in the form of equations that were both mathematical and graphic. For example, the reaction forming water is represented:

$$2H_2 + O_2 \rightarrow 2H_2O.$$

Priestley had observed that the volumes of gases combining and reacting were always in simple numerical ratios. This was expressed by Gay-Lussac, who related it to the Daltonian idea of atoms and atomic weight. If one Daltonian atom of oxygen weighed 8 times one Daltonian hydrogen atom, then at the same pressure one volume of nitrogen weighing seven times one volume of hydrogen, and the single volume of oxygen would combine to give one volume of NO.

It now appeared that the important physical properties of gases, pressure and volume, were independent of the chemistry of the gas. If one combining volume of any gas were taken and its pressure compared with the pressure of one combining volume of any other gas at the same temperature, the two were the same. Heavy gases like chlorine, light gases like hydrogen, active gases like oxygen, or relatively quiescent gases like carbon dioxide, it made no difference which were compared. If the combining weight of the gas were taken at a given pressure, would occupy a standard volume. The mechanical interpretation of this observation was made in 1811 by Amadeo Avogadro. Since reactions proceeded by the combination in simple numerical proportions of atoms of the reacting gases, and since volumes of the gases reacted together in the same simple nu-

merical proportions, each volume must hold an equal number o
particles (N_o) (Figure 22). The number N_o of particles of a
gas was directly proportional to the volume of the gas and the
pressure of the gas; the greater the number of particles, the
greater the volume and the greater the pressure. The gas law
should read: $PV = nRT$, n standing for the proportionate number of particles, P, V, and T for pressure, volume, and temperature, and R, the constant of proportionality.

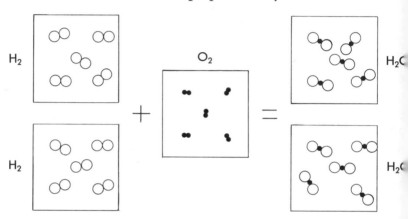

Fig. 22. *Avogadro's number.* Avogadro explained the simple proportion
in which gases combined by the assumption that a standard volume o
any gas contained the same number of discrete particles.

These particles could be single atoms, or they could be made
of more than one atom—diatomic, triatomic, etc. Fixed ai
(CO_2) consisting of one combining weight of carbon and two
combining weights of oxygen, was made of triatomic particle
as in Dalton's model. These particles are *molecules* and w
now assert that most common gases, oxygen, nitrogen, chlorine
hydrogen have diatomic molecules, while neon, helium, argon
etc., have molecules made of single atoms. We speak of a *gram
molecular weight* as the sum of the atomic weights of th

atoms making up a molecule, expressed in grams. Hydrogen with a diatomic molecule and an atomic weight of 1.00. is given the gram molecular weight of 2.00. One gmw of any gas, at the temperature of O°C. and the pressure of the atmosphere, will occupy the standard volume of 22.4 liters. It took more than fifty years to determine Avogadro's number and this is now taken as 6.02×10^{23}.

The neat mechanical reasoning of Dalton, Gay-Lussac, and Avogadro, even though seconded by the accomplished scientist Ampère, was ignored for most of the nineteenth century. The chemist more than any other scientist is empirical. He has the advantage of dealing directly with his subject matter. If it resists him, he can boil it, fuse it, roast it in charcoal, or dissolve it in acid. His problems are similarly direct, and their solutions may often be the weight of a substance or the determination of the answer to a direct question—will A react with B? If the answer is yes, then it may lead to other questions equally direct and equally capable of straightforward answer. How much A combines with how much B at the temperature T? The chemists of the early nineteenth century had to resolve all the complexity of a world put together of close to one hundred different elements in at least 100,000 common compounds. Questions of interpretation or of meaning faded into insignificance. The basic theory of elements and reactions as it appeared in Lavoisier's textbook (with some additions) was good for nearly a century of exploitation. Assuming only Lavoisier's text, the applications that could be derived from it were so vast that it is not surprising that the continuation of theory was largely ignored. Moreover, the applications of chemistry were practical. Here for the first time were the fruits of science that Bacon had promised two centuries before. In the form of soaps, munitions, illuminating gases, metals, dyes, etches, ceramics, paints, etc., they touched the lives of every man. Newto-

nians and Cartesians, liberals and conservatives, the pious and
the heretical alike were swept up in the flood of applied sci
ence, and some blessing, some damning, are drowned in i
today. Intellectuals and anti-intellectuals, positivists and ideal
ists, Marxists and capitalists, we are born, fed, clothed, ferti
lized, wounded and healed, sterilized, and ultimately embalmed
in the universal flood of applied chemistry.

The chemists of the early nineteenth century, following
Lavoisier, set the tradition of chemical pragmatism. They used
the directly determined equivalent weights of the element
rather than the atomic weights. The idea that the atomic
weights would all turn out to be multiples of the unit weight
of the hydrogen atom (Prout's hypothesis) was a sad failure
There seemed to be no numerical order to the atomic weight.
nor any relationship between these and other properties. The
directly determined equivalent weights were the basis of the
vast empirical analysis and synthesis that flooded the world
with practical results. A Kepler and a lifetime of labor to re
solve eight minutes of arc seemed far away from this new turn
of science. The chaos of chemical constitution not only lacked
all law and order, but the triumphs of empiricism seemed to
preclude a rational enquiry.

In one respect at least, the chemists were compelled to try
to organize this chaos of experience. In order to train more
chemists, to teach, to preserve the results of their experimenta
tion, a degree of organization is necessary. Simply to list the
results of analysis in indexes requires a system. In 1837, James
Dwight Dana, a mineralogist at Yale, published the *System o
Mineralogy* classifying the minerals into chemical groups, the
native elements, oxides, sulphides, silicates, etc. The element
themselves were understood to fall into families with simila
properties. For example, lithium, sodium, and potassium con
stitute strong alkalies. Fluorine, chlorine, iodine, and bromine
were known as the halogens, salt-formers. Other chemists, par

ticularly Dimitri Mendeleev (1834–1907), confronted with the task of writing a handbook of chemistry, invented the periodic table.

"I selected the bodies with the smallest atomic weight," Mendeleev wrote in 1869, "and ordered them according to the magnitude of their atomic weights. Thereby it appeared that there exists a periodicity of properties and that even according to valence, one element follows the other in the order of an arithmetical sequence." Mendeleev's sequence was essentially in this order:

Li	Be	B	C	N	O	F
Na	Mg	Al	Si	P	S	Cl
K	Ca	—	Ti	V	. . . .	

Within each column, the elements shared common chemical properties. All the elements of the first column will combine with oxygen in the proportion 2:1. All the elements in the second column will combine with oxygen in the proportion 1:1, and all in the third column will combine in the proportion 2:3, etc. Previously, the law of simple combining proportions had given rise to the concept of valence. If the combining proportion 2 is assigned to oxygen, then to every element there can be assigned a number, the *valence* for computing its combining proportion with oxygen or with the elements which will combine with oxygen. Considering the common positive valences, Mendeleev could label his columns 1 to 7, the numbers standing for the valence n in the combining proportion 2: n-oxygen. Within each row, and between rows, the arrangement was in order of ascending atomic weight. The third column, third row, Mendeleev left blank. He recognized that titanium coming after calcium in the order of ascending weight had chemical properties placing it under silicon rather than aluminum. Accordingly, he assumed that an element not then known would fit in the position under aluminum.

Once his system was set before him, Mendeleev concentrated on the orderly relationships which it must entail. Not only did he predict the discovery of new elements to fit in the gaps in his table but he also asserted that their atomic weights could be determined and a detailed account of their chemical behavior could be deduced from a consideration of the chemical behavior of the elements surrounding it in the table. The discoveries of the predicted elements followed in rapid order and the periodic table of the elements became a fundamental pillar of chemistry, and almost the only organizing concept of the subject. In the ability to narrow down the search for new elements and to identify these by their properties, the table became of great use. In the vast chaos of things as they are the great need of the chemist is for concepts to organize his research. Recently, James B. Conant, a chemist, has expressed this concept as the aim and driving force of science: the need to reduce the degree of empiricism. The reasons behind the periodicity of the elements and a theoretical explanation of the table would have been regarded by the nineteenth-century chemist as hypotheses, and irrelevant to the work that was to be done. The periodic table itself could be compared to Kepler's Laws, purely empirical and completely successful in predicting the positions and velocities of the planets. An explanation of the periodic table would be like the Newtonian theory a complete system of fundamental laws from which the observed regularities could be deduced. This explanation would wait for fifty years of physical advance. Ultimately, all explanations in chemistry must rest upon physics.

VITALISM vs. MECHANISM

Although the nineteenth-century chemists eschewed metaphysics, attended their churches, and served their kings and countries, they were concerned with the structure of matter, and the stigma of materialism inevitably fell upon them. They had ignored the atomic theory and the construction of strictly mechanical explanations for their subject, but they could not restrict the bounds of matter to exclude man. The tangible world of the senses included living things and these in turn could be resolved into their chemical constituents. A man could be resolved into so much water, so much carbon, so much nitrogen, so much calcium and phosphorus. But this seemed little better than the analytic procedures of the early Renaissance iatrochemists who would have found a man resolved into a tiny heap of ash, a puff of air, a puddle of water, and a flicker of flame. The vanity which had originally fixed on the geocentric universe now came to rest on the nature of life and the special position of man. The strange resentment, suspicion, and mistrust that were at first attached to warlocks and wizards and later clung to the astrologers and alchemists now fastened on the scientists. Newton, the most God-fearing of men, was charged with impiety; Priestley, a minister of the Gospel, was accused of atheism. To Newton's physics, that had established mechanism as to Galileo's telescope there could be no effective answer. But when Leonardo had treated the mechanics of the arms and legs as lever systems, when Paracelsus had spoken of the body as a chemical system and Descartes, as a machine, and now when chemists insisted that living things, even men, would fit on the rack of the periodic table and the wheel of the equivalent weights, the opposition came down hard. The greatest of all the battles of science was fought over the idea of life. It is a battle which still continues although the contestants on both sides have shifted ground. In the mid-nineteenth century the battle centered on the composition of living things. The one side, the mechanists, accepted the La-placean boast: given the positions and momenta of all the par-

ticles in the universe at a given instant, then all the past and all
the future could be calculated from this. For the mechanists
living things, like all things, were physical-chemical systems.
They founded a science of experimental medicine. In chemistry, they started the analysis of the compounds that made up
living things. Most of these turned out to be compounds of
carbon with hydrogen and oxygen in varying degrees of complexity. These carbon compounds were called organic and their

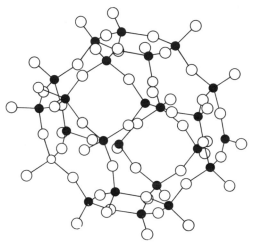

Fig. 23. *Structural chemistry.*

study is the field of organic chemistry, at least as large as all
the rest of chemistry together.

The carbon atom we now consider as tetrahedral in shape
with four bonds enabling it to link to other atoms in three
dimensional arrays. The possibilities of carbon atom linkages
are practically infinite. More than thirty thousand different
organic compounds have been identified in nature. More than
five hundred thousand have been synthesized. The modern
organic chemist uses carbon atoms like building blocks and

designs complex molecules to suit his purposes. Does he want a synthetic fiber? He has only to design a long stringy molecule. To make butter out of cottonseed oil, he bubbles hydrogen gas through to tack on hydrogen atoms and raise the melting temperature so that oil becomes grease.

The opposition to this unbridled mechanism was called *vitalism*. The vitalists first nailed their flag to the complexity of carbon compounds. No one had ever synthesized an organic compound and no one ever would, because the organization of carbon, hydrogen, oxygen, etc., into the stuff of living things required the breath or spirit of life—a vital essence. With the synthesis of urea in 1828 by the German chemist Wöhler, this particular position was lost. The floodtide of organic chemistry swept over the vitalists, engulfing them in oleomargarine, high octane gas, and nylon. Nor was the vitalist position really sound, for why should it have been allowable for a silkworm or a spider but not a man to synthesize a fiber? The vitalists were forced to retreat and adopted the view that the more complex organic compounds intimately associated with the vital processes, the proteins, could not be synthesized. The atoms making up single protein molecules may number thousands. Although the problem of their analysis, that is, the determination of their kind and relative quantities, was long since settled, we are only now beginning to understand the patterns in which they are arranged. The individual protein molecules do not seem very far from the filterable viruses, which are indubitably life. The vitalist view of the unattainability of protein synthesis was expressed as recently as 1947 by the French biophysicist, Lecomte du Noüy, who reported that if the ingredients of a protein molecule were shaken at the rate of five hundred trillion times per second, the time needed to form one such molecule in a volume equal to the whole earth would be 10^{243} billion years.

Both vitalists and mechanists argue from faith, and the overwhelming pressure of du Noüy's statistics has not turned anyone from organic chemistry to less uncertain tasks. Undeterred by the prospect of 10^{243} billion years of trial, S. L. Miller, a graduate student working with H. C. Urey at the University of Chicago, succeeded in his first trial in synthesizing a number of amino acids. Following ideas of Urey on the origin of the earth and the nature of the primeval atmosphere, Miller circulated a mixture of water, methane gas (CH_4), ammonia, and hydrogen over an electric spark. At the end of a week, analysis of the system revealed a variety of amino acids, some of them commercially useful. The amino acids are the principal building blocks of the proteins, and while this synthesis does not create living creatures or even the simplest protein, it does go a long way toward explaining the origins of life. Nor need it offend the true believer for Genesis does not say that God created life, but rather that He bade the earth and the waters to bring forth living creatures. In the beginning God created the atoms, hard, round, unchangeable, and indestructible through all their combination and dissolution, and to these there could have been given the ability to bring forth life. J. R. Oppenheimer remarked that as yet nothing has climbed out of the test tube and walked away. The conflict between vitalism and mechanism in this simplified form, du Noüy being the exception, was confined to the nineteenth century. More fundamental questions than the ability to synthesize living things remain. What is the nature of thought and intelligence? Are all the hopes and fears of men, the poetry as well as the accounting, manifestations of an all pervading mechanism? Are emotions themselves, as James and Lange asserted, the sum of the physiologic changes undergone by the organism at the time? Are all our reactions conditioned reflexes, and are we like Pavlov's dogs, animals to salivate on signal—the chemical effluvia of inorganic process?

We may not choose to see ourselves in this image and some of us turn instead to images of instinct battling with conscience to produce ego. In dealing with the mentally ill, one school of thought holds that we need only uncover the repressions of the past; the other more mechanical school holds that the disordered mind is like the watch that has stopped. Kick it and it will start again. It is possible that future generations will regard our understanding of mental illness as we regard the treatment of disease in Paracelsus' day, when the choice lay between vitalist magic and mechanist mercury and sulphur.

One important aspect of mechanism has been illuminated recently by the development of the modern high-speed digital computer. Do these machines think? Certain significant aspects of thought are definitely within the powers of the machine. Since most processes of modern analytic mathematics can be considered as mechanical and reducible ultimately to combinations of the addition of one and zero, the machines are capable of indefinitely complex computations. Moreover, this entails memory which, for the machine, can be signals in the form of punches in a card, or more sensitively, magnetized spots on a tape or a wire grid. The machine is capable of learning: that is, it can modify its behavior on the basis of its experience. Now obviously no machine has yet produced an acceptable violin sonata, but the question is not whether or not a machine is capable of thinking like Beethoven. Few men are. Nor is it necessarily a question of thinking as a human being thinks. Animals too think. Can the machine think as well as an ape, or a dog, or a mouse—or even lower on the scale of things, a simple creature like the limpet, fitted by nature to scavenge the narrow edge between the sea and the land, and equipped to tell wet from dry and up from down, so that placed in water it moves up and removed from water, it seeks a way down? Perhaps the question could be put in reverse: Does a limpet think? Does a mouse? If originality is the stamp of thought, how many of us are thinking, and how many of us are simply parroting the tapes which were fed into our memory units?

In other respects the existence of the computing machines can be a most disturbing insight into the nature of life. It can be shown logically that machines can be built which would be capable of reproducing themselves. Machines which build other machines are called machine tools. These can be operated by men or by properly instructed controlling machines such as computers. While the machine might not be able to control its environment, this would not be a necessity and many simple organisms are dependent for their existence on being immersed in nutrient solutions. Even man's control over his environment is restricted to narrow limits. He can heat his home when the temperature outside falls to 20°F. below zero, but at 100°F. below zero, serious problems would arise. Nor would the machine's lack of understanding of its own mechanism or of its purpose prevent it from existing, reproducing, and even evolving. Human beings have only recently acquired the rudiments of understanding of the human mechanisms, and our ideas on purpose are often lacking. We reproduce, take in the nutrients with which we are provided in the environment in which we find ourselves, breed thoughtlessly, and pass away. The task of constructing machines to do this might be extremely difficult but it is possible. No aspect of the process of manufacture of such a machine exists which is not already being performed mechanically. The plans by which the parent machine operates can be copied and installed automatically to direct the new generation of machines. The control mechanisms can be built and the machine tools of the factory can be built. It has even been suggested that small errors in the machine's copying of its plans would result in some cases in improved machines and in other cases in inferior machines, and thus by a process of natural selection the machines would evolve—possibly into something closely resembling man.

The complete idea of mechanism which came into existence in the eighteenth century has had its effects on every field of thought. Although it was based on the study of physics, it was extended into all the fields of science. Chemistry in particular was the field most consistently developed in accordance with the mechanical philosophy and the field most successful in terms of immediate practical results. Physiology and the other biological sciences were based in turn on the new chemical and physical ideas. Mechanism influenced the development of the social sciences, so strongly in fact that it might even be more accurate to refer to these variously as social mechanics and psychomechanics, and many writers today speak of social physics to indicate the strength of the connection. The extension of the idea of mechanism into arts and letters—the *pointillism* of Seurat or the cubism of the twentieth century are examples—only indicate how deep was the impression made by mechanism on modern thought. Mechanism in the latter half of the nineteenth century had behind it two hundred years of successful development. For the mechanist, the world was determined. The world of the present was completely described by the velocities and configurations of the particles making it up. These were atoms, small, indestructible, differing one from the other in the sequential fashion of the periodic table. The world of the present had been determined by the configurations of the past and these in turn determined the configurations of the future. Further, since these were in essence mechanical and applied alike to living things as well as nonliving, to thought as well as action, all were predetermined manifestations of the real, material world. For the mechanist, this was not simply a point of view. It was truth. The laws of science were similarly absolute truths and on the discovery that something like phlogiston would not explain experiment, it became false. The mechanist was aware of the vast complexity of the world but he had confidence in the organizing power of science. Ultimately and for the mechanist this meant, in not too much more than a hundred years, the world would be explained and science would be complete. Hermann Helmholtz, the great German physiologist and physicist, wrote:

> Finally, therefore, we discover the problem of physical science to be to refer natural phenomena back to unchangeable attractive and repulsive forces whose intensity depends wholly upon distance. The solubility of this problem is the condition of the complete comprehensibility of nature.
>
> . . . its [science's] vocation will be ended as soon as the reduction of natural phenomena to simple forces is complete and the proof given that this is the only reduction of which the phenomena are capable.

The machine of the solar system is the model for all mechanism. Timeless, unchanging, fixed in the eternal scheme of things, its history is an arbitrary *fait accompli,* its future like its past, no different from its present. From the beginning to the end, one year is like another year, and the world is therefore neither new nor old; for in a static universe, a world without change, a year is no different from infinity.

10. History in Science

THEORIES OF KNOWLEDGE DESIGNED TO AC-
COUNT FOR MATHEMATICAL AND THEOLOGI-
CAL AND SCIENTIFIC KNOWLEDGE THUS DO
NOT TOUCH ON THE SPECIAL PROBLEMS OF
HISTORICAL KNOWLEDGE; AND IF THEY OFFER
THEMSELVES AS COMPLETE ACCOUNTS OF
KNOWLEDGE THEY ACTUALLY IMPLY THAT
HISTORICAL KNOWLEDGE IS IMPOSSIBLE.

R. G. COLLINGWOOD, 1946

IN 1897, William Thomson, Lord Kelvin, addressed a gathering
of scientists on the subject of the age of the earth. Kelvin's
special field was thermodynamics, the study of heat and energy
relationships. Applying these to the heat balance of the sun
and of the earth, he concluded by unassailable physical reasoning that the earth could not have been at habitable tem-

peratures for much longer than twenty million years. A long tradition of geological research that had resulted in the collection of thousands of specimens of rocks and fossils located in the museums and universities of the world was in conflict with Kelvin's conclusion. The method of physical deduction from unassailable first principles was in contradiction with a relatively loose and ill-defined history of life and of the earth. The chain of logical reasoning that led from the assumptions of mathematics to physics to chemistry to biology and to the theory of evolution was long and often vague. The biological sciences in general lacked the direct contact with observational evidence of fundamental principles that characterized the work of Kelvin. The geological sciences appeared to be nothing other than the application of more fundamental sciences. Kelvin, in bypassing the results of geology, was directly applying deduction from physical fundamentals. The triumphant mechanism that had met and challenged man's most deeply cherished notions and ancient traditions and the everyday Aristotelianism of common sense would surely make short shrift of the loose approximations, the vague generalities, and the sweeping claims of the geologists.

We now know that Kelvin was wrong. Ignorant of radioactivity in 1897, his whole science of thermodynamics resting on the apparently firm pillar of the law of the conservation of energy, Kelvin's calculations were incomplete. For the geologists who refused to abandon their own far lengthier estimates of the age of life on earth, clinging like Aristotelians to ideas from which Kelvin's physics had cut away the supports, physical deduction was not the only path to knowledge. Mechanism, and even more broadly, mathematics and logic itself were subordinate to history. The fact that later discoveries revealed Kelvin's omissions and justified his method of determination of geological ages by physical procedures is immaterial. The history of the earth in this sense remains unchanged by the progress or lack of progress of physical theory. Du Noüy's statistics on the probability of the chance occurrence of a protein molecule are meaningless when confronted with the synthesis of amino acids. Regardless of the perfection of the logic or the theory, the "brute, stubborn, irreducible fact" remains.

Seventeenth-century men were born in a closed universe, a relatively tiny egg which could be crossed by a light beam in an hour or less. The shell of this egg was the sphere of the fixed stars and already in the beginning of the seventeenth century cracks in the shell had appeared. Although born in this egg, seventeenth-century man died in an infinite universe. The narrow bonds of space had been shattered in the revolution begun by Copernicus and completed by Newton. During the seventeenth century, the telescope had been raised to a high degree of accuracy. Newton's invention of the reflecting telescope, Huygens' invention of the pendulum clock, Hooke's development of spring clocks, the spring-driven clockwork mechanism (equatorial) which would keep a telescope pointed on a given celestial position while the earth revolved beneath it, the cross-hair which would enable direct measurement of the position of the telescope, the vernier which made for readings of a fraction of the instrument scale: all these enabled astronomers finally to detect parallactic displacement. The nearest star to earth is alpha Centauri. The parallactic displacement of this star, greater than that for any other star in the heavens, is only a fraction of a second of arc. When this is worked out geometrically, this nearest of all stars is found to be 270,000 times the distance from the earth to the sun or 4.29 light years.* This is a distance so great that if the earth and

* A *light year* is the distance traveled by light in the course of a year. It is $186,000 \times 60 \times 60 \times 24 \times 365\frac{1}{4}$ miles.

the sun were to be represented on a chart by points one foot apart, alpha Centauri on the same chart would have to be located fifty-four miles away. The great conglomeration of stars that make up the Milky Way we now understand to be our island universe in the shape of a great armed spiral. The sun is located on an outer arm of this spiral on the order of 50,000 light years away from the center. Other galaxies are visible to us as points of light that under the telescope resolve themselves into spirals of enormous numbers of stars, each island universe in itself on the order of 100,000 light years across. The distances between these island universes are correspondingly great. Astronomers today speak of supergalaxies, agglomerations in space whose member particles are themselves galaxies rather than individual stars. Before these immensities the human mind retreats. We cannot set bounds to this universe because we cannot conceive of an outermost limit. There is an old riddle which asks how many sides to a circle. The answer is two, an inside and an outside. We cannot conceive of a boundary to our universe which would separate the inside from the outside and therefore we speak of the infinite universe. Nor can we conceive of an end to the vast populations of stars in the universe.* Medieval cosmology with its quaint nest of concentric spheres about man, the microcosm, was shattered forever when Copernicus first tampered with the stuff of the heavens. But although seventeenth-century man received the notion of infinite space with relatively slight emotion, the idea of infinite time is somehow more disturbing. It is difficult for us to place ourselves in the position of seventeenth-century man and understand his attitudes toward time and history. Not only was the concept of earth history lacking, but the idea of history

---

* At present most astronomers are back to a cosmological theory of a finite number of stars in a universe which, though finite in the sense of being measurable, is boundless.

itself was of the most primitive sort. In the seventeenth century there was little impetus to study history because the history of the earth from the Creation to the Crucifixion was known, and on the best of evidence. The world had been created in 4004 B.C. at ten o'clock on a Sunday morning, as Newton's contemporary, Archbishop Ussher, once calculated. History was the lives of the patriarchs and the chronicles of the kings. Beyond that, the classical authors and the medieval churchmen brought one up to date. William Stukeley, an Anglican parson who examined the monuments at Avebury and Stonehenge, could rightly see that they were vastly older than the Roman occupation of Britain because Roman roads led right across the sites, as if they had not been, even in that time, enough of an obstruction to notice. Since the pre-Roman inhabitants of Britain were known to Stukeley as the Druids, and since no such people as Druids are mentioned in the Bible, Stukeley reasoned that the Druids were in the Bible (or else how could they have existed?) but under another designation. From the timing of the ruins Stukeley came to the conclusion that the Druids were the patriarchs of the Bible, these being the only inhabitants of the earth in that ancient period. Therefore the language they spoke was Hebrew, and Hebrew and Celtic were one and the same tongue, and therefore the religion they practiced was the true faith, a kind of premature Anglicanism.

The rising mechanism said little about time and change. In the beginning the clock was made and set running. It ran from the start as it ran at the present and as it would run in the future. Even for Newton and Priestley (who once asserted that he automatically took the heterodox side of every question) the Bible was the complete history of the world. Newton spent much of his time in an ingenious kind of biblical chronology. By references to the configurations of the heavens in the Bible, Newton was able to place dates on some of the events of the Bible and compare these with the timing of the Argosy. For Newton, like Stukeley, Priestley, and Archbishop Ussher, had broken the boundaries of space, but remained imprisoned in a narrow egg of time. There was biblical sanction for this temporal economy, but there was also biblical sanction for an opposite view. "One generation goeth and another generation cometh; but the earth abideth for ever," said the Prophet.

The Greeks too had thinkers who believed that time was limitless at either end, and who opposed to a mechanical view of the world, the notion of a world in continual flux, a world in which everything was change. The static Hebrew world view completely overshadowed this idea and came ultimately to dominate the thinking of the West up to the time of the Renaissance. Then in the seventeenth century the floodgates of investigation were opened wide. All over Europe the scientific collector of curios appeared, digging for relics, uncovering fossils, ruins, inscriptions; pinning butterflies and pressing leaves. The results of this furious activity were assembled in collections or cabinets of curiosities, some of which like the cabinet of the English merchant, John Tradescant, became museums. Gradually with the weight of this material and the examination of it the idea of history painfully emerged. Not only was there a history to man, but there was also a history to the earth. The history of the earth is the science called geology.

In the seventeenth century, arrowheads found in England were called fairy darts and were worn around the neck as charms. One of the first geologist-archaeologists, Edward Lhuyd, took issue with this view. ". . . they are just the same chip'd flints the natives of New England head their arrows with at this day . . . whence I gather they . . . were once used in shooting here, as they are still in America," he wrote. Lhuyd also collected fossils, which were known as figured stones. These were of two kinds: crystals whose uniform angles and plane faces appeared artificially perfect, and fossils of definite plant and animal appearance. A controversy over the nature of these fossils dated back to the time of the Greeks and was to continue to the nineteenth century. Were they as Leonardo da Vinci, Jerome Cardan, and the heretic French potter Bernard Palissy asserted, the remains of once living creatures? If so where were their descendants? No living species were to be found as fossils.

The mechanists of the seventeenth century leaned to physical and chemical explanations. Just as crystals of salt grew from solutions or the calculi that plagued the good physicians of the Royal Society grew in the gall bladder or the kidneys, so they maintained the fossils were strictly natural products produced in the rocks by percolating solutions. They only *resembled* living shellfish, but noticeably differed in details. Even Lhuyd, who was botanist enough to classify correctly the plant fossils he found in the coal measures, adhered to a mechanical-chemical theory of their origin. "It seems nothing more strange or unaccountable," he wrote to the naturalist and philologist John Ray in 1698, "that delineations of leavs should be naturally produc'd in this cole slat & c. than that representations of gnats should be sometimes found in the fossil amber of Prussia and of spiders in the cole-slat in England."

Part of the insistence on a mechanical theory of the origin of fossils was in opposition to a pious attempt to use the fossils as evidence of the great flood. Two centuries earlier, Leonardo had pointed out that cockles were found in the mountains of northern Italy, miles from the shore, and that these notoriously slow animals could never have negotiated such a distance in forty days. Voltaire, always anticlerical, maintained that they were the remains of travelers' lunches. Robert Hooke, with a perspicacity that transcended the mechanism of his time, tried to reason through the controversy by setting up other

avenues of knowledge than the merely mechanical or the traditional. He first distinguished between the two kinds of figured
stones, between those crystals, calculi, and efflorescent growths
with shapes characteristic of the substance of which they were
composed (our minerals) which would indeed grow from
solution, and those of shape independent of their substance,
the petrifactions having various shapes characteristic of the
former life to which they had belonged. He set the aims for
a new kind of science.

> The doctrine aimed at, is, the Cause and Reason of
> the present Figure, Shape and Constitution of the Surface
> of this Body of the Earth, . . . Now, because when we
> look into Natural Histories of past Times, we find very
> few, if any, Footsteps of what alterations or transactions
> of this Nature have been performed, we must be fain
> to make use of other helps than what Natural Historians
> will furnish us with, to make out an account of the His-
> tory thereof; Nor are there any Monuments or Medals
> with Literal, Graphical, or Hieroglyphical Inscriptions
> that will help us in this our Inquiry, by which the writers
> of Civil Histories have of late Years been much assisted
> from the great curiosity of modern Travellers and Col-
> lectors of such curiousities.

But later he saw that such helps were indeed forthcoming.

> If in digging a Mine or the like, an artificial Coin or
> Urne, or the like Substance be found, no one scruples to
> affirm it to be of this or that Metal or Earth he finds them
> by trial to be of: Nor that they are *Roman, Saxon, Nor-
> man,* or the like, according to the Relievo, Impression,
> Characters, or Form they find them of. Now these shells
> and other Bodies are the Medals, Urnes, or Monuments
> of Nature whose Relievoes, Impressions, Characters,
> Forms, Substances, &c. are much more plain and dis-
> coverable . . . to correct natural Chronology . . . nor will
> there be wanting *Media* or *Criteria* of Chronology. . . .

As peoples and civilizations have passed away, surviving now only by virtue of lost coins and fragments of urns, so Hooke continued,

> . . . there have been many other species of creatures in former ages, of which we can find none at present; and that tis not unlikely also but that there may be divers new kinds now, which have not been from the beginning.

Unlike ideas in science, ideas of history are not subject to experimental test. We cannot ever *know* history in the empirical sense of the word "know," because we are dealing with the past and the past is gone forever. But the events of the past have left their traces, mute evidences of the changes that have taken place. The volcanic ash and lava rising from the quiet marshes of coastal New England are vivid testimony of a violent past. Geology is concerned with sorting out this kind of evidence, evaluating and interpreting it. There is no shortage of geological evidence; it lies all about us. The earth on which we stand is the somewhat blurred picture we seek to unravel.

Like the rings in a tree which can be counted back to give the age of the tree and measured to determine the relative rainfall during a past growing season, the steady accumulations of sedimentary rocks reveal the conditions of their deposition. In New England clay pits, fine bands from one-quarter to one-half inch in thickness record the seasonal accumulations of debris in former ponds accumulated at the close of the ice age. In modern ponds, during the winter freeze, the fine dark organic particles settle to the bottom to be followed in the summer by the coarser clays and sands brought in when the pond surface is free of ice. The bands may be counted, each light and dark pair representing a year. Sometimes thousands of years of bands are found in a single pond. Recognizable sequences of climatic changes are found in the bands. Fifty years of long winters might be followed by ten years of extremely narrow dark bands and then thirty years of broader ones again. Such a sequence at the bottom of one clay pit might correspond to a nearby sequence at the top of another and in this way the record of the clay bands has been extended over thousands of years. In Scandinavia, where deposition of this sort is now proceeding on the margins of contemporary glaciers, the record can be continuous right up to the present.

Similarly, many rocks are observed in mountains and the sides of rivers lying one on top of another in definite sequence. Leonardo had observed the stratification of rocks in the mountains of Tuscany. He noted that the strata on one side of a valley continued after interruption on the other side. He reasoned from this that they had formerly been one continuous sheet, later cut into by the river. The river was therefore younger than the rocks. By the time of Hooke's appeal for a historical science, Nicolaus Steno, a Dominican correspondent of the Royal Society, formulated the rules or axiomatic principles which would serve as guides to the new history.

The first of these is the principle of superposition for sedimentary rocks, and its corollary, the principle of injection. The sediments settle from suspension on the bottom of a pond or sea, and therefore, Steno asserted, the upper layers in any sequence of strata were formed after the lower layers and must be younger. By a similar line of reasoning, if a vein or crevice in one rock is filled or injected by an intrusion of another, then the host rock must have solidified first, then cracked, and then, last and youngest event, the filling material consolidated. Steno's second principle is called the principle of initial horizontality. Many of the strata of Tuscany were folded or inclined, some even standing vertically. But since these were sedimentary strata, consolidated sands, clays, or gravels and limes, they must have been deposited initially as flat layers, essentially parallel to the surface of the sea. Finding them inclined was evidence that after their consolidation the crust of the earth had undergone deformation. There is an architecture to the crust of the earth and the pattern as we find it is a record of the process of construction. Steno's third principle, the principle of lateral extension, expressed the idea that strata were continuous until terminated. If a part of a stratum were found in one spot and part of the same stratum nearby, it could be assumed that the two were continuous, and if they were not now continuous, as in Leonardo's instance of the sides of the river valley, then the intervening event or material was younger than the strata. The geologist today, in constructing the basis of information for his geological ideas, plots the positions of the rocks he finds. Much of the rock of the surface may be concealed by vegetation or soil or glacial debris, but wherever there is no evidence to the contrary the geologist may complete his map by extrapolation.

The final assumption of geological science is the law of faunal succession. Evolving from the appeal of Hooke, from ideas of Huygens, Lister and, in the eighteenth century, Guettard and Desmarest, William Smith, an English engineer-surveyor early in the nineteenth century and the French naturalists, Cuvier and Brogniart, conceived of the identification of strata by means of their fossil contents. Smith was employed in the construction of canals across England and as the workmen dug through the inclined strata in their courses, Smith collected the fossils that turned up, carefully recording their position and their environment on his maps. After some time, he became familiar with the associations of certain fossils with certain rocks and with their sequence. He visited a member of the newly formed geological society and recognizing his fossils, described the kinds of rocks in which they had been found and the order of their occurrence. For it was Smith's observation that if a certain set of fossils were found in one locality above another set of fossils, then in all other localities in which these two sets might occur, the order of occurrence of their faunal assemblages was always the same. From this notion came the idea of a geological time scale. As history might be divided into the reigns of various kings, geologic history was divided into the *periods* during which the *systems* of rocks were deposited, each system characterized by a distinctive assemblage of fossils. In this way during the nineteenth century rocks were arranged in chronological order, and either from the fossils they contained or from their positions above or below other rocks in the chronological sequence they were assigned a definite geological age. The rocks of Devonshire belonged to the age of fishes and this preceded the coal age. Meanwhile in New York, rocks with fossils reminiscent of those of Devonshire were found and assigned to an Eriean System. Being essentially of the same age as the Devonshire rocks, the name Eriean was dropped and that period of the earth's history was assigned the name Devonian. In America as well as England (and the rest of the world), Devonian rocks precede the coal age, and this in turn precedes the age of reptiles and so on down the scale to the ice age and the age of man.

The geological time scale, though relative in that the ages of rocks were given in geological times and not in years, still demanded an enormous lengthening of the age of the earth. In place of the narrow six thousand years or so of Deuteronomy, vast periods of time for the erection and destruction of mountain ranges and continental basins were required. Much of the earth's crust was a record of upheavals and changes of land and sea that had taken place before the first appearance of life. Great sequences of strata contained only invertebrate life. Mammals did not appear until the uppermost section of the geologic column. As for man and human history, this appeared so recently as hardly to have begun to make an impression on the record. The extension of space of the Newtonian synthesis was to be matched by a parallel extension of time.

Not all the battles of the early geologists were fought over fossils and floods. Abraham Gottlob Werner, 1749–1817, had earlier put together a complete system of geology based on observations in his native Germany. He held that the rocks accumulated in a definite sequence, the hardest like the granites coming first from a pasty primeval sea. His views were completely inapplicable to observations made elsewhere, but Werner was a highly knowledgeable mineralogist with great experience in the ancient mining districts of central Europe. Students came from all over the world to study mining with Werner. He taught them practical mineralogy and successful techniques for the recognition of ores, assaying, mining methods, extraction of metals from ores, etc. That they returned also devotees of his quaint theoretical geology was a regrettable side effect. Werner's system, known as Neptunism, was opposed by the Scotch physician, James Hutton. Hutton studied the granites of his native Scotland and the configurations of these were so far from those of strata that he soon determined that they had been formed from molten rock, which had moved into place from below. This principle of injection flatly contradicted Werner's assumption that granite was the oldest of the rocks. Hutton found tongues of granite following into crevices in sedimentary rocks above, indicating that the granite was younger. In other cases, he found sediments made of boulders of granite, indicating that these sediments were younger than the granite. The conclusion was that all granites were not of the same age, that Werner's system with its primeval pasty sea and its step-by-step beginning-to-end account of the earth was too rigid and fixed. For Hutton the past had not been the occasion of a fanciful series of great events which had marked the landscape into the form we find today. Rather, the earth had undergone a series of changes in which forces of construction built up the continents only to have the erosional forces of wind and water wear them down. The visible characteristics of the rocks were the evidences of their history —the layered rocks were originally sediments, the unlayered formed from melts.

In the early part of the nineteenth century, Baron Cuvier led a continental school of thought that rejected the Huttonian idea of processes of geological change. Cuvier was a catastrophist. He thought of geological change in terms of catastrophic events: earthquakes which opened yawning gulfs, sudden floods inundating continents. For Cuvier, the geologic past was very different from the present. Cuvier was a remarkably accomplished zoologist and he was the first man whose grasp of comparative anatomy was sufficient to enable him to reconstruct from skeletal fragments animals now extinct. Given only a part of the skeleton of a hitherto unknown species, Cuvier could classify the animal, filling in the missing bones and even describing the animal's habits. This was not guesswork on his part. The teeth of a carnivore are distinct from the teeth of a herbivore, the leg of a running animal like the horse is quite distinct from the leg of a cat. To the specialist, the skeletal structure of reptiles is as distinct from that of amphibians as would be that of insects from us. Cuvier's dramatic success in peopling ancient France with giant reptiles and flying lizards and elephants gave him enormous prestige, which he did not hesitate to use to advance his opinions. He prided himself on being a man of science—of the mechanistic, strictly deductive science of his time. Hypotheses for him, as for Newton, were inadmissible. Accordingly, he explained the sequential populations of extinct animals by his catastrophic theory. The fauna of the past had been destroyed in great cataclysms in which the sea and the land had exchanged places; volcanoes had erupted on a worldwide scale, earthquakes had opened rifts for the rivers to flow in. Later, the present world fauna appeared. Cuvier's contemporaries conceived of this as separate creations. As the clockwork universe had been created in one time, faunal assemblages were created in the same static manner. Like the seventeenth-century mechanists who had rejected Hooke's insistence that fossils were the remains of once living creatures in favor of a physical-chemical theory of fossils forming like crystals out of solution, Cuvier formulated a mechanistic theory of life. To this was opposed the distinctly nonmechanical idea of evolution and growth.

Jean Baptiste Lamarck, who wrote the first thorough evolutionary scheme, thought of himself as a mechanist and his scheme as mechanical, because he based it on a fancied law of progress. In the final analysis, Lamarck's feeling for progress was aesthetic and analogous to Kepler's feeling for harmony. But in a mechanistic age Lamarck could not appeal, as Kepler had, to Pythagorean idealism. Lamarck and his champion, Geoffroy St. Hilaire, were too much Frenchmen of the Enlightenment to retreat to the turgid German nature philosophy, a precursor of the Romantic movement. They fought their battle (Hilaire entered into a famous series of debates with Cuvier) on Cuvier's grounds, on the grounds of mechanism. The rigid, methodical Cuvier demolished them. Lamarck's evolution was a historical idea and its evidence and defense were not based on mechanism or even physics and chemistry. For Cuvier, the idea of history did not exist and geology was for him, as for Lord Kelvin many years later, merely the application of physical deduction. He could not conceive of other kinds of science; he could not conceive of other sources of knowledge. Cuvier won acclaim in the Academy of Sciences and later served the Republic, Napoleon, and the restored

Bourbons with impartial success, while Lamarck died in poverty. The dictatorial techniques of the Napoleonic era extended even to scientific debate.

English geologists tended to follow Hutton. Sir Charles Lyell expressed the core of Huttonian philosophy in the famous doctrine of *uniformitarianism*. The events of the past were like those of the present, and the present was the key to the past. Werner and Cuvier had built systems on the idea that the processes of the past were completely different from the processes of the present. It was a separation in time as Aristotle had separated the physics of the earth from that of the heavens. The past was the time of miracles, of creations and catastrophes. Lyell asserted on the contrary that the natural processes of the present were those which, operating over long periods of time, were responsible for the present configuration of the earth's crust. The Colorado River, trickling at the bottom of its immense canyon, was responsible for the cutting of the canyon, and not a fancied sudden rift. The delta of the Nile had been built by the steady repetition over thousands of years of the annual floods of the Nile, and not by a single sudden deluge. The earth's record was a continuous record and change was always going on.

It was in this tradition that young Charles Darwin was trained. At first headed for medicine, he found dissection uncongenial. It was with half a thought of taking holy orders that he pursued his university career, displaying in it a considerable flair for natural science. Both of Darwin's grandfathers, Erasmus Darwin and Josiah Wedgwood, had been members with Priestley of the Lunar Society at Birmingham. Erasmus Darwin had proposed a theory of evolution much like Lamarck's, written up, however, in verse, and therefore never treated seriously by professionals. Young Darwin had been exposed to Wernerian Neptunism (which he despised) at Edinburgh and a more conventional, descriptive-collecting kind of geology at Cambridge. He obtained the post of naturalist on a government survey expedition to the South Pacific from 1831 to 1836, the famous voyage of the *Beagle*. On the trip out, Darwin had the opportunity to read the newly published *Principles of Geology* of Lyell.

Lyell's ideas, which are the basis of the classical geologic thought of the latter nineteenth and early twentieth centuries, were the essence of antimechanism. In contrast to the dogmatic Cuvier, who explained earth history on the basis of his preconceptions, and then arranged his observations to bolster his opinions, or to Werner whose ideas, based on observations in Germany alone, contradicted flatly observations in other places, or to the English geologists Sedgwick, Murchison, and Henslow who followed Smith and confined their work to the meticulous description of strata and their fossil contents, Lyell postulated no laws and laid down no history of places not yet studied. Instead, he described processes of geologic change and interpreted observations as the results of these processes acting through time. For Darwin, confronted on the single voyage with a variety of geologic phenomena nearly equal in sum to the total that had been previously studied by geologists, Lyell's *Principles* were a method of organization and interpretation. In place of telling Darwin what he would find, the *Principles* were open-ended. Lyell described processes of erosion and deposition as he had seen them and understood them. But these were not offered as the sum of geologic processes. In observation, other processes would make themselves manifest. Each phenomenon would contain within itself the trace of its history.

On the voyage of the *Beagle*, Darwin's function was as naturalist, a post difficult to imagine in an age of specialization but perfectly reasonable in 1830. The whole of nature was his con-

cern. In consequence, although his first publications were i
his own field of geology, he had spent much of his time observ
ing organic nature. In particular, the birds of the Galápago
Islands had made a deep impression on him. The Galápago
Islands are a small isolated group nearly five hundred mile
from the South American mainland. The fauna of the island
display relatively little variety but that little is strikingly odc
The islands are the home of the giant sea turtles, anima
whose weights may reach a ton and which the sailors of th
Beagle could disable by simply turning them over. In goin
from island to island, collecting on each one, Darwin wa
struck by the lack of variety. It was obvious that only a fe
species had reached the islands from the mainland. The birc
of the Galápagos illustrated the peculiarities of the island
fauna. A species of finch was found throughout the islands an
this species was only slightly different from a species whic
Darwin had observed on the mainland. But within the limite
environment of the islands, the finches had differentiated s
that those on each island could be distinguished from those o
other islands, although all the Galápagos finches could be re
ognized as closer together than to the mainland variety. Da
win could see that the species were modified in contradictio
to the accepted views of science that this could not be so. O
his return to England, he began to collect notes on the divers
fication of species.

> I worked on true Baconian principles, and without
> any theory collected facts on a wholesale scale, more
> especially with respect to domesticated productions, by
> printed inquiries, by conversation with skillful breeders
> and gardeners, and by extensive reading. . . . I soon
> perceived that selection was the keystone of man's suc-
> cess in making useful races of animals and plants. But
> how selection could be applied to organisms living in a
> state of nature remained for some time a mystery to me.

About a year later, Darwin chanced to read "for amusement," he wrote apologetically, the *Essay on Population* of Malthus (1798). The *Essay* was an attack on the idea of progress and the views of such men as Godwin and Condorcet. The human race is not improving, Malthus asserted sourly.

> Throughout the animal and vegetable kingdom nature has scattered the seeds of life abroad with the most profuse and liberal hand. She has been comparatively sparing in the room and nourishment necessary to rear them. The race of plants and the race of animals shrink under this great restrictive law. And the race of man cannot by any effort of reason escape it. Among plants and animals its effects are waste of seed, sickness and premature death. Among mankind, misery and vice.

For Darwin this was the moment of revelation as for Archimedes the act of immersion in the bath, and for Newton the fall of an apple. The struggle for existence of Malthus was the means of natural selection. Of the vast numbers of seeds of any species, only a few could live to maturity. Any advantages, however slight, would count in that continual struggle, and pass in turn to succeeding generations. The artificial selection which in a relatively short time could separate the species of dog into the Pekingese and the Great Dane, was matched by natural selection operating over the immense reaches of geologic time. In Malthus' England, conditions of life were unbelievably severe. Food was poor and scarce. Medical attention was reserved for the rich and often a hazard more dangerous than lack of medical attention for the poor. Famine periodically struck the provinces and in Ireland Dean Swift had proposed with savage irony that the children of the poor would make good meat being tenderer than beef and tastier than pork. Hanging was the most merciful of punishments which in Swift's day could be administered to a seven-year-old child for a petty theft. Conditions in other parts of the world were at least as severe. It took great courage and strength and intelligence to survive. Our ancestors were the few hardy survivors of great trials.

With the same precision that Newton had shown, Darwin worked for twenty years on what was to be a multivolumed *Principia* of evolution. But the idea was abroad and the English naturalist Alfred Wallace observed in the Malay Peninsula the same variations among species of neighboring islands and having read Malthus, came to the identical conclusions as Darwin. It was a case of parallel discovery like that of Newton and Leibniz and the calculus, but it did not lead to a controversy. Darwin acknowledged Wallace's independent discovery and Wallace acknowledged the labors and skills of Darwin. What was for Wallace a brilliant insight was only the opening idea of Darwin's theory. Patiently and exhaustively, Darwin had collected and discussed records of artificial selection and of diversification of species. The fossil record, enormous in Darwin's day, fell into a new and meaningful order in the light of Darwin's theory of evolution, and his own and Wallace's observations on the geographic distribution of species could not be explained on any other basis.

The twenty years of caution that had preceded Darwin's publication were designed to assemble an irrefutable battery of evidence for the change of species. Mindful of the defeat of the same doctrine espoused by Lamarck and St. Hilaire, and the ridicule that had descended on his grandfather, Darwin was entering the lists as more of a zoologist than Cuvier, more of a geologist than Lyell. Although in the first publication the descent of man had not been discussed, it was definitely implied. Twelve years after the initial publication of *The Origin of Species,* Darwin was ready for the significant postscript *The Descent of Man.*

A great storm broke over Darwin's head on the publication
of *The Origin of Species*. Darwin and evolution were attacked
from the pulpit and from the lecture rostrum. In the scientific
journals as well as the scientific societies, in the universities
as well as the seminaries, the attack on Darwin was bitter and
prolonged.* Science itself, the new philosophy for which Bruno
had burned and which Galileo had abjured, had in large part
hardened into obdurate dogma. The anti-evolutionists cited the
authorities, the opinions, and the experience of such thorough-
going scientists as Cuvier. Richard Owen, the foremost biologist in England, and Adam Sedgwick, the dean of British
geologists and Darwin's mentor at Cambridge, wrote damning
reviews of the original Darwin-Wallace papers. The Anglican
clergy led by Bishop Wilberforce attacked in particular the
evolutionary origin of mankind. Following Cuvier's precedent
in the debates with St. Hilaire, Wilberforce, in a debate with
Huxley, turned to ridicule as a weapon. Would the distinguished zoologist care to acknowledge apes for his grandpar-
ents? Thomas Henry Huxley was not after all in the position
of Galileo at his trial. He would rather, he replied, have a
miserable ape for a grandfather than a man highly endowed
by nature and possessing great means and influence and yet
who employs those faculties and that influence for the mere
purpose of introducing ridicule into a grave scientific discussion.

The nineteenth century was not the seventeenth century
and if evolution had its emotional opponents, it had its firm
supporters as well. An era of dogmatism in science was drawing to an end. As the Renaissance scientists had taken their
cases to the public by eschewing the Latin of scholarship for
the Italian vulgate, the later nineteenth-century scientists ap-

* In *The New York Times* of July 7, 1957, Jacquetta Hawkes, described as
archaeologist and amateur geologist, appealed for a new doctrine to challenge Darwinism.

pealed to the new democracy for a decision. Huxley met Wilberforce in public debate and the intellectual equipment of the
Bishop was not equal to the occasion. In a series of beautifully
written papers and lectures addressed to the somewhat idealized concept of the intelligent workingman, Huxley gained
widespread acceptance for the theory of evolution. Lyell saw
that the idea of evolution of living things accompanied and
paralleled the geologic idea of a changing and evolving earth
In general, geologists who had been inspired by Lyell's uniformitarianism were ready for evolution. Those whose background included the strict mechanistic views of Cuvier saw
evolution as an attack not only on catastrophism and Cuvier's
idea of multiple creations, but on the foundations of science
itself.

In the United States, Louis Agassiz, the Swiss naturalist a
Harvard, symbolized all of nineteenth-century science. Agassiz
abilities as teacher and popularizer of science, his position o
eminence at Harvard, his positive convictions and firm manne
of expression, lent him a unique authority. In addition, there
clung to Agassiz the glamour of the rebel. He had brought the
theory of the ice age to the United States and explained the
boulder-strewn landscape of New England as the product o
the last great catastrophe, an era of glaciation when the en
tire northeast was buried beneath a huge moving cap of ice
For this, Agassiz had been assailed by the devout. His evidence
of glaciation were their evidences of the deluge. To provincia
America, the arrival of Agassiz, famous pupil of Cuvier, was a
event of the greatest importance. American scientists strug
gling for recognition welcomed this bulwark of their cause
Americans respected European scholarship and the Franco
German learning in particular that Agassiz represented.

It was unfortunate that immediately upon his arrival Agassi
was drawn into the civil conflict that was then beginning. A

European of the mid-century, Agassiz arrived with a prejudice against slavery and no previous acquaintance with the Negro. His first views of Negroes in the south horrified him. Appealed to by Morton and Nott, apologists for slavery, who were studying the differences between the Negro and the white races, Agassiz lent his name and prestige to the racist doctrines of pluralism. Although other naturalists like John Bachman, Audubon's associate, maintained that all mankind was one, the arguments for unity were largely scriptural. Agassiz set the stamp of scientific justification on the doctrine that the superior white race was entitled and even obligated to maintain the inferior Negro race in a permanent state of tutelage. At the close of the Civil War, Agassiz, requested by Lincoln to prepare a scientific report on the capabilities of the Negro for the guidance of the federal government, entered his beliefs in the total incapacity of the Negro for independent, civilized existence. He did, however, recommend that the Negro be granted complete civil quality.

The doctrine of the pluralist origin of the races of mankind was the static notion of mechanism. In Europe, it evolved into the vicious anthropology of the Comte de Gobineau, revived in the racist mania of modern times. Against the apparently irrefutable logic of science, against the prestige of the older and wiser European learning of Agassiz, the opponents of slavery asserted Genesis. Agassiz' opposition was made up of fundamentalists like Bachman who would brook no latitude in the meaning of the story of Adam and Eve, of Quakers who denied the evidence of the laboratory for the testimonies of their inner light, of fanatics like John Brown, of the philosophical New England transcendentalists, the gentle Unitarians. To science and reason and logic they opposed a faith in the unity of mankind. In 1512, a Papal Bull had declared the Indians of the New World to be true descendants of Adam, with souls capa-

ble of reaching to God. Reason and mechanism, all the weight
of science as it was then constituted, and the self-esteem of
Europe were ranged on the pluralist side. Speaking for the
unity of mankind was an outmoded fundamentalist theology
and the nonadmissible testimony of human values. Just such
a collector of mystical notions must Bruno have appeared in
the sixteenth century to the enlightened, Aristotelian scholastics. For Agassiz there was no alternative to pluralism, for if
mankind could diversify from a single stock, then so could the
animal and plant varieties, and if varieties, then one would
have to admit the modification of species. For Agassiz, the
fixity of species was a fundamental truth as incontrovertible
as the fixity of the earth for Galileo's inquisitors. Accordingly
1859 with the publication of *The Origin of Species* found
Agassiz publishing his life's work in opposition. His introduc-
tory "Essay on Classification" had appeared within months of
Darwin's paper. Agassiz, who had been so long beaten with
the clubs of fundamentalist theology, had worked God's hand
into every species, and in a savage review in the *American
Journal of Science* he accused Darwin of irreverence. The
theory of evolution, Agassiz asserted, was ungeological, by
which he meant that it was nonmechanical.

> . . . a scientific mistake, untrue in its facts, unscientific
> in its method, and mischievous in its tendency. . . . In-
> stead of facts we are treated with marvelous bear,
> cuckoo, and other stories.

Darwin's friend, Asa Gray, the Harvard botanist, in a cautious review in the same journal tried to show that evolution
was not in conflict with religion. "I am determined to baptise
your book," he wrote to Darwin. It remained for William James
to point out that since the seventeenth century scientific questions had not been settled by appeals to orthodoxy. Gradually
evolution won widening acceptance, first by the educated pub-

lic, and slowly as older men died and their places were filled
by younger men, by the scholars of science. No other theory
has ever been offered to attempt the organization of the fossil
record. The unity of mankind has become accepted social doctrine; the scientific basis on which it rests, the assertion of the
unity of all living things through the theory of evolution, is
contradicted only by the ignorant or the intellectually vain.
Darwin was not a seer like Bruno who thought of God as per-
meating the universe. He was not a poet like his grandfather.
A good Victorian, an English gentleman, he would have re-
coiled from the excesses of Kepler's harmonies or his Germanic
theology. But the impulse toward harmony, the drive toward
intellectual comprehension which had produced the heliocentric universe and the three laws of Kepler, had found expression in Darwin in the theory of evolution. There was a history
to life and a history to the world and this could never be reduced to the unchangeable attractive and repulsive forces of
mechanism. The phenomena of nature were only in part subject to the processes of physical deduction. Beyond logic, beyond reason, there lurk in the jungle of experience the "brute,
irreducible, stubborn facts" of existence. The phenomena of
nature of the present are unique. They have in at least one
respect, their past, a distinction from all other phenomena. The
history of the world is at least as much a part of its order as
the mechanism.

The theory of evolution in part fed upon and in part contributed to the spread of the idea of progress. The idea of progress is unique with us. For the Greeks who had entertained
every other idea, for the Hebrews, this idea was foreign. It is
today so deep a part of our culture that the realization that it is
only a faith and not a necessary truth comes as a shock. The
idea of progress is the idea that at some future indefinite date
mankind will reach a state of happiness on the earth. It in-

cludes the eradication of warfare, of disease, of poverty, of prejudice. Furthermore, the progress of mankind is inevitable for it is in the nature of things and the nature of man that a better world must evolve. The physical and psychical nature of man is such that he must move inevitably in the direction of the future.

This idea, which is an article of faith with us, would have struck the melancholy Greeks as incredibly naïve. The Greeks thought of history as a cyclic process with civilization rising out of barbarism and returning again to a state of unknowingness. One could tell where in the cycle one's own civilization was placed. For Plato, the golden age had passed and his own times were the degenerate relics of a greater glory. It was impossible, however, to tell how many cycles had gone before or how many were yet to come in this age of nonhistorical thought. The Judaeo-Christian tradition was far more submissive. The world was a temporary stasis; a brief flare out of nothingness beginning with the Creation and concluding with the Last Judgment. How could there be improvement in the face of Almighty God? The cautious men of the Renaissance with their extensions of the dimensions of existence turned at first to the recovery of classical learning. The age of Greece and Rome was the golden age, the age of mathematics, of astronomy, of poetry, of art. The recovery of Greek scholarship was a tremendous awakening to the provincial Europeans, and at first they tended to react by a sense of inferiority to the past. With time and the development of Renaissance civilization Europe recovered self-confidence. In the age of reason, following the Newtonian demonstration that the intellect of man was capable of mastering the universe, the idea of progress appeared. For the *philosophes* and the *Encyclopedists* of the Enlightenment, man had only to crush the forces of ignorance and superstition to advance. The steady growth in complexity of the fossil record, the tree of life with its beginnings in one

celled organisms and its finest fruit, the mind of man, seemed
a warranty of progress.

The science of geology, fundamentally historical, with its
introduction of the theory of evolution, was the first major set-
back to the triumphant mechanism of the Enlightenment.
Other reactions against mechanism culminated in the romantic
movement of the latter nineteenth century. The romantic movement turned away from reason and away from the idea of
progress. The spread of science and education, the steady improvement in world standards of living did not appear to increase the sum of happiness in the world, or to reduce misery
and cruelty. The problem of evil remains with us, elevated by
some schools of psychology to a fundamental principle. The
confidence that Laplace expressed in the ability of the human
intelligence to fathom the determined universe has been cast
into doubt. The universe appears to be not a static machine
but an evolving complex, complete with a past, and at least as
much a historical entity as a mechanical entity. The laws of
mechanics operate within the larger framework of history and
there are no laws of history. The cyclical, recurring, orderly,
and regular machine of the Newtonian synthesis as an achievement of the human intelligence was matched by a concept at
least as grand, the concept of organic evolution, of the unity
of all living things, of the tree of life and man at its summit.
The simile of the clock and its wheelworks has been gradually
replaced in science by the simile of the highway. Our universe
is not a treadmill, in constant motion yet always in the same
place. It is an evolving system coming out of the past and
heading into the future. The first mechanists, like children,
knew nothing of the past, but boldly constrained the future
to their image of the present. As science grew, as it turned
inward and downward, it acquired depth and continuity.
Whatever was lost in assurance and confidence was more than
made up in the breadth and profundity of history.

11. Heat, Work, and Energy

I HAVE HERE . . . A NEW INVENTION IN
MECHANICKS OF PRODIGIOUS USE, EXCEEDING
THE CHIMERA'S OF PERPETUAL MOTIONS FOR
SEVERAL USES. THE WEIGHT OF THE AIR
PRESSES DOWN ON THE VACUUM WHICH IS
LEFT BY FIRE.

ROBERT HOOKE, *Lampas*, 1677

THE NINETEENTH century saw the rise of the energy principle, an idea so thoroughly bound to the principle of causation, so simple and withal so fertile, there seemed no doubt that here at the root of things was the absolute. There was a fixed sum of energy in the universe. Energy could neither be created nor destroyed. There was a fitness to things, an essential proportionality that must always prevent an effect greater than its cause or the emergence of something out of nothing.

186

There were two aspects to this idea. The first in point of time became the second law of thermodynamics—the idea of the proportionality of all energy processes. The second was the idea of conservation. The two became the foundations of an exact science of heat, energy, and work, just as the principle of the conservation of matter had become the foundation of a science of chemistry. From the two laws expressed mathematically, the operations of the calculus could derive a host of hitherto unforeseen and unsuspected relationships, which could be sought for and found in nature. The process of derivation of the implications of the two laws of thermodynamics is still going on. Thermodynamics is as applicable to the atomic-powered engines of the *Nautilus* as it was to the paddle-wheeled propulsion plant of Fulton's *Clermont*. It is fashionable today to suggest that thermodynamics grew out of the steam engine, rather than the other way around, but the history of the first man-made prime mover will not bear this out. The development of the steam engine is rather a beautiful example of the interrelationship between theory and practice. At every stage, the requirements of practice led to advances in theoretical understanding, and these in turn provoked the further exercise of empirical ingenuity.

Hero of Alexandria built the first steam engine but this was a curiosity and a toy. The Greeks had no concept of machine power. A slave society, the use of that most perfectly automated of all machines, the human being, left them with little incentive to exploit even the power of animals. In the middle ages, a general world underpopulation encouraged the more efficient use of animals and the exploitation of wind and water power. At sea, sailing methods were gradually improved and skilled sailors came to replace galley slaves. The steam engine grew directly out of mining problems, both as invention mothered by necessity and also out of the pumping technology that mining had evoked.

Classical mining methods began with lowering a slave tied by his feet down a shaft with a bucket and a tool or driving a captured tribe into an adit, fencing off the entrance, and exchanging small quantities of food and water for ore. But such methods, although they succeed in keeping down costs, are hardly competent to deal with the highly intricate problems of locating and extracting ores. Once the obvious deposits at or near the surface of the earth were skimmed off, mines would have to be sunk deeper where they would encounter flooding ground waters, cave-ins, problems of haulage and ventilation which no degree of desperation on the part of harried slaves could overcome. A skilled artisan class of slaves grew up to meet this need.

During the middle ages, miners, particularly in Central Europe, were ingenious individualists who risked the dangers of life underground and of poisonous extraction processes above ground to supply a small but steady stream of metals for the common use. To drain the mines they used chains of dippers rotated by waterwheels or oxen at the surface. They developed the ordinary suction pump and early in the seventeenth century approached Galileo with the problem of its improvement. The suction pump will lift water a maximum of 32 feet. Galileo erroneously attributed this limit to a cohesive strength of the water, but his pupils Torricelli and Viviani reasoned correctly that it was instead the pressure of the atmosphere which forced the water up a pipe from which the air had been exhausted. They proved this by showing that the height to which a column of mercury would rise in an evacuated tube was in the same ratio to 32 feet that the weight of water bore to the weight of mercury. From this slim beginning can be traced the careers of nearly every scientist of note in the latter seventeenth century; Pascal who wrote to his brother-in-law, Périer, to carry an inverted tube of mercury to the top of the Puy-de-

Dôme and thus proved that the air had weight; Otto von Guericke, Burgomaster of Magdeburg, who fashioned the first air pump; Boyle who undertook the famous series of experiments with Hooke on the relationships between the pressure and volume of the air.

To cope with the gradual deepening of the mines below thirty-two feet, Saxon miners had devised a stepped series of pumps all operated from a single shaft. Each would lift water about fifteen feet into a sump from which the next could take it on up. But the limits of the strength of draught animals were soon reached. As many as five hundred horses were harnessed to a single string of pumps at one English mine. Animal power could not be concentrated at the point of use.

For the Baconians of the seventeenth century, the purpose of science was the solution of just such problems as this. Boyle and Hooke were aware that their researches on the spring of the air contained the clue to the solution. Hooke worked closely with Denis Papin, a Huguenot refugee who brought to the Royal Society his invention of the pressure cooker (Papin's steam digester) and prepared with it a *philosophical dinner*. Papin had also worked on the design of a steam gun, a long cherished project of Leonardo da Vinci. Hooke suggested that a vacuum could be produced by condensing steam in a closed vessel, and Papin thought that the vacuum could be transmitted for a distance through a pipe just as air was transmitted for the diving bell that Hooke had tried and in which he had come close to drowning. Here were the basic mechanisms for a steam pump. One such pump had been designed by Baptisa della Porta before 1600. In 1698, Thomas Savery constructed a steam pump which was tried with indifferent success in the mines. Savery's pump consisted of a crude water boiler connected by a valved pipe to a steam chamber. A pipe with a valve opening into the chamber was the suction end. A second pipe with a valve opening out of the chamber was the discharge end. Steam was admitted to the chamber and then condensed to form a partial vacuum. Water rose into the chamber from below to make up the reduced pressure and then more steam was admitted to the chamber under pressure to drive the water up the discharge pipe. The device required steam under high pressures and the machinist's techniques of the seventeenth century were too crude to construct boilers and valves which would operate consistently. In addition, the boiler and fire were located within the mine and when the machine was shut down for repairs, the rising mine waters would drown it. But the chief drawback to Savery's engine was its gross inefficiency. It consumed far too much fuel for the work it was supposed to do.

The first working steam engine was constructed about 1712 by Thomas Newcomen, an English blacksmith, possibly utilizing information supplied by Hooke. Instead of trying to force the water up a pipe by steam pressure, the Newcomen engine was a prime mover, a general source of power applied in this instance to the rods of the old-fashioned suction pumps. It was a true engine and it could be applied to any turning or moving task. In Newcomen's engine, steam was admitted from a boiler to a cylinder and then condensed by a jet of cold water. The pressure of the atmosphere then forced a piston down on the partial vacuum in the cylinder. As more steam was admitted, the piston would be forced up and the cycle repeated. The end of the piston was attached to one end of a rocker beam and the string of pump rods was attached to the other. Since the steam had only to overcome the pressure of the atmosphere, it was never at high pressures and there was no danger of the boiler exploding. The mining problem had been solved and Newcomen engines were installed in almost every English mine in a short time. Among their other advantages, the Newcomen engine, as a prime mover, was used to operate the pumps already in the mines. They were simply substituted for the large teams of horses that had formerly been used.

An empirical advance of the magnitude of Newcomen's was bound to be closely followed by the Baconian scientists of the eighteenth century. James Watt, an instrument-maker of Glasgow, was employed in the laboratories of the University of Glasgow, and one of his tasks was the repair of models of the Newcomen engine. He discovered that the models were not nearly so efficient as the actual engines. The smaller the model, the more fuel it consumed compared to the work that it could do. Intrigued by the problem, young Watt consulted Joseph Black, the discoverer of carbon dioxide, who taught medicine at the University. Black had distinguished the idea of quantity of heat from the older idea of degree of heat. If two objects are left together for a time, heat will flow from the hotter to the colder. If no heat flows, the two are at the same *temperature*. This was the degree or quality of the heat. The heat itself was believed to be a weightless and intangible fluid (caloric) flowing in and out of bodies. Two pieces of steel, one small and one large, might be at the same temperature, but Black considered that the larger would contain more heat than the smaller, even though the degree of the heat was the same for both. Black observed that different substances differed in their capacity to take up caloric, and he thought of this as a capacity for heat storage. By careful measurement, he could determine that the heat given out by one pound of water would raise the temperature of nearly ten pounds of iron. He thought of this as showing that water possessed ten times the capacity for heat of iron. In modern terminology, one *calorie* is the amount of heat which will raise the temperature of one gram of water by one degree centigrade.

Black's second discovery was of a marked increase in this

capacity for heat storage at the precise temperature at which a substance was changing state, as from a solid to a liquid or a liquid to a gas. Addition of heat to a mixture of ice and water does not raise the temperature of the mixture until the last of the ice has melted. And withdrawal of heat from a mixture of a solid and its melt does not lower the temperature of the mixture until the last of the liquid has changed over to solid. At the boiling point of water (100° C.) each gram of water will absorb 540 calories without experiencing the slightest change in temperature. The 540 calories are required to change the gram of water to steam. Similarly, about 80 calories are required at 0° C. to change a gram of ice to water. This heat, absorbed (or relinquished) without a change in temperature, Black called *latent heat*.

Using the concept of specific heat, Watt calculated the effects of changing the size of the Newcomen engine. On steam entering the cylinder, it had first to heat up the brass of the cylinder walls and then only could it begin to work. When the cooling jet of water was sprayed into the cylinder at the end of the power stroke, the cylinder walls were also cooled down. The heat absorbed by the walls of the cylinder at each stroke was wasted. The greater the proportion of brass cylinder to steam volume, the more waste. Decreasing the size of the engine decreased the steam volume more than the weight of the brass so that the smaller the engine, the greater this waste of reheating.

The work of the steam engine is accomplished by the expansion of steam, which begins above the temperature of 100° C. To avoid the wasteful heating of the engine itself, Watt devised a separate condenser (Figure 24) which could be maintained at a low temperature. At the end of the power stroke the moving piston uncovered an exit port leading to the condenser. Steam condensing to water lowered the pres-

sure in the condenser and the steam of the cylinder moved in
to take its place. The cylinder itself was maintained at the
high temperature of the working steam and therefore had to
be heated only once. Watt's invention greatly reduced the
amount of fuel necessary to operate the steam engine, which
meant that it would now be possible to apply it to moving
vehicles and boats carrying their own fuel and to mines other
than coal mines. The difficulties of machining cylinders and
pistons that would hold their pressure at first prevented Watt
from manufacturing his engines, but with the development of
machine tools, notably Wilkinson's cannon borer, Watt and

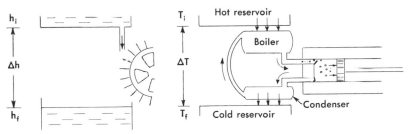

Fig. 24. *Watt's engine compared to a water engine.* "The amount of
work produced is limited by the quantity of heat and the difference in
temperature through which it falls."—Carnot

his partner Boulton began mass production. They offered their
machines free to mining companies which were equipped with
satisfactory Newcomen engines in return for the fuel savings
over the first three years of installation, and rapidly displaced
the Newcomen engines from the world market.

THE CARNOT CYCLE

As Watt was one of the earliest modern engineers, combining in his person the mechanical skills and the theoretical un-

derstanding necessary for this most significant technical development of his century, Sadi Carnot was one of the earliest modern scientists. His father, Lazare Carnot, was a mathematician employed by the French Revolutionary Convention to organize the resources of France to meet the demands of the revolutionary wars. The older Carnot had studied the operations of water machines in great detail. The younger Carnot saw in his father's work the clue to the understanding of the mechanical effects of heat. Determined to forge a theory of heat engines, Carnot in 1824 published an epochmaking paper, "Reflexions sur la puissance motrice du feu."

> We may justly compare the motive power of heat with that of a fall of water. The motive force of a water fall depends on the height and quantity of fluid: the motive force of heat depends upon the quantity of caloric employed and what we may call the height of its fall, that is to say, the difference in temperature of the bodies between which the caloric is exchanged.

Carnot conceived of two heat engines operating in a cycle so that one would drive the other. The first engine accepts heat from a high temperature source and is driven by the heat falling to a low temperature sink. Only a part of the energy of the heat source can be obtained as useful work because the lowest temperature at which the heat may be rejected is that of the sink. The work done by the heat in its cascade down the temperature falls is used in the second engine to raise the same amount of heat back to the temperature of the source. Because he accepted the concept of caloric as a material substance, Carnot thought that the amount of heat (caloric) rejected at the low temperature sink must be the same as the amount accepted from the high temperature source. Similarly, the work obtained in the first engine would be just sufficient to restore the original situation by driving the second engine in reverse. Neither the forward engine nor the reverse engine could obtain a different amount of work from the same quantity of heat flowing between the same temperature limits. If there could be any difference in the efficiency of the two engines, then the more efficient engine driving the less efficient engine in reverse could raise the same quantity of heat to a higher temperature than the original temperature of the source. On the next operation of the cycle, the same quantity of heat would fall through a greater temperature difference and thereby deliver more work than necessary to keep the cycle going. Obtaining excess work in this way simply by rearranging the existing energy would be perpetual motion of the second kind (as opposed to simply creating energy out of nothing). Perpetual motion, Carnot asserted, would be impossible and therefore the work derived from the fall of a given quantity of heat between definite limits of temperature would always be the same.

In the hands of William Thomson, Lord Kelvin (1824–1907), Carnot's idea that the motive force of heat depends solely upon the quantity of heat and the difference in temperature through which it falls led to the concept of the absolute temperature scale.

All thermometers are essentially arrangements for converting what Galileo would have called a secondary or subjective property, temperature, into an objective and measurable property such as the volume of a gas, or the length of a column of mercury, or an electrical voltage. The common mercury thermometer is calibrated by immersing the bulb in a mixture of water and ice and marking on the tube the position of the column of mercury. Then the same thermometer is immersed in boiling water and the height to which the mercury rises is again marked on the tube. The distance between the two marks is divided into 100 equal parts, marked from 0° to 100°. A temperature change sufficient to cause the mercury to rise by one of these parts is taken as a temperature change of one degree Centigrade. In the same way thermometers could be constructed using the expansion of a gas or the change in resistance of a wire between the same fixed points, the ice point and the steam point. But a difficulty arose. The various thermometers were in only approximate agreement. The exact value and hence meaning of temperature itself remained uncertain. For example, if it were assumed that the mercury thermometer was the true measure of temperature and that an increase in length of half the difference of the mercury column between the ice point and the steam point represented a temperature of 50°, then all other kinds of thermometers would be very slightly off. Held at that same temperature, the increase in volume of a suitably constructed gas thermometer would not be exactly half the difference of the ice point to steam point volumes. The gas thermometer would not read exactly 50° but rather a slightly higher temperature. In the same way, a resistance thermometer would not agree exactly with either the mercury or the gas thermometer.

Which was correct? A practical thermometer could be constructed using any of the thermometric properties but a scientific concept of temperature would have to be independent of the properties of one or another substance. In Carnot's principle, Kelvin glimpsed the idea of an absolute value of temperature, a value which would be independent of the particular operation of measurement. The ideal Carnot engine operating over a unit temperature difference with a fixed flow of heat would always yield the same amount of work.

> In M. Clapeyron's paper various experimental data . . . are brought forward, and the amounts of mechanical effect due to a unit of heat descending a degree of the air-thermometer, in various parts of the scale, are calcu-

lated from them . . . The results so obtained indicate
very decidedly that what we may with propriety call
the value of a degree (estimated by the mechanical effect
to be obtained from the descent of a unit of heat through
it) of the air-thermometer depends on the part of the
scale in which it is taken, being less for high than for low
temperatures.

The characteristic property of the scale which I now
propose is, that all degrees have the same value; that is,
that a unit of heat descending from body A at the temperature T° of this scale, to a body B at the temperature (T—1)°, would give out the same mechanical effect,
whatever be the number T. This may justly be termed
an absolute scale, since its characteristic is quite independent of the physical properties of any specific substance.

Carnot's principle became the second law of thermodynamics. The development of the first law of thermodynamics
was slow and its applicability to Carnot's new science of heat
and work was not at first realized. The first law expresses the
idea of the conservation of energy. In any process, the sum of
the initial energies must be equal to the sum of the final energies. The New Hampshire expatriate, Benjamin Thompson,
who became Count Rumford of the Holy Roman Empire and
married Lavoisier's widow, had shrewdly disposed of the caloric theory while supervising the boring of brass cannon in
Bavaria. Noticing that the boring tools became greatly over-
heated, Rumford, a convinced Baconian, saw an opportunity
for the overthrow of the caloric theory. One of the few scientific statements that Bacon had made was that heat was simply
the mechanical motion of the particles of bodies, an assertion
accepted in the seventeenth century by Boyle, Hooke, and
Newton among others but discarded in the eighteenth century
in favor of the caloric idea, which appeared to promise quantitative results. Rumford wrote:

> From whence comes the Heat actually produced in the mechanical operation above mentioned?
>
> Is it furnished by the metallic chips which are separated by the borer from the solid mass of metal?
>
> If this were the case, then, according to the modern doctrines of latent Heat, and of caloric, the capacity ought not only to be changed, but the change undergone by them should be sufficiently great to account for all the Heat produced.

Upon experiment, Rumford found that the heat capacity of the brass chips was the same as the heat capacity of the brass with which the operation started. The heat came not from the brass but from the friction, the mechanical work done on the brass. Further Rumford noted that the heat that could be drawn from the brass was inexhaustible, since the brass that had already yielded large quantities of heat retained its original heat capacity.

> It is hardly necessary to add, that anything which any *insulated* body, or system of bodies, can continue to furnish *without limitation,* cannot possibly be a *material substance;* and it appears to me to be extremely difficult, if not quite impossible, to form any distinct idea of anything, capable of being excited and communicated in these experiments, except it be MOTION.

Julius Robert Mayer, physician on a German vessel in the tropics, thought in terms of fundamental philosophical principles. A man of science (as all physicians were then considered), Mayer in the course of bleeding his patients noticed that the venous blood of his European patients remained a bright red until they had acclimated themselves to the tropics. Mayer explained this by the mechanistic view that the body heat of animals was produced by chemical combination of food with oxygen. Mayer reasoned that in hot climates, unable to dispose of body heat, less food would be combined with oxygen and the excess oxygen in the bloodstream would color it bright red. The sailors on Mayer's ship had blue venous blood and in their case, the oxygen had gone to produce work. Using published values of the heat absorbed by expanding gases, Mayer computed the amount of heat equivalent to a given amount of work, and stated the principle of the interconvertibility of energy and the conservation of energy.

In the period in which Mayer worked, science had congealed into an organized profession with its journals and its standards and a certain rigidity of thinking. Mayer's article with its grandiose enunciation of fundamental doctrine, coming from an obscure physician, failed to satisfy the notions of scientific method then hardened in European scientific circles. His paper was rejected by the German physics journal because it lacked new experimental data but it was ultimately published (1842) in a journal of agricultural chemistry. Meanwhile the same idea had inspired another amateur, James Joule, a Scottish brewer, to a series of fundamental and precise experiments during which he demonstrated the interconvertibility of heat and mechanical energy and heat and electrical energy. A given amount of work appears with the expenditure of a given amount of heat. Both are forms of energy.

Although experimental, Joule's work was rejected at first by the Royal Society of London, but its importance was recognized by Kelvin, who saw in it the resolution of the problems raised by Carnot's principle. Contrary to Carnot's original idea, the amount of heat absorbed at the top of the cycle was greater than the amount of heat rejected by the engine at the bottom of the cycle. Something had disappeared, namely heat. Something else had appeared in its place—work. In simplest form, the first law expresses the idea that heat and work are interconvertible forms of something more general. This general idea, of which Descartes had a glimpse in seeking to conserve the quantity of motion in the world, was the concept of energy. It was the energy which was conserved in the Carnot cycle, or indeed in any other autonomous system. It was the amount of heat less the work done which remained the same throughout the cycle and this could be expressed for the rapidly developing science of thermodynamics as a fundamental assertion; energy is conserved.

Carnot died of cholera at the age of thirty-six after he had recognized that heat was not conserved but before he understood how to reconcile his principle of the motive force of heat with Joule's principle of the heat equivalent of work. Except for Carnot's classmate, the steam engineer B. P. E. Clapeyron, the significance of Carnot's principle was lost. It was in Clapeyron's work that Kelvin learned of Carnot and it was therefore in the mind of Kelvin that the two principles of Carnot and Joule came finally to resolution.

Rudolph Clausius, a German theorist whose attention was called to this subject by Kelvin, rephrased the Carnot principle in a beautifully imaginative step. An ideal engine, in order to convert all the heat flow into work, would have to operate between some starting temperature and the absolute zero. If the final temperature is above 0, then some heat must be rejected at that temperature. The efficiency of the process is limited by the temperature. Since the efficiency of the process is known to begin with, it affords a constant standard with which to compare results. The proportion of heat unavailable for useful work (calories rejected per degree above absolute zero) is the same throughout the operation for a machine operating with maximum efficiency. Ordinary machines operating at less than maximum efficiency do not convert all the heat flow between the operating temperatures which could in theory be converted to work. At the end of the operation, therefore, the value of the proportion of calories rejected per degree, increases. Clausius termed this proportionate measure of the unavailability of energy the *entropy*, and phrased the laws of thermodynamics in the twin statements:

> The energy of the universe is constant.
> The entropy of the universe is always increasing.

The analogy to water power is in order. There is as much water at the foot of the falls after it has fallen as there was at the top of the falls in the beginning. But, although the quantity of water is the same, it is no longer available for useful work. Ultimately, we could imagine all the water in all the world arriving at sea level. It would then be totally unavailable for work for it could no longer be dropped into a hole unless one was previously pumped out.

Entropy is the first example in science of a purely mathematical idea for which the mind has no intuitive feeling. It is impossible to conceive of a physical model for entropy. We think of heat as a fluid flowing in or out of bodies until, this being disproved, we think of it as the random motions of the parts of bodies. For force, for energy, for motion, for hot and cold, and for temperature we feel an intuitive understanding. It is not at all true that we sense these things directly. Like entropy, these are concepts. We do not sense heat and temperature, although we sense effects of these to which we have assigned the names heat and temperature. They remain ideas, concepts by which we organize our experience. We perceive length. Do we perceive time? Or can we be said to perceive the change of distance divided by time which we call motion? For numbers and geometric forms we feel an intuitive understanding, but the concept of entropy is elusive. There is perhaps no better example of the conceptual quality of science than the idea of entropy. A pure idea, it has no existence in the physical world apart from the minds of the students of this world.

To the latter nineteenth-century philosophers, the realization that every process in the universe is accompanied by an irretrievable degradation of energy appeared to put limits to the universe. The clock of the mechanists would not in this view last forever. While it loses no energy as Laplace's *Celestial Mechanics* demonstrates, it is nevertheless a spontaneous process and steadily, inexorably, the energy which is conserved by the first law is rendered increasingly unavailable by the second. The entropy of the system increases steadily, moving in the direction of the final *Wärmetod,* or heat death, when the last temperature difference in the universe will disappear and all the bodies in the universe will rest in the ultimate conformity of death.

The concept of entropy broke the mechanistic circle. Processes, even mechanical processes, were now seen to change with time. There was an evolution, not merely to living things as Darwin had asserted, but even to the inorganic world. The past was the direction of low entropy, the future the direction of high entropy. The element of historicity enters into all phenomena, organic and inorganic, natural and humane. The Deistic clockwork universe vanishes along with the absolute character of mechanical law. Science, which had become a closed system with the extension of mechanics, was now seen to be open-ended. For the concepts of science were all, without exception, like entropy the products of the human mind, and what one man had done another could hope to improve on.

There was a richly satisfying character to the new science of thermodynamics as Kelvin and Clausius formalized it in the latter nineteenth century. Like the Newtonian synthesis, it rested on a minimum of assumption; the beautifully simple first and second laws. Its applicability appeared boundless. All heat, energy, and work phenomena could be explained by relationships deduced directly from the two laws. This included heat engines as they were known then and the jet and rocket engines of today. The phenomena of weather, of chemical reaction, of geological processes, of the economy of the body, were all subject to the lucid rule of thermodynamic law. Aircraft and submarine, water pump and electrical resistance, furnaces and refrigerators, comet and earthquake wave alike, all testified to the universality of the new science. Like Newtonian gravitation, thermodynamics offered no hypothetical explanations, no models of the phenomena it described. For whether a gas were made of atoms or molecules or of a continuous stuff was no concern of thermodynamics. It was sufficient to know only that it had a pressure, a volume, and a temperature. The nature of heat, whether simply the sum of miniscule motions of a weightless fluid or anything else, is irrelevant. Chemistry, the periodic table, the laws of combining proportions neither confirm nor contradict the body of thermodynamics, but thermodynamic results and data govern the phenomena which chemistry interprets in its laws. Thermodynamics like the theory of gravitation offers no explanations, no models of the tiny machines of nature which Hooke, a microscopist, sought in all phenomena. Instead it deals with the inexorable relationships between the thermodynamic coordinates, pressure, volume, temperature (and composition). These remain empirically verifiable and independent of mechnistic hypothesis. They are *macroscopic*. A theory which, on the contrary, attempts to describe the fine structure of matter is a *microscopic* theory. It is the old distinction which Newton made with Hooke and Huygens. For Newton, in describing his decomposition of white light into colors, offered no explanation and (at the time) no hypothesis of the nature of light. Was it to consist of small bodies or of waves in the ether? The *microscopic* * hypothesis was immaterial. White light still resolved into the colors of the spectrum as Newton had determined them. The best example of microscopic theory would be the modern conception of the structure of the atom. At least twelve subatomic particles are identified and described in this most recent triumph of the microscopic, hypothetical, development of science.

Unlike Newtonian mechanics, thermodynamics was immediately and immensely useful. The story that is told of two Swedish technical students who sat in a class on thermodynamics and dreamed up the gas refrigerator, the heat pump to maintain foods at a constant low temperature, which operated entirely on the energy of a gas flame, illustrates, if trivially, the breadth of thermodynamic applications. A "pure" theory, thermodynamics rests on the inductively firm base of the first and second laws. From these, the operations of the calculus derive an enormous variety of hitherto unsuspected relationships among the thermodynamic coordinates and functions. A rigid theory, the derived relationships are sought and found in experiment among measurements of strictly definable coordinates (pressure, volume, temperature and composition). The classical development of physical science offers no subject of more grace and elegance than thermodynamics.

---

* The use of the term "microscopic" to refer to a theory of the structure of matter or light or heat, etc., does not imply that the hypothetical fine structure is visible under any kind of microscope, including the electron microscope, but rather implies that the hypothetical fine structure is beyond the reach of direct methods of observation.

12. The Microscopic Model

HERE IS A BOOK INTENDED TO EXPOUND THE MODERN THEORIES OF ELECTRICITY AND TO EXPOUND A NEW THEORY. IN IT THERE ARE NOTHING BUT STRINGS WHICH MOVE AROUND PULLEYS, WHICH ROLL AROUND DRUMS, WHICH GO THROUGH PEARL BEADS, WHICH CARRY WEIGHTS; AND TUBES WHICH PUMP WATER WHILE OTHERS SWELL AND CON-TRACT; TOOTHED WHEELS WHICH ARE GEARED TO ONE ANOTHER AND ENGAGE HOOKS. WE THOUGHT WE WERE ENTERING THE TRANQUIL AND NEATLY ORDERED ABODE OF REASON, BUT WE FIND OURSELVES IN A FACTORY.

PIERRE DUHEM, 1914

THE HEIGHTS to which thermodynamics rose, the purity of its intellectual concepts were, if admirable, somewhat like the unrealistic demands of excessively austere religion. Surrounded on all sides by the vigor of the world of phenomena, by observations of almost infinite complexity and chaotic profusion, few physical scientists adhered to the pure faith, with the comforts of the lower church of mechanism so readily at hand. Hooke's search for the tiny machines of nature by which all microscopic functions were performed, the deterministic boast of Laplace, Helmholtz' call for the reduction of all phenomena to the inverse square forces between particles, seemed to offer a shorter route to the final comprehension of the world about us. The regular orderly world, the lawful reflection of God's mind, the Pythagorean ideal which was ultimate reality, was not to be sought in abstract concept but in explanation and model. "My object is to show how to make a mechanical model," wrote Kelvin, "which shall fulfill the conditions required in the physical phenomena that we are considering, whatever they may be."

> . . . when we have vibrations of light to consider, I want to show a model of the action exhibited in that phenomenon. We want to understand the whole about it; we only understand a part. It seems to me that the test of "Do we or do we not understand a particular subject in physics?" is "Can we make a mechanical model of it?"

Of all the microscopic and mechanistic theories, the theory of matter as consisting of discrete small bodies, the theory of atomism, was the scientific heresy that would not stay down. The world of phenomena at every turn seemed to bespeak the atom. In the latter half of the nineteenth century, parallel to the development of thermodynamics, and often by the same individuals who were simultaneously forwarding the thermodynamic edifice, the science of mechanics was successfully applied to the atomic idea and the kinetic-molecular hypothesis was the result. It proved as successful in every prediction as the rival development of thermodynamics.

The hypothesis that matter consisted of small, irreducible particles was a sufficient but not a necessary explanation of many common observations. For the Greeks Epicurus, Leucippus, and Democritus, it seemed a necessary accompaniment of materialism. Matter would have to have form and real, rational number. The seventeenth century found Hooke and Boyle considering that a corpuscular theory would account for the mixing of liquids into a homogeneous mass, for the regular shapes of crystals, and for the elasticity of air. Newton, hypothesizing, could not conceive of gravity transmitted across empty space and filled space with a particle ether, as did Huygens. Newton's speculative light corpuscles had shapes, as did Huygens' crystal atoms, or Boyle's air springs, and therefore parts and thus could hardly be irreducible, ultimate bits. For Lavoisier the question was metaphysical, but for Dalton, Avogadro, and finally Mendeleev the rule of fixed combining proportions and the periodicity of the properties of the elements could only be explained by the atomic idea.

In 1827, an English botanist, Robert Brown, observed what appeared to be the thermal motions of elementary particles. Pollen grains on the surface of a liquid droplet, seen under a high powered microscope, moved back and forth in a ceaseless and senseless agitation. Never still for more than an instant, they darted across the field of the microscope, shook and vibrated in a constant, random motion. It was exactly the kind of motion which Bacon had conceived as the fine structure of heat, along with the seventeenth-century mechanists and later, the Count from New Hampshire at his cannon in Bavaria. Brown's phenomenon attracted widespread attention. When it was discovered that the pollen did not need to be alive to engage in the Brownian dance, that the motions continued

with no sign of any slackening whatever, it was asserted tha
they were a confirmation of vitalism and a means of tellin
the organic from the inorganic worlds. But it was later dis
covered that any particles light enough could be observed i
a similar motion. The dust motes in a beam of sunlight ca

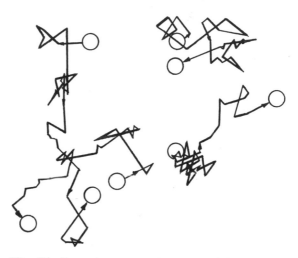

Fig. 25. *Brownian motion.* Positions of the Brownian particles at intervals of one second. Since the
Brownian particles are large enough to be seen,
an accurate average size and mass can be calculated. From this and from the averaged motion
of the particles, applied to the Jouleian figure for
the average velocity of the colliding molecules, it
is possible to compute the mass of the colliding
molecules and the value of Avogadro's number.

sometimes be seen in Brownian motion. A chamber of cigarett
smoke under the microscope appears like a spotted jelly. Th
spots suspended in the viscous air quiver restlessly an
eternally. Here were the visible traces of the ceaseless motior
of the molecules of the air. The particles, bombarded on a
sides by moleeules in random motion, danced like corks in

untain. The conversion of heat to work and work to heat had
mechanical explanation. When a hand is rubbed rapidly
cross a table surface, a large motion disappears. In its place
mething new, heat, appears. The large motion has been
onverted into a multitude of minute motions of the particles
f the hand and the table top. A few liters of air contain on
e order of 10^{23} molecules. We compress the air and the large
otion squeezing it together is converted into the many small
otions of 10^{23} particles. The thermometer faithfully records
n increase of temperature. Rumford and Joule, but not Mayer
ho leaned toward the grand conception, asserted not only
at heat and motion (kinetic energy) were interconvertible,
ut something even more radical. Heat *is* motion.

The theory assumes that a gas consists of a great number of
articles which are absolutely alike, moving about at random.
s these particles collide with each other and the walls of their
ntainer, they rebound perfectly, losing no energy in the
llisions. Bernouilli substituted a single motion of a single
rge body for the sum of the random motions of the many
nall particles. He was able to show that the macroscopic prop-
ties by which gases were ordinarily described such as tem-
erature, pressure, etc., could be related to the mechanics
the substitute body.

A century later (1848) Joule was able to derive expressions *

* A particle of mass m traveling with a velocity v in a box of side length l
ll change momentum by $2mv_x$ for each collision with a single wall of the
x. There are $v_x/2l$ collisions per second, hence

$$F = \frac{mv_x^2}{l}; \quad (F = \text{force}).$$

For N particles, $Nm = M$; $\quad F/l^2 = P$; $\quad (P = \text{pressure}, V = \text{volume})$,

$$PV = M \frac{v^2}{3}$$

$$= \frac{2}{3} E; \quad (E = \text{Kinetic energy}),$$

$$= nRT \quad (n \text{ is the number of gmw, R is the gas constant}).$$

relating the experimental quantities of pressure, mass, an
volume, to the behavior of the hypothetical molecules. Joul
assumed a box containing a single particle of a gas travelin
with a definite velocity. The impacts of the particle on th
walls of the container account for the pressure of the gas
Adding a second particle with the same mass and velocity a
the first would double the pressure. Reducing the volume of th
box would increase the number of impacts and hence the pres
sure. But this was Boyle's law, determined empirically nearl
two hundred years earlier. The simple assumptions of th
molecular theory led directly to the results of experiment.

In the same way Joule was able to derive the laws of Dalto
and Charles (pressure or volume of a gas is proportional t
temperature). Raising the temperature of a gas according t
the molecular theory meant speeding up the particles an
therefore increasing the number of impacts with the walls o
the container and therefore increasing the pressure. Fittin
observations of pressure, mass, temperature, and volume int
his equations, Joule calculated that the average velocity of
molecule of water vapor at 100° C. was more than 1 mile pe
second. This was the first molecular quantity to be evaluatec
Although the molecules themselves could not then, as eve
today, be seen, felt, isolated or weighed, but remained purel
hypothetical, the kinetic-molecular calculations led to precis
values for molecular quantities.

In 1865, Joseph Loschmidt calculated the number of mole
cules in a cubic centimeter of gas under standard conditions. B
dividing this number into the weight of the gas, a figure for th
weight of a single atom could be obtained. Since the relativ
weights of all the elements were known from measuremen
determination of the absolute weight of one atom was enoug
to determine the absolute weights of all. In 1905 and late
Einstein looked to the Brownian motions as the most direc

evidences of the reality of the molecular world. The French physicist Jean Perrin, watching particles of smoke under the microscope, used the average velocity of the visible particles and the laws of impact to calculate the average velocity of the bombarding molecules responsible for the visible motions. Perrin was able to calculate Avogadro's number N_0. The number of particles in a gram molecular weight of an element is now taken as 6.02×10^{23}.

Kinetic-molecular explanations of a world of phenomena were rapidly developed—the rate of diffusion of a dye through a liquid, for example. The sharp rise in temperature of a metal in being struck was now understood to be the increase in thermal vibration of the atoms of the metal. The solid state, the liquid state, the gaseous state were seen as degrees of orderly arrangement of atoms. In a solid, the atoms were arranged in regular orderly array, each referred to a position in a pattern called a space lattice. This could be related to the crystal form. As the temperature of a solid was increased, the vibrations of the atoms about their positions in the lattice increased. From considerations of this sort, it was possible to calculate the heat capacities of solids. As the motions of the atoms became more and more violent with increasing temperature, they reached the point where the average energy of the individual atom was sufficient to overcome the forces holding it in its lattice position. At temperatures above this the atoms mingled freely, disregarding their assigned positions. At such temperatures the substance was a melt. At still higher temperatures, the violent thermal agitation of the particles exceeded all the forces tending to hold them together and the substance reached the vapor stage. The phenomenon of latent heat, the energy required to transform a quantity of solid into liquid or liquid into vapor, was also explained microscopically. During the time of fusion or vaporization when the temperature remained

constant, each atom was individually breaking from its position
When the last vestige of the old structure disappeared, th
temperature could again rise with increment of energy.

Even the effective size of the atom could be computed
From the atomic weights, which are multiples of the weight o
a hydrogen atom,* and Avogadro's number, the number o
atoms to occupy a given quantity of material can be deter
mined. For example, a cubic centimeter of water (H_2O) weigh
1 gram. Two grams of hydrogen and sixteen grams of oxyge
(eighteen grams in all) contain N_o particles. The cubic centi
meter therefore contains $\frac{1}{18} \times N_o$ particles and each partick
must occupy one divided by $\frac{N_o}{18}$ cubic centimeters or $\frac{18}{N_o} =$
2.99×10^{-23} cm³. By assuming geometric arrangements for th
atoms that would complement the regularities of crystal form
exact dimensions could be assigned. Atomic radii are effectivel
on the order of 10^{-8} cm.

For chemistry, the ability to visualize the actual patterns o
complex molecules, the directness with which numerical result
could be considered, the ingenious mechanical explanations o
chemical reactions, explosions, diffusion, and material processe
of all sorts were overwhelming. One by one, the holdout
against atomism surrendered. In vain, the physical chemist
philosopher-historian Pierre Duhem protested and pointed ou
that none of these advances had required the kinetic-molecula
theory; that all had proceeded by induction from experimen
and then and then only had been interpreted by gross mechani
cal models. The kinetic-molecular theory, like a thief in th
night, crept into the minds of men and capped the discoverie
to which abstract theory had led them.

* The atomic weights are actually determined relative to oxygen which i
assigned the weight of 16 even units. On this scale, hydrogen has the atomi
weight of 1.008.

> The theory of osmotic pressure . . . had reached maturity and constitutional vigor when the mechanical models and kinetic hypotheses came to bring to it the assistance it did not ask for, with which it had nothing to do, and to which it owed nothing.

The atom, the molecule, the positions and motions of these were the hypotheses of a mechanical model. An atom could not be seen by any process of magnification. It could not be weighed; it could not even be isolated from its hypothetical fellows. It has even been demonstrated that this uncertainty of concept is permanent. There was no kinetic-molecular result which could not be obtained independently from abstract theory. And there were many aspects of abstract theory to which the kinetic-molecular hypotheses did not apply, gravitation for example. Yet, since its inception the atomic idea has grown steadily, unbidden possibly, but coming nevertheless to the assistance and explanation of idea after idea, always holding out the will-o'-the-wisp of the final ultimate explanation—the reduction of all science to the fundamental postulate: in the beginning God created the atoms and the inverse square forces between them, the "reasons of mechanics . . . (by virtue of which) . . . the true philosophy conceives the cause of all nature's effects."

The kinetic-molecular theory itself was destined for still greater triumphs. In the hands of the American, Willard Gibbs, the Englishman, James Clerk Maxwell, and the German, Ludwig Boltzmann, it was linked irretrievably to thermodynamics by the cement of the mathematics of probability. A new science, statistical mechanics, emerged. Like the residents of drought-stricken New England turning impartially to prayer, divining rods, and hydrogeologists, the new science of statistical mechanics employs the pure theory of thermodynamics with the full assistance of the atomic hypothesis. The mechanism of a single

particle taken 10^{23} times over with appropriate statistical techniques is equated to the abstractions of thermodynamics.

"The atomic theory," Boltzmann wrote, "yields results that
are independent of any other theory, and may not be obtained
in any other way. For it speaks a world of physical, chemical
and crystallographic facts. This is not a theory to be criticized
but to be advanced."

As it is a mistake to cling to an idea after it has been shown
to be obsolete, simply because we like it, so it is a mistake to
reject an idea that has been shown to be useful, simply because we do not like it. The drive to intellectual economy
cannot blind us to reality. Against reason, against logic, against
order itself, the brute, stubborn, irreducible world remains.
Like Galileo's bits of glass and metal, like Kepler's eight minutes of arc, the atoms will not down, but when they have been
beaten out of one position, they race around the corner ahead
of us like a patient dog to wait until we shall need them again.

13. Electricity and Magnetism

. . . MANY PHILOSOPHERS CITE THE LODE-
STONE AND ALSO AMBER WHENEVER, IN EX-
PLAINING MYSTERIES, THEIR MINDS BECOME
OBFUSCATED AND REASON CAN NO FARTHER
GO.

WILLIAM GILBERT, 1600

WITH THE publication of the *Principia,* mechanics and the study of celestial phenomena which had been for the Greeks the whole of science became increasingly the province of the mathematical theorist. The cultivated amateur, the gentleman of the eighteenth century, his mind molded by classical studies, turned to other fields of science. Many of the members of the Royal Society were physicians and not trained to the subleties of the developing calculus. It was with relief that they turned to the ancient topic of electricity and the simple experiments which were at once so easily performed and so strikingly incomprehensible.

The study of electricity began with the observation by the Greeks that amber, when rubbed, had the property of attracting bits of chaff. The Greek word for amber, *electron*, came to apply to the property. The amber of the Baltic coast had been valued as a gem since prehistoric times and figured as a major item in the trade that stretched across the Eurasian land mass. Tacitus wrote of the amber trade in his book on the Germans. The Arabs called it *carab* and used it in pre-Moslem religious ceremonies according to William Gilbert (1540–1603), physician to Elizabeth I. While Gilbert, whose special interest was the magnet, knew of the attractive powers of amber, and distinguished these from the attractive powers of the magnet, he was apparently unaware of the parallel repulsive properties of electricity. Otto von Guericke, the versatile Burgomaster of Magdeburg, knew, however, that when a bit of chaff had been drawn into contact with an electrified body it immediately flew away, repelled by an invisible force.

In Elizabeth's time, phenomena such as these appeared mysterious and magical. John Dee, Elizabeth's alchemist, was alternately subsidized and persecuted as the hope of profit through his transmutations overcame or declined before the dread of the black arts that he was believed to practice.* By the eighteenth century the mystery was gone, replaced by the mechanical reasoning of a self-consciously intellectual age. When Benjamin Franklin arrived in France to plead the American cause, he stepped from the boat wearing a coonskin cap; the representative of a nation of philosophical savages, a member of the Academy of Paris and the Royal Society of London, and an electrical savant of great originality. To the eighteenth

---

* Elizabeth II in our own time employed a dowser to locate a lost ring in Buckingham Palace, with results which were never publicized.

century, the frontier vigor symbolized in the coonskin cap, the republican ideals of liberty (and property) went inseparably with the scientific enlightenment. The France to which Franklin appealed successfully for men, for arms, for ships, and for money had been well prepared to admire the tamer of electricity. At the court of Louis XV, the savants of the Paris Academy had performed electrical experiments and discoursed on them to an admiring circle of nobles and mistresses of the King. A century before, prowess in knocking each other from the backs of horses distinguished gentlemen; a century later, it was to be skill in pursuing a ball about a grassy field. In the eighteenth century, a concomitant of birth and breeding was a full acquaintance with the mysterious behavior of glass rods rubbed with cat's fur.

The electrical phenomena known in the Age of Reason were briefly as follows: nonmetallic bodies could be excited by friction to a state in which they attracted small bits of down, or pith, or paper, etc. The attractive virtue could be led or conducted along metallic wires but not along thread or other nonmetallic materials. The attractive virtue acted, like magnetism, at a distance through the empty air or even, as von Guericke suspected, through vacuum. If the electrical virtue was imparted by contact to the test particle of pith (or fine leaf gold), then the particle was repelled instead of attracted. "This principle is," wrote Charles du Fay in 1734, "that electrick bodies attract all those that are not so, and repel them as soon as they are become electrick, by the vicinity or contact of the electrick body." Du Fay, in addition, made a second most pertinent observation. There appeared to be two distinct electricities, very different from one another. One of these, he called *vitreous electricity*, and the other *resinous electricity*. He had discovered that the electricity excited in glass, crystal, cat's fur, wool, and similar materials would always attract electrified bodies of amber, copal, gum-lac, silk, etc. Either kind of electricity could be imparted by contact to a test ball of wood or ivory, which would then behave in exactly the same fashion as an electrified vitreous or an electrified resinous material. Small bits of pith suspended on fine threads made excellent indicators. In modern terminology, we would say that like charges repel, opposite charges attract. Du Fay seems to have thought of electricity as a fluid or element in the mechanical fashion of the times, weightless and invisible like caloric.

The systematic study of such delicate phenomena seems to have waited for the development of sensitive instruments for measurement and amplification of the effects. Von Guericke had developed the first continuous static generator, which by the eighteenth century had evolved into the form of a large wheel with inset lumps of amber or other material. As the wheel was rotated, the amber was electrified by passing fixed brushes of cat's fur. The electricity so generated in the amber was picked up on wire brushes and led away by wires to metallic spheres. The charges that can be developed by this mass production method are very substantial and the early experimenters ran considerable risks. On approaching such a charged sphere, the experimenter was often met by a violent spark as if the electricity, too impatient to wait for contract, had leaped across the intervening space. Experimenters began to substitute a second sphere close to the first in metallic contact with a large unelectrified body such as the ground, to receive this kind of spark. Electrostatic machines, as the generators are now called, can produce sparks leaping across gaps of many feet, always to the accompaniment of violent noises, and the peculiar smells in the air which the medieval experimenters took as indication of the presence of devils.

Pieter van Musschenbroek of Leyden (1692–1761) nearly paid with his life for his disregard of antique superstitions.

Trying to see if water could be electrified, he led the electricity from a static machine to a jar of water with a wire. Happening to touch the wire while holding the jar in his other hand "The arm and the body was affected in a terrible manner which I cannot express; in a word, I thought it was all up with me." The possibilities of this means of storage of large amounts of electricity in Musschenbroek's Leyden jars were rapidly investigated. At Louis XV's court, the Carthusian monks of the Paris convent were arranged in a circuit 900 feet long to receive the discharge of a Leyden jar. At the moment of discharge, the entire line of monks hopped into the air. Electricity in small amounts did not appear to be harmful. It seemed as if, on the contrary, it had a beneficial effect, enlivening the dull, loosening the tongue, and imparting some of its fiery spirit to even the mildest of men seized unawares by a playful experimentalist. The use of electricity for medical purposes, electrotherapy, began in the eighteenth century and has continued to the present. The electric shock is employed today in the treatment of the mentally ill, in much the same spirit as the repair of a watch by a sharp rap on the case. Recently, shoe-shine parlors in the southwest installed trays of radioactive mud in which patrons may treat their feet. John Wesley, the evangelist, thought that electricity must be the soul of the universe and with some small apparatus he imparted it to his followers.

A major role in the eighteenth-century development of a science of electricity was played by Benjamin Franklin, who retired from his occupation of printer in order to devote the remainder of his life to scientific studies. In this resolve he was interrupted by the rebellion of the colonies. No enemy of learning, Franklin had already become a cultural leader of Philadelphia, the largest city of the colonies, but he was now to devote his full time to philosophy, by which he meant the application of Baconian experimentation on a variety of subjects to extend the Newtonian mechanism. In Boston, chancing to observe an itinerant lecturer named Spencer go through the bag of electrical tricks, Franklin offered to buy Spencer's apparatus and on acquiring this, began his experimentation.

In a series of letters to the Royal Society, Franklin publicized the results of his experiments. He first determined that a pointed conductor was the most efficient means of discharging electrified bodies. The individual particles of the electric fluid in their mutual repulsion tried to get as far from each other as possible and thus spread out over the charged body. A point would by this reasoning acquire the highest density of charge. If the electricity generated by an electrostatic machine were conducted to a sphere and a second body connected to a large sink for electricity (the ground was such a sink) was brought near, the charge in the sphere when great enough would leap to the second body. By making the second body in the form of a point, this discharge was most effective at the greatest distances.

In place of the two fluids, the vitreous and resinous, of du Fay, Franklin introduced the radically different notion of one fluid in different degree. Instead of working with relatively small effects, Franklin used an electrostatic machine and Leyden jars and his observations were of sparks. He thought therefore of electricity as "electric fire" and it was his most significant observation that the strength of the electric spark depended on the density of electrification of the points between which the spark jumped. He noted that a spark would leap from either kind of electrified body, vitreous or resinous, to a neutral point. Further, he noted that the spark from one kind of electrified body to the opposite kind was of greater strength than the spark of either to the unelectrified body. Since he had performed his experiments with a glass tube, he labeled the electricity he had so produced on the glass *positive*. He thought of this electricity as a corporeal substance, a fluid drawn out of the person rubbing, and accumulated on the tube. The rubbing material was therefore left with a deficiency of the electric fire and to this kind of electrification he gave the name *negative*. Unelectrified bodies he thought of as a common store.

Franklin had seen through the apparent diversity of two kinds of things and placed them upon a single scale, much as the caloric theory had displaced the older notion of a separate heat and cold. Further, Franklin's scale distinguished between the quality, the *concentration* of electricity, and the quantity, the *amount* of electricity. This was the same distinction that the thermometer had introduced into the topic of heat. The density of electricity, like the degree of heat (temperature) was measured on the linear scale of Figure 26. The degree of electricity came to be called *potential* and later *voltage*. The amount of electricity held at a given level of potential was the *charge*. Like heat flowing from high temperature to low temperature, like water flowing from a high to a low level, electricity was conceived as a weightless mechanical fluid flowing from a high potential to a low potential. The flow of electricity manifested itself in the heat and light of the spark. The evolving science of thermodynamics was to have no difficulty in subsuming electrical phenomena by analogy with heat and water power. In fact, Joule's first measurements on the principle of conservation of energy were of the electrical equivalent of heat.

Franklin's most famous experiment was that of the kite. From the appearance of lightning, the smell of ozone in the air after a flash, the fire, and the shock to living things, Franklin could reasonably assume that lightning was the electric fire with which he had been experimenting. He proposed to obtain lightning in a Leyden jar and there experiment with it to verify

what was at the time simply a reasonable idea. Franklin turned
to the device of the kite, which he had last used in childhood as
a sail to carry him across a Boston pond. Sending up a well-
built kite in a thunderstorm, he charged a Leyden jar and with

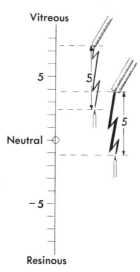

Fig. 26. *Franklin's Scale of Potential.* The
same intensity of discharge is obtained in
descending the same distance of the potential scale no matter where along the scale
the distance is taken. Doubling the charge
or quantity of electricity to descend a given
distance will double the intensity of the discharge.

it performed the experiments that showed the properties of
electricity obtained in other ways, such as demagnetizing a
nail, kindling a fire, etc.

The effects of Franklin's discovery were literally electrifying.
His identification of the lightning and thunder universally
associated with supernatural power as the corporeal, mechani-

cal phenomenon, electricity, was in itself of the character of miraculous revelation. Franklin seemed like a sage from a nobler world, soothing the fears of mankind. To the philosophers of the Age of Reason it was one more blow, as great perhaps as had ever been struck, against the forces of ignorance and superstition which they thought of as the enemy. In Newtonian mechanics, the rationalists found the ordered world-system to fit their ideas, but the *Principia* was after all a remote and forbidding territory of hostile theorems and implacable geometry. Franklin's lightning was immediate to the perception. Franklin had not only rationalized the lightning but with his invention of the lightning rod he had rendered it powerless. To the more literal-minded, both in the camp of the clericals who deplored Franklin's impiety and the anticlericals who hailed the backwoods savant,* it appeared that Franklin had disarmed the Deity and rendered the awful visitation of divine chastisement an impotent if dramatic display of frustrated rage. In France, Buffon, who had already been forced to retract his naturalistic theory of the origin of the earth, arranged for the translation of Franklin's letters, while the Abbé Nollet, who had scourged the Carthusian monks with his Leyden jar, indignantly wrote that he would prefer church bells to lightning rods. The church steeples of Europe, graceful spires projecting high above the surrounding villages, were ideal points of greatest potential difference, and it had long been a source of disquiet that churches of God were so frequently singled out for destructive visitation.

When, as was inevitable, the new group of theoretical physicists, their skills whetted by a century of mathematical refinements of the theory of gravitation, turned their attention to the

* There were probably fewer raccoons within the confines of eighteenth-century Philadelphia than in twentieth-century Manhattan. Franklin was neither the first nor the last politician to capitalize on an irrelevant symbol.

phenomena of electricity, they were able to subsume it rapidly under the all-embracing mechanistic idea. The work of Coulomb in particular was typical of the mathematical precision and experimental nicety that was the boast of French science. The forces of attraction and repulsion that characterized electrical and magnetic phenomena were believed to fall off as the inverse square of the distances involved. If it is simply assumed that the force extends equally in all directions, this implies the diminution of the force in proportion to its spread; that is to the square of the distance involved.

Joseph Priestley had reasoned from the analogy with gravitation that if electricity obeyed an inverse square law, the force on a charged particle at the center of a charged sphere would be nil. Newton had used the calculus to deduce that the force of gravity at the center of a sphere must be zero. Priestley prepared a sphere which he charged and then through an orifice inserted a charged particle at the end of a thin rod. He showed in this way that there was no force between the particle and the sphere when the particle was at the center of the shell. Since he obtained the same effect for electricity that Newton had obtained from the inverse square law for gravitation, Priestley reasoned that the electrical law must be the same mathematically.

In the experiments which Coulomb performed, he was able to determine an empirical law for electrical attraction that he called the fundamental law of electricity.

> The repulsive force between two small spheres charged with the same sort of electricity is in the inverse ratio of the squares of the distances between the centers of the two spheres.

The attractive force between oppositely charged bodies also obeyed an inverse square law. In a similar set of experiments Coulomb determined that the inverse square law governed the attraction between unlike and the repulsion between like *magnetic* bodies. Coulomb was acting on faith. The insensitivity of his instruments gave him results that he could not always construe into the simple inverse square relationship. ". . . in these three trials the difference between theory and experiment is $\frac{1}{10}$ for the last trial compared with the first, . . ." he wrote. The fanatical insistence on perfection that led Kepler to reject the Copernican discrepancy of eight parts in 21,600 would have led Coulomb into a blind alley. Instead he rested his faith on the inverse square relationship. The laws he had determined were the laws of mechanism. Electrical phenomena, magnetic phenomena, indeed all phenomena must fundamentally rest upon the idea of particles and the inverse square forces acting along the lines between their centers. Electricity, like magnetism, was a fluid material made of particles in the form of "molecules." These particles and their momenta and positions would enter into the calculations of Laplace's universal knowledge. And the task of the reduction of all physical phenomena to mechanical terms had been brought closer to completion by the work of Coulomb.

Not long after, about 1798, Henry Cavendish, the discoverer of hydrogen, reported his direct determination of the law of gravitation by the use of a torsion balance. The trinity of mechanical laws stood complete:

$$f_g = \gamma\, \frac{m_1 m_2}{r^2}$$ the law of universal gravitation (Newton-Cavendish);

$$f_e = k\, \frac{z_1 z_2}{r^2}$$ the fundamental law of electricity (Coulomb);

$$f_m = K\, \frac{p_1 p_2}{r^2}$$ the fundamental law of magnetism (Coulomb).

The gravitational, electrical, and magnetic forces (f_g, f_e, f_m) were all proportional to the inverse square of the distance (r).

Three constants of proportionality, γ, k, and K were known by direct measurement. The degree of the force involved depended on the quantity of the material being attracted or repelled; on the product of the masses of the particles, m_1 and m_2 in gravitation; on the number z of the electric charges on each attracting body for electricity; on the density p of the magnetic fluid for the case of magnetic force. While gravitation, electricity, and magnetism remained three distinct areas of physics, the universality of mechanistic law seemed well established. In the watery sunshine of the dying eighteenth century, the simple clarity of science, like the spirit of the new American republic and the ideals of the Declaration of the Rights of Man, was the optimistic expression of a confident mankind. But the nineteenth century did not usher in the millennium, and the simplicities of mechanism had yet to meet their first check. The fluids and their forces had been identified. Electrostatics had been founded. But the motions of these fluids were still unknown.

The great leap from electrostatics to electricity in the form of a current of charge was an advance due to the humble frog. That Job of the animal kingdom, as he was styled by Claude Bernard, has been subjected to continuous persecution since at least the sixteenth century, when Harvey used it to demonstrate the circulation of the blood. Another physician, Luigi Galvani, professor at Bologna, now began the study of electrokinetics at the same time that the careful work of Coulomb was bringing electrostatics to a conclusion. For a hundred years the pall of Galileo's condemnation had hung over Italy. Too provincial for mathematics or theoretical mechanics, the Italian investigators in the privacy of their laboratories turned to the new phenomena of the electrostatic machine, and the Leyden jar, or the older and safer study of medicine. In Galvani's laboratory in happy disorder a dismembered frog lay on the same table as an electrostatic machine. By pure chance, which the more orderly laboratories of England and France would have excluded, a visitor happened to crank the electrostatic machine while at the same time poking at the leg of the frog with a scalpel. Galvani had discovered a detector of electricity. The spasmodic contraction of a recently severed frog leg was the first *galvanometer*.

Galvani's experiments were repeated and varied ingeniously by Alessandro Volta, who soon discovered that the frog's leg was a trivial irrelevance and that the phenomenon had nothing to do with any hypothetical animal electricity. Instead, any fluid or semifluid such as water, water-soaked leather, blotting paper, etc., which would conduct electricity, would generate electricity when placed between two dissimilar metal plates. By taking silver and copper coins and stacking them in a pile with brine-soaked cardboard or leather between each pair of coins (dissimilar) the strength of the effects were multiplied. The voltaic pile to which we now refer as the electric battery produced the same effects as the Leyden jar but produced them continuously and without the necessity for previous charging. Volta made the further observation that the degree or density of the electricity of the voltaic pile was decidely less than that of the Leyden jar. In modern terms, the chemical battery produces electricity of low *voltage* (or potential). The voltage of static effects is relatively high. But the voltaic pile effect is continuous while the Leyden jar effect is momentary. The quantity of electricity produced by the battery is large compared with the quantity involved in electrostatic effects. The metal discs of the pile imposed a perpetual action or current of electric fluid.

Within the year (1800) William Nicholson (1753–1815) determined that the silver coins were of low (negative) potential with respect to the zinc or tin of the pile and began the investigation of the chemical activities that were involved. The electric current obtained from the voltaic pile or battery would decompose water into hydrogen and oxygen. Further, the action of the voltaic pile was not perpetual because there was a rapid deterioration of the metal plates involved. The current of electric fluid flowing around a circuit from the zinc terminal of the pile to the silver heated the wire as it passed. Energy was being produced. The source of this energy was the chemical energy of two dissimilar metals separated by a conducting brine. As more electrical energy appeared and was converted into heat energy, less chemical energy remained. Like heat, the mysterious electric fluid was weightless; like heat it could be generated in inexhaustible quantities as in the electrostatic machine, like heat it could be made to disappear while something else appeared in its place. The exhaustion of the electric fluid in Volta's and Nicholson's experiments was accompanied by the production of heat or light, or the work of a moving frog's leg, as the exhaustion of heat in a steam engine was accompanied by a corresponding production of mechanical work. The conclusion for electricity appeared to be the same. Like heat, electricity was a form of energy, not matter, not substance. As in the case of heat, purely mechanical ideas would never serve to explain electrical phenomena. Since electricity was freely convertible to heat, the laws of thermodynamics must apply to electricity.

The parallel between electricity and heat could in some ways be extended to magnetism. That electricity and magnetism were related was early suspected. One of the effects of a Leyden jar discharge was its ability to demagnetize an iron nail. As one could speak of the level of heat (temperature) or the degree of electricity (potential), it would be proper also to speak with Coulomb of the density of the magnetic fluid (intensity). And the quantity of heat (calories) corresponded to a quantity of electricity (charges) and a quantity of magnetism (pole strength). The direct connection was first shown by the Danish physicist Hans Christian Oersted in demonstrating electrical effects on magnets to his classes at the University of Copenhagen. Oersted found that the flow of an electric current in a wire produced a magnetic force which could be detected by a simple compass needle. In contrast to all forces that had been known up until that time (1820), the force produced by a current in a wire turned a compass needle, not toward the wire (or away from it), but in a direction at right angles to the line joining the center of the needle to the wire. The force was neither repulsive nor attractive. It was non-Newtonian and it was nonmechanistic. If a series of very small button compasses are placed on the page (Figure 27) and a wire with current flowing up it is pushed up through the middle of the page, the compasses will point in directions tangent to circles centered on the wire and in a counterclockwise sense. If the terminals to the wire are reversed, so that the current flows down through the page, the compasses will reverse so that, still tangent to the circles, they will girdle the wire in a clockwise sense. Oersted had made a discovery of fundamental importance. Here was an empirical phenomenon totally outside the mechanistic conception. The force which turned Oersted's compass needles appeared with the flow of electricity, and ceased when the electricity ceasted to flow. While Coulomb's inverse square law gave the magnitude of the force, it said nothing about the direction. Why should the needles point in the counterclockwise sense? The implication was that the universe was essentially lopsided. Certainly the simplicities of Newtonian mechanism seemed abruptly contradicted by this simple observation, for nothing in the *Principia* was relevant. A totally new kind of force had appeared and the simplest assumptions and hopes of mechanism seemed inadequate for

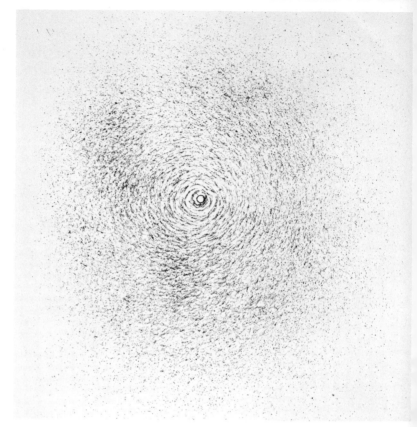

Fig. 27. *Oersted's experiment.* The magnetic field about a current-carrying wire.

its explanation. At the same time, the discovery of Ocrsted proved for the first time a direct connection between electricity and magnetism.

Henry Rowland (1848–1901), performed an experiment similar to Oersted's, which proved the connection between the electric current and static electricity. If a current produces the Oersted effect and a static charge does not, and if a current is a flow of charge along a wire, then the motion of static charges would be a current. Rowland devised a modification of the electrostatic machine that enabled him to whirl charged glass plates at high velocities next to a magnetic needle. The effect was that of a current of electricity and the needle responded accordingly. Furthermore, Rowland found that the strength of the deflecting force depended not only on the inverse square of the distance of the needle, but also on the velocity of the moving charge. The laws of Newton and Coulomb not only said nothing about the direction of this force, but also had nothing to say about the effect of the velocity of the moving charges.

Electrical and magnetic phenomena had at first appeared to be susceptible to mechanical interpretation. Electrical and magnetic fluids were conceived which, acting with the mutual attractions and repulsions of mechanism, accounted for the greatest variety of the first observations. With the discovery of a means of generating a continuous flow of electricity, the immaterial character of the fluids became more apparent. Oersted's discovery was of an entirely unsuspected phenomenon. Nothing in mechanics had prepared the experimenters for a new geometry of forces. And although they had expected a link between electricity and magnetism, this link in the form of Oersted's discovery, was not accompanied by any explanation. It was a fact that magnetic needles pointed not toward or away from current carrying wires, but tangent to circles perpendicular to the wires. And it was a fact that if the current flowed along the wire in the direction of advance of a right-handed screw (from high to low potential) then the needles pointed in the direction of turn of the screw. Not a deduction from the *Principia* or the century of superb mathematics which had amplified and consolidated the universal mechanics, Oersted's results like Galileo's bits of brass tubing and glass were

beyond reason, beyond logic. They were empirical, lying in no
man's mind, conceivable by no process of philosophy. Was the
world right-handed? It appeared to be so, and for the mind
contemplating the possible properties of empty space, this
was a fact of an entirely different order from the assumption
that one and one are two. For the human game of mathematics
in the field of number theory, one and one are two and this
is a mental process and in the mind. But no process of reasoning, no fundamental assumptions could have predicted Oersted's results. Beyond man, beyond the idea, there is the
universe of the right-handed screw, of the gravitational constant; the universe where the velocity of light is c and entropy
is always increasing.

14. Ether and Light

THAT WHICH HATH BEEN IS THAT WHICH
SHALL BE; AND THAT WHICH HATH BEEN
DONE IS THAT WHICH SHALL BE DONE: AND
THERE IS NO NEW THING UNDER THE SUN.

Ecclesiastes

MECHANICAL PHENOMENA, machines themselves, are
really static. They show change which is repetitive and therefore no change at all. Although the earth is in motion about
the sun, it will appear to be motionless if we inspect it at
365¼-day intervals. A pendulum swings but always in the same
arc, always with the same period. Mechanical phenomena are
rhythmic phenomena, repeating themselves in time. The machine is the human replica of the rhythmic processes of nature,
along with music, along with art. The Pythagorean music of the
spheres is in the deepest sense heard by men, even by insects

and plants. The periodicities of nature are expressed in the regular form of the crystal, and the song of the wood thrush as well as the monthly swelling of the moon.

The first connection of these regularities by analogy to the wave is lost in antiquity. Supposedly Pythagoras first attached number to the notes of the scale, but surely the makers of reed pipes and lyres had discovered these regularities before the time of the pyramids. Aristotle understood the concept of the sound wave as a periodic disturbance of the air and related the length of the wave to the length of a sounding pipe. Galileo described the dependence of the pitch of the note upon its frequency. The seventeenth-century atomists, particularly Boyle and Hooke in their pneumatic experiments before the Royal Society, had developed a full concept of the transmission of sound as waves in the air. By exhausting the air from a glass jar containing a bell, they were able to show that the spring of the air was necessary to transmit the sound of the bell; for although the clapper could be seen striking the bell, no sound could be heard when the air was exhausted. By the same token, light did not require air for its propagation because the contents of the jar could be seen as easily without air as with. The simplest of molecular assumptions fit this concept of sound waves. If the air is to consist of small hard molecules like marbles, then the characteristics of an air wave may be calculated from Newton's laws of impact in the same way that the transmission of a blow at one end of a row of glass marbles can be calculated. Newton, in fact, derived a formula for the velocity of sound with the assumption that the air consisted of just such identical particles in rows.

The well-developed mechanical sense of the seventeenth-century investigators, Hooke, Huygens, and Newton, would not allow a fundamental discrepancy between the propagation of light and of sound. For Huygens in particular, the Cartesian mechanistic universe, an all-pervading plenum of strictly logical necessity, demanded a parallel between light and sound.

> . . . when one considers the extreme speed with which light spreads on every side, and how, when it comes from different regions, even from those directly opposite, the rays traverse one another without hindrance, one may well understand that when we see a luminous object, it cannot be by any transport of matter coming to us from this object, in the way in which a shot or an arrow traverses the air. . . .
>
> We know that by means of the air which is an invisible and impalpable body, sound spreads around the spot where it has been produced by a movement which is passed on successively from one part of the air to another; . . . Now there is no doubt at all that light also comes from the luminous body to our eyes by some movement impressed on the matter which is between the two; since, as we have already seen, it cannot be by the transport of a body which passes from one to the other. If, in addition, light takes time for its passage . . . it will follow that this movement, impressed on the intervening matter, is successive; and consequently it spreads, as sound does, by spherical surfaces and waves.

Does light require time for its passage? Galileo thought it must, but without clocks, without instruments, it was impossible to tell. Galileo proposed that two men carrying lanterns, climb to the peaks of two distant hills. One of them would uncover his lantern, and the other, on seeing the light, would uncover his in turn. When the first man saw the flash of the second lantern, he would understand that the velocity of light would be the distance to the other lantern and back divided by the time that had elapsed. But the velocity of light was far too great for this to be a practical experiment. For Galileo to have detected the passage of an interval of one second of time, the two lanterns would have had to be 93,000 miles apart or a distance of nearly four times around the earth. The velocity of light was indeed determined in the seventeenth century and the method was indirectly owing to Galileo. It was determined from astronomical measurements by Olaus Roemer in 1676.

> In 1666 [wrote Voltaire] Colbert, jealous of the new glory [of the English Royal Society] wished France to partake of it; and at the request of savants, obtained Louis XIV's agreement for the establishment of an academy of science. . . . Colbert drew by means of heavy pensions, Cassini from Italy, Huygens from Holland, and Roemer from Denmark. . . .
>
> The public was astonished to see a chemistry that sought neither philosopher's stone nor the art of prolonging life beyond the limits of nature; an astronomy that did not predict the future, a medicine independent of the phases of the moon.

Roemer suggested that the regular rotations of the satellites about Jupiter made it a clock of absolute accuracy set up in a position from which it could be read from anywhere on the earth. By 1676, such astronomers as Roemer were in possession of pendulum clocks, telescopes, observatories, and under the benign wing of Colbert, the freedom to explore the world "rejecting all systems." Roemer told the Royal Academy of Paris that the eclipse of the first satellite of Jupiter, due two months from that date, would be ten minutes late. His dramatic prediction of what amounted to a substantial departure from uniform motion (the period of the Medicean planet in question was only 42½ hours) was based on eight years of careful observation. Following the eclipse, which occurred ten minutes late as he had predicted, Roemer explained that the discrepancy was due to the finite speed of light (Figure 28). While the satellite with its period of 42½ hours circles Jupiter with clocklike precision, beating out equal intervals of time, the earth moves away from Jupiter on its orbit about the sun.

As the earth gets farther and farther from the clock, light must travel the intervening distance and the eclipse, taking place at the correct time, will be observed on earth late by the amount of time required for the light to travel the extra distance. By careful observation, Roemer was able to determine that it took a ray of light 22 minutes to cross the diameter of the earth's

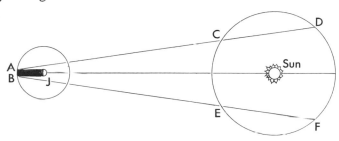

Fig. 28. *Roemer's determination of the velocity of light.* The satellite is seen emerging from the shadow of Jupiter at B while the earth is at E. Forty-two and a half hours later, the satellite has revolved back to B. The earth by this time has moved to F. The light from B must travel the extra distance from E to F, and the satellite is observed at B later than its appointed time. On the other side of the sun, as the earth moves from D to C (toward Jupiter), the satellite's period of revolution is apparently shorter.

orbit. Using the modern figure for the diameter, the velocity of light would appear to be:

$$\frac{186,000,000 \text{ miles}}{22 \times 60 \text{ seconds}} = 140,000 \text{ miles per second.}$$

The modern figure for the velocity of light is now given as 186,000 miles per second.

While Huygens could see the impossibility of anything *material* traveling at such a fantastically high velocity—

. . . more than six hundred thousand times the velocity of sound. This however is quite another thing from

being instantaneous, since there is all the difference between a finite thing and an infinite.

he could at the same time see that a wave motion could be
transmitted by hard round spheres which were in contact. The
spheres would remain in place like the particles of rope or like
the cork on the surface of the sea. It would be the disturbance
itself that would move. Referring to the example of the marbles
in a row struck at one end, Huygens wrote:

> . . . the motion passes as in an instant to the last of
> them, which separates itself from the row. . . . Whence
> one sees that the movement passes with an extreme ve-
> locity which is the greater, the greater the hardness of
> the substance of the spheres.
> But it is still certain that this progression of motion is
> not instantaneous, but successive, and therefore it must
> take time. . . .

Isaac Newton was a mechanist and an atomist along with his
century but he was also the first theoretical physicist, and if
he thought in mechanistic terms, he was still precise in his
publication. He would admit no hypotheses and in his method
of mathematical reasoning from observation, he avoided explanation and cause. Why did bodies attract one another? What
is light? Such questions lead us to:

> . . . [the] very first cause which certainly is not me-
> chanical; . . . Whence is it that Nature does nothing in
> vain; and whence arises all that order and beauty which
> we see in the world? To what end are comets, and
> whence is it that planets move all one and the same way
> in orbs concentric, . . . what hinders the fixed stars from
> falling upon one another? How came the bodies of ani-
> mals to be contrived with so much art, and for what ends
> were their several parts? Was the eye contrived without
> skill in optics, and the ear without knowledge of sounds?
> . . . And though every true step made in this philos-

ophy brings us not immediately to the knowledge of the
First Cause, yet it brings us nearer to it, and on that
account is to be highly valued.

If he banished hypotheses from the body of his work, he
could not refrain from incorporating them into his thinking.
His optics had been criticized by Hooke and Huygens for offering no explanations, no *model* of light but only the laws governing its behavior. In a pique at Hooke, Newton, who had as
a young man carefully studied Hooke's *Micrographia*, withheld
publication of his *Optics* until Hooke's death. In the back of
the *Optics* he appended the famous queries, a set of discussions
in which the pent-up mechanism of a lifetime of hypothesis
finally appeared. Here were all the speculations, beautifully
reasoned, of Newton the visionary, which had been so sternly
repressed by Newton the purist.

Once previously, in a letter to Boyle, Newton had entertained the idea of Huygens' ether of hard round particles and
speculated on these as a mechanism for gravitation. He now considered the possibility of the ether as a medium for the transmission of waves of light. It would have to be of an elasticity
490 billion times that of air, and at the same time 700,000 times
rarer than air in order both to transmit light at the velocities
observed by Roemer, and at the same time offer no appreciable
impedance to planetary motions in the course of about 10,000
years (which Newton thought would suffice for the time span of
the universe). These difficulties did not seem impossible to
Newton. If the rarity of the ether appeared unbelievable to
anyone,

> Let him also tell me how an electric body can by fric-
> tion emit an exhalation so rare and subtile, and yet so
> potent, as by its emission to cause no sensible diminution
> of the electric body, and to be expanded through a
> sphere, whose diameter is above two feet, and yet to be

able to agitate and carry up leaf copper, or leaf gold, at the distance of above a foot from the electric body?

But the whole idea of an undulatory or wave theory of light Newton felt, broke down when one considered the phenom cnon of double refraction in Iceland spar, recently described by Bartholinus. This mineral, an exceptionally well crystallize variety of ordinary calcite, cleaves in optically excellent para lelopipeds (rhombohedra). A ray of light passing through th spar is refracted in the ordinary way, just as a ray of ligh passing from the air into water is bent toward the perpendic ular to the surface on entering the denser medium. In addition a second ray appears which is more strongly refracted. Becaus of this, anything seen through Iceland spar may appear double

Huygens had explained refraction by the wave theory o light. Transparent objects contained the fine particles of ether which were not as free to vibrate as they were outside such bodies and therefore waves were slowed down on entering water, or crystal, or glass. If a beam of light consisting of vas numbers of spreading spheroidal waves encounters a surface o a denser medium at an angle (Figure 29) the waves at on end of the beam will be slowed before the waves at the othe end, and the front of the beam will therefore swing on itsel changing the direction of the beam. It seemed to Newton tha double refraction required two distinct interpenetrant ethers each transmitting light with a different velocity, in order t account for double refraction. He preferred to ascribe the phe nomenon to some original property of the rays rather than t multiply these hypothetical ethers. "And for rejecting such medium, we have the authority of those the oldest and mos celebrated philosophers of Greece and Phoenicia, who mad a vacuum, and atoms, and the gravity of atoms, the first princi ples of their philosophy; . . ."

Newton suggested a corpuscular hypothesis. Light was t

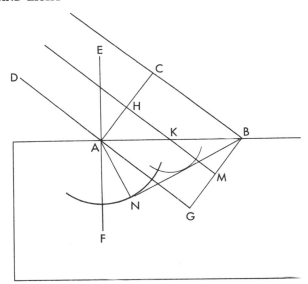

Fig. 29. *Huygens' construction for refraction.* While
light travels along the upper ray CB, light spreading
from the point A through the relatively resistant medium reaches N. As each point on the surface is
reached by the wave disturbance, it becomes itself
the center of a spreading wave. The line NB tangent
to these wavelets is the refracted wave front instead
of the line GB which would have been the wave
front if the light was not slowed down in the medium.

onsist of very tiny particles, corpuscles. The corpuscles of
ach color were alike. White light was a mixture of all kinds of
orpuscles. The corpuscles had shape, that is to say, sides, some
f them having sides with properties enabling them to be re-
racted by Iceland spar in one way, and others having sides
nabling them to be refracted in the other way. If the wave
heory was a simpler hypothesis in that it required only the
ne kind of hypothetical particle, the ether, or perhaps two
thers, the corpuscular idea had the advantage that it could

more easily explain the transmission of light across empty
space and in straight lines.

Both ideas had a consistent and mechanical explanation for
all the properties of light. For the rectilinear propagation of
light, the wave theorists could argue that light waves were so
tiny that the tendency for waves to change direction, to flow

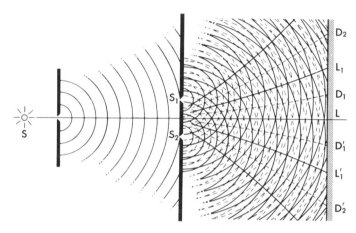

Fig. 30. *Diffraction of light.* Huygens' principle states that
every point in space becomes a source of spreading waves.
The crests of successive waves starting from S_1 and S_2 are
shown in solid black. The lines L_1, L, and L'_1 are lines along
which the waves from both S_1 and S_2 are in position to reinforce. Along the lines D_2, D_1, etc., the crests from S_1 cancel
the troughs from S_2 and vice versa.

around an obstacle, would not be noticeable for gross obstacles.
Besides, when light was passed very close to a fine obstacl
such as a knife blade there was a tendency to wave interfer
ence, similar to what might be observed on the edge of a bar
rier in the sea (Figure 30). Newton explained this by assum
ing an attractive force between matter and the corpuscles of
light. Since these were of sizes proportionate to their position

n the spectrum, the attraction of matter would tend to sort
hem out, much as a magnet would sort out passing bodies of
varying degrees of magnetism. By this means, Newton explained the different refractions undergone by the different
colors. White light entering a glass prism was divided into the
colors of the spectrum because the glass attracted each size of
corpuscle differently. In the wave theory, the same phenomenon of colors was explained by the assumption that each color
was caused by waves of different wave lengths, the red end
of the spectrum being the longest waves and the violet end the
shortest waves, but like sounds of different frequencies in air,
all traveling with the same velocity.

Both hypothetical models and fine structures for light were
consistent in their mechanisms and in their explanations of
the optics of the seventeenth century. Both rested on hypothetical substances, weightless, or of weight too slight to be measured. Both were theories of particles and the forces between
them; the corpuscular theory required a great many kinds of
particles, and even required that these have shapes, but for an
ge approaching an atomistic chemistry this was not a serious
bjection. The wave theory required but the one kind of particle, the ether particle, although later developments in physics
might add additional ethers to transmit electrical and magnetic forces.

Thomas Young (1773–1829), a child prodigy who read at
the age of two and renounced the use of sugar at the age of
sixteen because of his opposition to slavery, settled the question in favor of the wave theory by his invention of the principle of interference, an idea imperfectly advanced in Hooke's
Micrographia and then ignored for nearly 150 years.

> When two undulations, from different origins, coin-
> cide either perfectly or very nearly in direction, their
> joint effect is a combination of the motions belonging

to each. . . . It has been shown that two equal series of [water] waves proceeding from centres near each other, may be seen to destroy each other's effects at certain points, and at others to redouble them; and the beating of two sounds has been explained from a similar inter- ference.

If light is passed through a pin hole to a screen, the patterr on the screen will be a spot. If the experiment is performec very carefully, there will be color fringes about the spot– which Newton explained as due to the differential attraction of matter on the kinds of corpuscles. If a second pin hole i, made next to the first and the second is covered for a momen' while light through the first records on a photographic plate and then the first is covered and the second uncovered, the resulting pattern is of two distinct spots on a dark field. But i light is passed through both holes at the same time, the patterr is light at the center with light and dark stripes further out. It i as if the light knows whether or not an adjacent hole is avail able. The two rays of light interfere with each other. If each ray was a stream of corpuscles, like the spray of bullets of a machine gun, there is no conceivable way in which the twc streams would interfere. But with the assumptions of Huygen, this phenomenon called *diffraction* is explained by Young anc even the nature and degree of the interference are described The light spots on the film are the directions in which the light is reinforced by constructive interference. The dark spot, are the directions in which the light has been canceled by destructive interference.

It would be fitting to record that Young's papers, whicl posterity has adjudged the first significant advance in optic, since the time of Newton, were so recognized by the worlc of science, but Young was to wait nearly twenty years before he was understood. His contemporaries described his papers as:

> . . . destitute of every species of merit. . . . We . . . dismiss, for the present, the feeble lucubrations of this author, in which we have searched without success for some traces of learning, acuteness, and ingenuity, that might compensate his evident deficiency in the powers of solid thinking.

Young's explanation for the diffraction of light made it an *experimentam crucis*. The hypothesis of the wave nature of light was confirmed. The corpuscular hypothesis of Newton was discarded. In vain would Duhem protest many years later that the phenomenon of diffraction of light, like all other optical phenomena, could be described completely and accurately with reference only to things that could be measured and seen, to gratings, angles, and distances; that the wavings of the hypothetical ether were a mechanical addendum that neither added to the phenomenon nor explained it in any way. The reduction of the complex phenomena of nature to a system of particles and the forces between them acting in the inverse ratio of the distances and along the lines joining their centers seemed certainly a closer goal after Young's experiment than before. The ultimate goal that Hooke had expressed in 1665 in the *Micrographia*, of visualizing the tiny machines of nature, the fine patterns of what to our coarser unaided senses seemed smooth continuum, was for light, at least, a *fait accompli*. Skillful instrument makers rapidly developed the tools for an enormously productive science of spectrography. The light from the sun, from the moon, and planets, from distant stars, from incandescent gases and solids was passed through the spectrograph and broken into rays, which were spread out on a scale and measured precisely. For scientists cataloging the frequencies of thousands of rays of light of all kinds, the suggestion that the wave theory was a superfluous hypothesis made no sense.

One minor contradiction tempered the success of the wave theory. On examination of the two rays of light into which a single ray was split by a fragment of Iceland spar, it was found that the rays were plane *polarized*. The spar could be fashioned into a kind of filter and if two filters were placed together in front of a beam of light, they could be turned into a cross position in which the beam would be canceled completely. This signified that, like water waves, light waves were *transverse*, the displacement of the medium occurring across the line of advance of the wave rather than as in the case of sound waves or the shock wave in a row of marbles, along the line of advance of the wave. Huygens' ether model of a row of marbles was for the wrong kind of wave. In order to transmit a transverse wave, a medium must have a shape to which it clings and to which it returns after displacement. The surface of the sea, if depressed for an instant, returns to its original shape initiating a spreading vibration. The displacement of the surface is up and down—across the radial lines of advance of the spreading wave.

The phenomenon of polarization of light was so clearly understood in wave terms that it served to strengthen the theory which diffraction had already established. On the other hand, it raised disquieting notions about the nature of the vibrating medium, the mysterious ether. Huygens had dismissed this as an interpenetrant sea of extremely hard, fine particles, so subtle as to penetrate all matter. The ether must penetrate transparent bodies in order for these to pass light. At the same time it must be so fine as to pass freely through the pores of opaque bodies like the earth and the planets without in the least offering these any resistance. This is in itself a contradiction, for the earth and the planets include transparent bodies such as water and glass. The fine Huygenian ether particles must on the one hand interact with the water slowing down light passing through it (the phenomenon of refraction) and on the other hand must offer no noticeable interaction to masses of water moving through space.

But this contradiction is of no real importance, since the ether particles which Huygens describes are for the transmission of longitudinal waves and the phenomenon of polarization proves that light waves are transverse. Substances like air or water or any kind of particle fluid cannot transmit transverse waves because they lack the property of resisting a change in shape.

Substances with shapes to which they cling, jellylike substances, saw blades, rigid solids, are required to transmit transverse waves. The greater the rigidity, the greater the rapidity of transmission. Newton's figures were quite correct. A rigidity 490 billion times that of air would be required to transmit waves at the velocity of light. The densest of tool steels would not even begin to approach the required rigidity. At the same time, the ether, in order to avoid interfering with the motions of the planets, would have to be 700,000 times rarer than air to permit the universe to last even 10,000 years. The ether could not be seen, touched, felt, or weighed since upon its free passage through the pores of all matter depended the stability of the universe. It could not be pumped from a jar like air. It had one property. It would transmit light.

The luminiferous ether so conceived was the creation of Huygens, although the Greeks had used the word for the material stuff that filled the universe. Huygens' story would not be complete without the mention of its conclusion. Toward the end of his reign, Louis XIV acquired religion. Colbert was dismissed in disgrace and Louvois appointed in his stead. The

Edict of Nantes was revoked and the Protestants were driven from France. Roemer returned to Denmark, Huygens to Holland, disdaining the patent of personal toleration offered him. Denis Papin fled to London with his steam digester, and his steam gun, to work with Hooke on the experiments that were to lead to the steam engine. Many of the other members of the Academy fled to Switzerland. The nucleus of French scientists remaining were employed by Louvois in what the Defense Department today calls "development," that is, useful projects such as designing the hydraulics system for the fountains of Versailles. The abstract questions that had agitated them, the velocity of light, the weight of the air, the figure of the earth, were abandoned. Louvois was not concerned with "what makes the grass green."

The wave theory of light was one of the triumphs of classical science. It provided a simple model in terms of which all optical phenomena could be explained. It was mechanical and rational. There was only one difficulty with it and this was the question of the medium of transmission. A string wave travels along a string. Particles of string do the waving. But a light wave travels in otherwise empty space and also in transparent matter. To account for the passage of a light wave it is necessary to postulate the existence of a vibrating medium—the ether. The ether shows itself in no other way than in the passage of light. The properties required of the ether are unlike the properties of either matter or energy. The contradictions inherent in the ether concept were eventually to bring down the whole house of classical Newtonian physics. As science developed in the latter nineteenth century, the improvements in instruments and measurements provided for a steadily accumulating series of observations in greater and greater contradiction with the ether model. Not even the wave theory of light was to be spared. In the revolution that was to bring down the whole of science, the *Principia* was to go the way of Ptolemy's *Almagest*. The foundations of space, of time, of reason itself, were to shake to pieces. Already, in the earliest discussions of the wave theory of light, the discrepancies that were to destroy it were present.

15. Probability and Chance

I DREW ONE CONCLUSION WHICH I BELIEVE
TO BE CORRECT: THAT IS, THOUGH THERE IS
NO SYSTEM, THERE REALLY IS A SORT OF OR-
DER IN THE SEQUENCE OF CASUAL CHANCES
—AND THAT, OF COURSE, IS VERY STRANGE.

FYODOR DOSTOIEVSKY, *The Gambler*

JEROME CARDAN (1501–1576), the sixteenth-century
mathematician and physician who was one of the few men
privileged to see the notebooks of Leonardo da Vinci, wrote
in his autobiography, "I gambled . . . at chess more than
forty years, at dice about twenty-five; and not only every year,
but—I say it with shame—every day." It was an era of flam-
boyance and melodrama—Italy at the height of the Renaissance
—and Cardan was not the least conspicuous figure in an era
that boasted a Copernicus as well as a Cellini. His life was a

frenetic alternation between poverty and wealth, between fame and disgrace. He witnessed the execution by torture of his favorite son and resigned the chair of mathematics at the University of Milan, only to accept the chair of medicine at Bologna. Imprisoned as a heretic, he lived to be pensioned by the Pope. He wrote 242 books, publishing 53 in the single year of 1543 alone. He wrote on every subject—astrology, the Virgin, teeth, fossils—but his chief love after medicine was the "cossick art" or algebra, so called after the Italian *cosa* for "thing" or *x*, the unknown. It is not surprising that when he set down his observations on games of chance—fifteen pages entitled *De Ludo Aleae*—he brought into play the same kind of reasoning that he used in his algebra. The book on chance was not only a kind of premature Hoyle, but included recipes for coping with the indeterminate that ranged from the distinctly practical (to cut the deck at a particular card, soap the back of the card) to a mathematics of probability and chance.

Like any other branch of mathematics, the science of chance consists of a systematic exploitation of the implications of a few very simple and highly general ideas. The primary idea underlying all of probability theory and statistics is the idea of contingency—of a chance event—an event wholly outside of the realm of cause or plan or purpose—an event, in short, outside law. That probability should have begun with gambling, as illegal in Cardan's world as it is in ours, is not surprising. The fall of a sparrow was after all in God's hand, but the fall of a card was outside the law.

A chance event, as the gambler understood it, is wholly unreal. It is something which may occur, but also may not. If it does happen, it is no longer a chance event; it is a certain event. It passes from the realm of probability to the realm of certainty. The two are not entirely distinct. Events which have already happened may be analyzed statistically. And the statistics in turn may be the basis for assigning probabilities to future events. Gamblers have always had a rudimentary concept of probabilities expressed in the notion of fair odds. The least mathematical of gamblers knows that a bet of even money is fair on the toss of a coin, but hopelessly unfair on the turn of a particular card. Cardan was the first person to assess the odds and to set down methods for their computation. He did not invent gambling any more than Eve invented sin, but the analogy is fair. The idea of chance in science is like the knowledge of good and evil in Eden.

A century after Cardan's death, the mathematicians Pascal and Fermat, again at the behest of gamblers, undertook to found a complete mathematics of probability. Still later, the great Laplace brought the full power of the calculus to bear. The disreputable origins of the science were ignored. As early as the seventeenth century, John Graunt, an English haberdasher, had collected figures on births and deaths which he used to prove that monogamy was the natural state of affairs. He had found that over the years there were consistently more male than female children born, but the vicissitudes of war and labor ensured a counterbalancing higher death rate for the males. In the nineteenth century the Belgian astronomer Quetelet found that nearly all human characteristics followed a normal distribution curve (that is, the number of samples at any distance below the average is the same as the number of samples an equal distance above). Today statistics intrudes upon our every activity. We are born items on a statistical compilation. Our future lives are influenced by the statistical positions we achieve on tests administered before we are able to walk. By averages we are called into the armed forces and by averages we are assigned to duty. Our lives reflect the joggling of the stock market curves and there are those who think we are dependent on the activity of solar flares. We cannot, except with the greatest inconvenience, place two dollars on a horse to win, but decisions affecting our lives turn on the flicker of a percentile point. Cardan, with his trivial daily wager, was an innocent by modern standards.

Statistics first found application in science in the kinetic-molecular theory. The motions of molecules of a gas were postulated to be random, the velocities of the molecules were averaged by Bernouilli, and more precisely by Joule. In 1860, James Clerk Maxwell and later, Ludwig Boltzmann investigated the frequency distribution of the energy among the particles of an ideal gas. From earlier work it was known that the average velocity of the molecules depended on the energy of the system. Unable to make precise predictions about the behavior of any one of 10^{23} individual molecules, the kinetic-molecular theory was nevertheless able to assert with great precision the value for the *average* velocity of the molecules at any given temperature. As a parallel if not exactly comparable problem, it was once computed that the *average* Smith girl has 1.3 children, a figure obtained by dividing the number of children of Smith alumnae by the number of alumnae. It is in some ways a meaningless figure. Of all the thousands of alumnae under consideration, not one actually has one and three tenths of a child. But whether any use can be found for the figure or not, its value as an average is as good as the data on which it was based. If the survey of alumnae and their children was complete and accurate, then the average is also complete and accurate.

A more useful figure might be an estimate of the distribution of the children among the graduates. Here we could imagine 130 children to be divided among 100 women. Thirty of the women could have two children and the remaining 70 could have one each. But it is reasonable to suppose that some will have none and some will have three and even four. We can imagine the problem as dividing 100 women into the categories, childless, one child, two children, three, etc. in such a way that the total number of children will be 130. The largest single group of Smith women will turn out to fit in the two-children category. Smaller groups will fit in the categories of one and three children. Still fewer women will have either no children or four children. A very few hardy souls will be found with more than four children, but none can have less than no children.

This distribution of 130 children among 100 women could be predicted entirely from the assumption that one Smith girl is more or less like another; in other words, the assumption that the individuals of the sample are indistinguishable. That being the case, the random accidents of life, marriage, fortune, and disease are distributed among them impartially, and the accompanying distribution of children must, according to the assumption, be equally random, equally a matter of chance. Accordingly, the distribution of 130 children among 100 indistinguishable women will be that distribution which is most probable: precisely the distribution we might calculate for 130 peas rained down upon 100 cups.

All of the 130 peas might fall into one of the cups alone. This is highly unlikely. Actually, since there are 100 cups, there are 100 ways of bringing about this unlikely distribution and any of the 100 cups could be chosen. It is unlikely because there are so many more ways of bringing about a less extreme distribution. For example, 65 peas could fall in one cup and 65 in another. Although this distribution also is unlikely, it is far more probable than the first. Any of the 100 cups could serve for the first, leaving any one of 99 to serve for the second, so that instead of 100 ways, there are 9,900 ways of bringing about this distribution. The probability of the second distribution is 99 times the probability of the first. The probability of a distribution which would spread the peas still further among the 100 cups rises sharply.

There are $100 \times 99 \times 98 \times 97 \times 96$ ways of dividing the peas so that twenty-six fall in each of five cups. The number of ways of reversing this, of having five peas drop in each of twenty-six cups, is astronomically greater. And even this distribution is not of very high probability, compared to a distribution which would have three peas in each of forty-odd cups.

The example, if trivial, suggests the method by which Maxwell and Boltzmann determined the distribution of the energy of a gas among its molecules. The probability of any one distribution depends on the number of ways in which such a distribution could be brought about. In the example of the peas, the probability of dividing the peas up so that twenty-six fell in each of five cups, itself a highly improbable distribution, was nevertheless ninety million times greater than the probability that all 130 of the peas would fall by chance into a single cup. If the sample was larger, for example 1,000 cups, the probabilities that are already overwhelming would be multiplied in this single instance by ten thousand. Putting it another way, if the peas were dropped and the cups inspected over and over again, for every single time that all the peas were found in the one cup, there would be ninety million times when twenty-six would be found in each of five cups.

These probabilities, overwhelming in the trivial sample of 100 Smith girls, approach certainty when the 10^{23} particles that make up a laboratory sample of a gas are considered. Attacking the problem of N particles sharing a given amount of kinetic energy, Maxwell reasoned that the least velocity of any of the particles was 0 while there was no theoretical limit to the maximum velocity. The curve will be asymmetrical. The skew curve, obtained by strict deduction from the assumptions of random motion and the operations of statistics, is described by a slightly different mathematics than the normal symmetric curve. The mathematics of the skew distribution is called the Maxwell-Boltzmann statistics. "It appears from this proposition," wrote Maxwell, "that the velocities are distributed among the particles according to the same law as the errors are distributed among the observations in the theory of the 'method of least squares.'" The distance of shots from a central target follow a skew distribution for similar reasons. No shots can come closer than the center and there is no limit to the width by which a shot may miss the center. Maxwell and Boltzmann had obtained a strict method for the description of the fine structure of a gas. If the temperature of the gas is raised by adding more energy in the form of heat, more molecules will travel at higher velocities. The average velocity will be higher.

The particles of a gas collide with each other and the walls of the containing vessel almost continuously. If we place a stream of fast particles all moving with the same high velocity in an empty box, in a very short time these will have collided with each other at random angles and interchanged velocities so that they will no longer travel all at the same velocity. Some at a given instant will be scarcely moving. Some will be traveling at much higher velocities than their original. Most will have acquired a velocity close to the average but slightly lower. If there are enough particles, the curve of their frequency distribution will rapidly reach the proper skew form. Even the time necessary to reach the skew distribution from another distribution is calculable. With ordinary samples it is practically instantaneous.

Consider a cube of gas at 0° C. and an identical cube of the same amount of the same gas at 100° C. Their distribution curves are represented in Figure 31. If the two cubes are placed side by side and the single wall separating them is

suddenly removed, then at the moment of removal, and before
the gas of the one cube has had an opportunity to mingle with
the gas of the other cube, the momentary appearance of the
distribution curve will be distinct from the skew. But almost
instantly, the faster molecules of the hot gas will collide with
the slower molecules of the cool gas, losing some of their velocity to these, and the resultant curve will again be the typical
skew curve, this time for the intermediate temperature 50° C.
The most probable distribution is the skew curve. This prob-

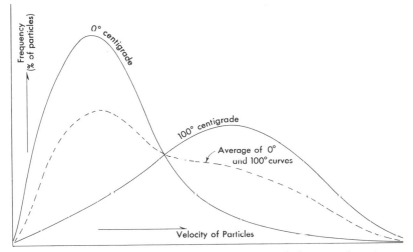

Fig. 31. *Frequency distribution of the velocities of the particles of a gas at separate temperatures.*

ability involves the behavior of 10^{23} particles. It is therefore
overwhelming. We might conceive that once in the course
of the total life of the universe, a box of gas might momentarily
by chance separate into the hot and cold fractions of the averaged curve of Figure 32, or even take a single value for the
velocities of all the particles. The laws of probability do indeed
predict that ultimately every possible distribution of velocities

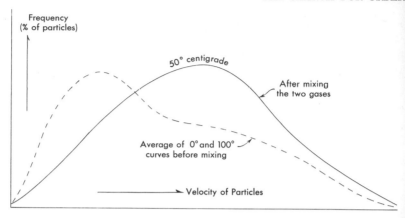

Fig. 32. *Frequency distribution of the velocities of the particles of a gas on mixing.*

will come about. Each has a finite chance. As the grains of the salt in the sea, being distributed in purely random fashion and being in constant motion, might conceivably for a moment concentrate in one ocean, leaving the others as pure fresh water, so the faster molecules of a gas might momentarily segregate. But the chance, though finite, is so small that it can be neglected.

A parallel problem would be to take a jar of white dust and a jar of black dust and mix these together. The result we say without hesitation will be gray dust. As we shake the jar containing the two dusts, there is a possibility that in billions of shakes in billions of years, the dust will momentarily segregate itself, the white powder on one side, the black on the other. There is the possibility that three monkeys seated at three typewriters will eventually produce all the works of Shakespeare. The possibility is finite but we neglect it.

When the two cubes of hot and cold gas were placed together and the faster molecules of the hot box rushed into the colder box, the energy of this heat flow could have been harnessed.

The moving molecules could have been made to turn a wheel or push a piston. Once the skew distribution was reasserted, however, the system is incapable of doing work. The energy of the system is the same after the two gases mix as it was before they intermixed. That is, the amount of internal energy of two units of gas, one at 0° C. and one at 100° C., is the same as the amount of internal energy of two units of gas, both at 50° C. No energy has been lost or gained in the process of mixing the gases. But before the two were mixed, work could have been obtained from the system. Now that the two are mixed, work cannot be obtained from the system. Something has been lost: the capacity for doing work. The measure of this incapacity for doing work, the measure of the degradation of energy, was what we had previously termed *entropy*.

Maxwell, always prone to Victorian whimsy, proposed a paradox. Conceive of a demon, stationed at a door between the two cubes of gas, which are initially at 50° C. Let the demon now observe the molecules approaching the door and when a fast one approaches, let him open the door, and when a slow one approaches, let him close the door. In a moment, the gas would be segregated into hot and cold portions without the expenditure of any work, or of any appreciable amount of work. Maxwell's demon is in violation of the second law. He reverses the flow of entropy. The hot and cold fractions of the gas, left to themselves, will revert to the intermediate temperature, and the flow of heat may be harnessed to perform useful work.

It remained for Ludwig Boltzmann in 1877 to cap the edifice of the kinetic-molecular theory by expressing in useful form the connection between the kinetic-molecular theory and thermodynamics. A kinetic-molecular model already existed for every aspect of thermodynamics, an explanation in terms of the microstructure which, Duhem said, "it did not ask for, with

which it had nothing to do, and to which it owed nothing."
The frequency distribution curve of the state of the two cubes
before they are mixed (Figure 32) is the curve of the system in a state of *low probability*. The skew curve resulting
spontaneously when the barrier between the cubes was lifted
is the curve of the state of *high probability*. Somthing increased
spontaneously, the probability. From the thermodynamic point
of view, the system before mixing was characterized by low
entropy or high availability of the energy for work. After mixing, the entropy had spontaneously risen to maximum value.
In any process the spontaneous movement in the direction of
highest probability is paralleled by the spontaneous movement
in the direction of highest entropy. Entropy, Boltzmann asserted, is a function of probability.

> We can calculate the state of equilibrium by investi-
> gating the probability of the different possible states of
> the system. The initial state will in most cases be a very
> improbable one and from it the system will progress to-
> ward more probable states until it at last reaches the
> most probable state, that is, that of equilibrium of heat.
> If we apply this to the second law we can identify that
> quantity which we commonly designate as entropy with
> the probability of the actual state. . . .
>   . . . In accordance with the second law . . . change
> must always occur in such a way that the total entropy
> of all the bodies increases; according to our present in-
> terpretation this means nothing else than that . . . the
> system of bodies goes from a more improbable to a more
> probable state.

Boltzmann observed that two sciences, kinetic-molecular
physics and thermodynamics, treat of the same phenomena.
In processes like that of the two cubes, the variable of kinetic-
molecular physics that increases is the probability. In thermodynamics, the increasing variable is the entropy. The connec-

tion between the two was induced by Boltzmann. Boltzmann's relation* expressing the functional connection between statistics and entropy is the foundation law of a new science, statistical mechanics. It is one of those simple and perfectly clear generalizations like Galileo's law of freely falling bodies, from which major conclusions may be drawn. In the experiment of the two cubes of gas, the entropy of the joint system was low at the start of the experiment and high at the conclusion of the experiment. The availability of the energy of the system decreased, although the energy was neither lost nor increased. From this kind of an experiment, it became clear that in any kind of spontaneous reaction, entropy, a macroscopic function of the thermodynamic variables, energy, pressure, volume, etc., must always increase. This statement is the second law of thermodynamics. It is an absolute law admitting of no exceptions and no modifications. In mathematical form, it admits of no modifications even in degree. It is a deterministic law and it is positive. In this universe, in this world, the degradation of energy proceeds inexorably; the increase of entropy is absolute. The world moves by a process admitting of not even the slightest remission toward a distant future in which all the energy of the universe will have arrived at the same temperature, in which all the water of the world will have reached the sea, a universe which will be not cold, but comfortable. The energy will be there. The world will be *warm*. But all traces of difference will have disappeared and change will be impossible in the universal sameness of things. In the world of the first and second laws, no other course of behavior is open to a system just as in the world of Newtonian mechanics no other path than the Keplerian is possible to a planet. These worlds are orderly, fixed worlds. Given only sufficient insight into the

* In one form, $S = k \ln P$; S is entropy, k is the gas constant per molecule, and P is probability.

laws, every facet of behavior is fixed and the future is precisely defined by the conditions of the past. The mechanism is
not the completely repetitive mechanism of eighteenth-century
mechanics. It has been modified by the idea of progression in
time of the second law. Instead of a fixed machine following
a circular path, the world is a changing machine following a
spiral path. The problem of Laplace, of determining the whole
of the past and the future given only the positions and momenta of the particles of the universe at a given instant, has
been altered slightly. We must know their entropies as well,
but then, once there, the solution is determined. The rule of
law is absolute.

But experiments such as that of the two cubes are also interpreted from the kinetic-molecular point of view. We picture
a world of fine structures, tiny mechanisms, a world of atoms
and the void. We have one skew frequency distribution curve
for the cube at 0° C. and one for the cube at 100° C. and a
combined double humped curve of low probability. With mixture, the cubes are now described by a new, single skew frequency distribution curve. The system has moved from lower
to higher probability states. From this point of view we regain
the first law of thermodynamics. It is seen now as simply an
old law of Newton's. In collisions of elastic bodies, the sum
of the kinetic energies of the bodies before the collisions is
the same as the sum of the kinetic energies after the collisions.
We also regain the second law. Any spontaneous reaction proceeds in the direction of increasing probability. The state of
probability of the universe is continually increasing. We
reinterpret entropy, which we had previously considered as
the measure of the unavailability of energy for useful work.
It is a measure of the probability of things. It is a measure of
the degree of confusion of intermixture of things.

The new law relating entropy and probability, for which

Boltzmann and the American J. Willard Gibbs are chiefly responsible, now subsumes the two separate sciences of kinetic-molecular physics and thermodynamics. Kinetic-molecular physics assumed the model of particles and the void and to this model applied the mechanics of Newton. Thermodynamics assumed the first and second laws (and certain qualifications known as the zeroth and third laws). The Boltzmann relationship postulates the connection between the two sciences and brings the results of these separate sciences under the single heading of statistical mechanics. From the Boltzmann relationship, the results of kinetic-molecular physics can be derived mathematically. From the Boltzmann relationship, the results of thermodynamics can be derived mathematically. It leads on the one hand to all the results of the model of particles and mechanical interactions between them. It leads on the other hand to all the results of the purely macroscopic assumptions of thermodynamics. But more than that, it leads to results which neither of the two parent sciences had conceived. From it can be deduced results of great significance in many of the branches of physics and chemistry, and therefore in geology and the life sciences, in communications and information theory. From it we can calculate rates of radioactive disintegration applicable on the one hand to the development of nuclear weapons and, on the other hand, to the development of atomic power and nuclear research in medicine, botany, and other fields. Even determinations of the ages of the rocks of the earth's crust hinge on the equations of statistical mechanics. We use it for calculations of heat flow and of diffusion rates. It is of major importance for the newly developing science of the solid state, for crystallography, for the beginnings of the understanding of metals, for the physical properties of solids, the study of which has already produced the transistor and through it, a revolution in electronics.

The Boltzmann relationship, the Boltzmann law, expressed in any one of several ways, is like Newton's law, of general applicability. When we apply the operations of mathematics to this law, as we applied mathematics to the postulates of the kinetic molecular theory in Bernouilli's derivation, we are led by the rules of mathematics to a volume of new and hitherto unsuspected relationships which to our great satisfaction we find are confirmed by nature. In the new science of statistical mechanics, we have miraculously recovered the mechanistic view. But now it is a statistical mechanism. In a single gram molecular weight of matter, it is the sum of 10^{23} separate mechanisms. Our model of the universe is again mechanical but now the machine even in its minor parts is of vast complexity. We can be very positive about our assertions. The shaking of the jar of gray dust will not separate it into white and black dust fractions in our lifetime, or even in the lifetime

Fig. 33. *"Elements of so-called chance."* Watercolor by Jackson Pollock.

of the solar system. We can rely upon the vast probabilities involved. But still upon our reliance the seeds of doubt have been cast. There is a finite possibility of a departure. There is a small possibility, so small as to seem absurd, but a possibility nevertheless, a finite thing. As Huygens remarked, between a finite and an infinite thing lies all the difference. The dust might separate on the next shake. The pieces of Humpty-Dumpty might fly together again. The universe in this view is not absolute, it is not determined. The second law is simply an expression of probability, of likelihood, overwhelming, it is true, but simply of likelihood. There remains chance; there remains possibility. The event of low probability is the event of luck. We have recovered free will.*

* Not entirely, because we always have the alternative method of tracing the exact behavior of each of the individual 10^{23} particles. The probabilistic approach in statistical mechanics is merely a convenience. We do not *have to* adopt it.

16. The Fall of Matter

. . . IN PLACE OF A FAMILY OF LINES OF
IDEAL FORCES, CONCEIVABLE ONLY BY REA-
SON, HE WILL HAVE A BUNDLE OF ELASTIC
STRINGS, VISIBLE AND TANGIBLE, FIRMLY
GLUED AT BOTH ENDS TO THE SURFACES
OF THE TWO CONDUCTORS, AND, WHEN
STRETCHED, TRYING BOTH TO CONTRACT AND
TO EXPAND. WHEN THE TWO CONDUCTORS
APPROACH EACH OTHER, HE SEES THE ELAS-
TIC STRINGS DRAWING CLOSE TOGETHER;
THEN HE SEES EACH OF THEM BUNCH UP AND
GROW LARGE. SUCH IS THE FAMOUS MODEL
OF ELECTROSTATIC ACTION IMAGINED BY
FARADAY AND ADMIRED AS A WORK OF GEN-
IUS BY MAXWELL AND THE WHOLE ENGLISH
SCHOOL.

PIERRE DUHEM, 1905

ALTHOUGH IT is safe to say that never before in the history
of the world has the philosophical doctrine of materialism

266

spread so far or so deep, it has for more than a century shared the scientific stage with a totally different concept. For every advance made by atomism, there has been a corresponding weakening in science of the doctrine of matter, indestructible and permanent. A totally new aspect of reality, the field, has played the same role in physics that atomism has played in chemistry. One by one, the characteristics that served to define an autonomous state of existence—matter—have been shown to apply only within narrow limits. One by one, new levels of experience have appeared within which materialism has proved at best an uncertain guide. The role that materialism could not play has been filled by the concept of field—perhaps the only idea in modern thought that was never anticipated by the Greeks. The relative unfamiliarity of the field idea should not mislead us into assessing it as of lesser importance. Materialism in science today is a skeletal wraith, so stripped of its attributes as to be unrecognizable. The field concept by contrast is a robust giant, yet to receive its first check after more than a century of pyramiding triumph.

The field was conceived by Michael Faraday (1791–1867), who began life as a bookbinder's apprentice with the unprofitable habit of reading the books he bound. Faraday attended a series of lectures by Sir Humphrey Davy, the head of the Royal Institution of Great Britain. In the best tradition of the century, he took verbatim notes and bound them in a carefully illustrated volume which he used as a recommendation to try to obtain employment with the Royal Society. It was not enough and Faraday remained an apprentice bookbinder. Later, by this time a journeyman, he approached Sir Humphrey himself with the notes and was hired on the spot. Davy thought that such careful attention to his lectures was a sure sign of genius. After a month he sent Faraday back to his bookbinding, saying that the boy was obviously not cut out for science, but shortly after he was obliged to rehire him. Reliable laboratory assistance is always rare. Faraday was totally untrained in science and mathematics but he was intelligent and he was willing.

The first independent researches of Faraday were built on Davy's life work. Davy had exploited the phenomenon of electrolysis: the inverting of the voltaic cell, which Nicholson had discovered in 1800 would decompose water into hydrogen and oxygen. Davy had systematically decomposed the alkalis and the alkaline earths, and isolated and described six new metals. His was the analytic imagination of the true chemist. He thought in terms of the differences of the alkalies where Faraday, with the synthetic insight of the physicist, looked for the identities in the process. Faraday began by carefully measuring the quantity of electricity and the quantity of material decomposed and at once made a most significant discovery. A given quantity of water was decomposed by a definite amount of electricity. All other conditions of the experiment were irrelevant. Further, the quantities of the elements decomposed by a fixed quantity of electricity were in the fixed proportions of their atomic weights.* Faraday had found what amounted to a unit combining quantity of electricity since named the *faraday* to commemorate the discovery. There was an atomistic interpretation of the faraday at hand. The faraday was a kind of electrical gram atomic quantity and must consist, like any gram molecular weight or gram atomic weight, of a fixed number of particles: the Avogadro number 6.02×10^{23}. The particles of electricity were later named *electrons*.

But Faraday rejected the conclusion as he had already rejected the atomistic premises on which it was based.

> . . . there can be no doubt, that the words definite
> proportions, equivalents, primes, etc., which did and do

* Actually of their chemical equivalents.

express fully all the *facts* of what is usually called the atomic theory in chemistry, were dismissed because they were not expressive enough . . . they did not express the hypothesis as well as the fact.

Electrolysis was essentially the conduction of electricity through liquids. Faraday's next researches were on electrical

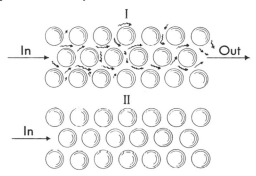

Fig. 34. *Faraday's model of conduction in an atomistic world.*
I. *Faraday's atomic model of a conductor.* Space must conduct electricity.
II. *Faraday's atomic model of a nonconductor.* Space must be a nonconductor of electricity.
Space cannot be both a conductor and a nonconductor, and therefore matter cannot be constructed of atoms.

conductivity, and he was again led to question the whole idea of atomism. How could any material conduct electricity if it were assumed to be discontinuous? If a copper bar consists of discrete atoms in empty space, then, in order for the bar to conduct electricity, space itself must be a conductor (Figure 34). But in that event, to explain a nonconductor like glass, space itself must be a nonconductor.

In considering the properties of empty space, Faraday had

gone to the root of the difficulties of all mechanism. Nothing exists, the atomists had maintained, but atoms and the void. The void could not of itself possess properties such as conductivity. Newton had balked at the idea of action at a distance that his *Principia* entailed. If the sun reached across empty space with powerful bonds to hold the earth in its orbit, how could the space itself be empty? Did it not contain at least the forces of gravitation? The attraction at a distance of the magnet or electric charge was no less marvelous than gravity because Coulomb had measured it and elaborate names of Greco-Roman origin had been applied to it.

Faraday studied the critique of mechanism written by Roger Boscovich (1711–1787), a Jesuit from the Adriatic whose speculations on space and time raised questions which were not to be answered for nearly two hundred years. Rather than material atoms, Boscovich thought of matter as composed of points which were the centers of forces spreading out to the ends of the universe. A century of electrical and magnetic experimentation provided Faraday with a basis on which to expand the plenum of Boscovich's forces into the concept of the field. Faraday rejected the idea of action at a distance and in doing so, rejected the fundamental notions of science since the time of the Renaissance and conceived of the first new philosophy of phenomena since Leucippus had dreamed of atoms and the void. For particles and void, Faraday substituted the continuum of the field. Empty space, Faraday asserted, is not empty, but rather it is permeated with a complex of forces, gravitational, electric, magnetic. In place of atoms and the void, Faraday, the untutored bookbinder's apprentice saw a single continuous reality, the field.

Newtonian mechanics (like Coulomb's) expressed the force between a planet and the sun. But what if there were no planet? What of the spaces between the planets? If the planet is removed, the force vanishes. The value of f in the inverse square function vanishes when the value of either of the two masses vanishes. To Faraday, this was close to removing the cow by the simple expedient of turning one's back. An essential constituent of the force remains, the part contributed by the sun. The sun is surrounded by a field of influence. When particles are placed in this field, they reveal the structure of the field by their behavior, just as bits of iron filings, by their pattern on a sheet of glass over a magnet, reveal the presence of the magnet and the direction of its forces, or just as the compass needle reveals the influence of the earth's magnetic poles.

Faraday suggested representing the field by lines of force, the number of lines giving the strength and the direction of the lines showing the direction of the field at any point. This remarkably simple conception at once enabled Faraday to represent gravitational fields, electrical fields, and magnetic fields. Faraday's very ignorance of formal mathematics had compelled him to direct his powerful imagination into pictorial channels.

The field concept was more than the hieroglyphics of a mathematical illiterate. It led Faraday to those discoveries of which Einstein and Infeld wrote:

> How difficult it would be to find those facts without the concept of the field! The expression for a force acting between a wire through which a current flows and a magnetic pole is very complicated . . . with the help of the field we immediately notice the character of all those actions at the moment when the similarity between [the fields] . . . is seen.
>
> We have the right to regard the field as something much more than we did at first. The properties of the field alone appear to be essential for the description of phenomena; the differences in source do not matter.

When Oersted had discovered that an electric wire exerted influence over a magnetic needle, he wrote that the fundamental law of electromagnetism was "that the magnetical effect of the electrical current has a circular motion round it." Faraday drew the lines of force of the magnetic field as circling around the wire. Experimenting (Figure 35) he found

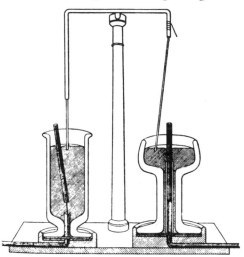

Fig. 35. *Faraday's motors.* Faraday's sketch of the bar magnet rotating about the current-carrying wire (left) and the wire rotating about the magnet (right).

that an electric wire revolved about a magnet, and a magnet revolved about an electric wire. This was the invention of the electric motor. It won Faraday election to the Royal Society although his employer Davy opposed him.

The field, to Faraday, was real and the lines of force were not hypothetical constructions but actual distortions of the field, as real as the strain in a stretched spring. The motions of the lines of force circling the wire were reality. They were invisible to the eye and intangible because the eye and the hand were not suitable detectors of magnetic fields. A magnet or a current-carrying wire in the proper position is a suitable detector and shows by its motion the reality of the circling motion of the lines of force. Either a wire or a magnet was suitable, because the *matter* of the test device was not reality but only a superficial appearance of the underlying reality, the field. Like the retrograde motions of the planets or the rising and setting of the sun, the matter of wire, magnet, battery, etc., was appearance; the gravitational action at a distance, mere mathematical illusion.

The link between electricity and magnetism could not run in only one direction. A feeling for symmetry of effect prompted Faraday in spite of repeated failures to search for the inversion of the Oersted effect- the electrical field that he was sure must accompany a magnetic field. Others, the French physicist Arago and the American Joseph Henry had come close to the discovery of what is now known as self-induction. Henry, the son of a day laborer, had become a teacher at the Albany Academy and spent his vacations in electrical researches. The month of August, when the academy was closed, was the only time that both schoolmaster and schoolroom were free for research. Henry worked on the development of electromagnets; from these he devised a telegraph which he freely disclosed to Morse and Wheatstone, the American and British inventors. While assembling an electromagnet for his telegraph, a connection broke and Henry observed a spark leap momentarily between the parting wires. The importance of this spark at the instant of *disconnecting* the circuit was immediately recognized by Henry. He proposed that a wire would ". . . become charged with electricity, which by its reaction on itself projects a spark when the connection is broken." The concept of the field makes the phenomenon clear. While the circuit is on, a magnetic field surrounds the wire. When the circuit is broken, the magnetic field falls in upon the wire and the energy that was put into the field in setting it up is restored to the wire as a surge of current and dissipated as a spark. In his August vacation of 1830, Henry obtained a surge of electricity from a separate magnet, thus completing the circle which Oersted had begun by his discovery of the magnetic effects of electricity. The following summer, Henry began the construction of a giant electromagnet for the production of large quantities of electricity but his vacation was over before he had put his observations together for publication. In the same year, Faraday had tried the old experiment of producing a magnetic field in one coil of wire, trying to detect an electrical effect in a secondary coil not connected to the first. Like Henry, Faraday was quick enough to observe that a momentary surge of current appeared in the secondary coil only at the instant of making or breaking the circuit which set up the magnetic field about the primary coil. Repeating the experiment, using a bar magnet for the magnetic field in place of the primary coil, Faraday found the explanation. A current flowed as he moved the magnet into or out of the secondary coil but no current flowed if the magnet was motionless. The surge of current that marked the setting up of an electrical field appeared only with the *motion* of a magnetic field. Connecting the circuit in the primary coil set up a distortion of the field detected as magnetic force, just as if a spring was stretched. When the circuit was disconnected, the distorted field sprang back to position. The *induction* of electricity in the secondary coil accompanied the springing in or out of the magnetic field. The motion of a magnet and the turning on and off of an electromagnet were simply ways of flexing the magnetic field.

Two months before his annual vacation in 1832, Henry, confident that he was years ahead of anyone else, learned that

Faraday's work, begun in 1831, a year later than Henry's discovery, had just been published. Faraday had been free to conclude his experiments and report on them to the Royal Society while poor Henry still dusted his erasers.

The incident was not without effect. America in 1832 smarted under a sense of cultural inferiority that the tradition of Benjamin Franklin was no longer sufficient to assuage. As Faraday, who had already invented the electric motor (a means of producing motion from electricity) now replaced his secondary coil by a rotating copper disc in order to obtain a continuous flow of electricity from mechanical motion, the enormity of the loss to American prestige became obvious and belated recognition fell upon Henry. He was appointed to Princeton and later became the first director of the Smithsonian and scientific adviser to Lincoln. He traveled abroad to meet and work with Faraday and others in the main stream of British experimentation. In his new capacity as administrator, he was able to funnel recognition and encouragement to the young American scientists who were beginning to appear on the scene.

The field concept was now intact. A changing electric field was accompanied by a magnetic field. A changing magnetic field was accompanied by an electric field. The pith balls of charge, the wires, solenoids, etc., vanished. The field was for Faraday the ultimate reality. And with the field, matter itself, materialism, and mechanism vanished. "I do not perceive in any part of space," wrote Faraday, "whether (to use the common phrase) vacant or filled with matter, anything but forces and the lines in which they are exerted." Just as a pith ball behaves electrically as a center of electrical force, Faraday conceived of it as a center of gravitational force. The gravitational field about the pith ball changes abruptly at a position called the surface of the ball but the field continues within the ball. Faraday had observed this continuity of the field by sprinkling iron filings on a magnet and a solenoid.* The lines of magnetic force pervade the magnet and the solenoid. Existence did not contain two separate entities, matter and space, but rather one reality, the field, of fluctuating intensity.

The reality of the field, the physical existence of the lines of force could be demonstrated by the agreement between equation and observation. The atomic theory had not been overthrown but it had been sharply limited in its applications, and its usefulness in interpreting important aspects of reality was at an end.

James Clerk Maxwell, who completed the field theory, was everything that Faraday was not. Maxwell had the education and the mathematical facility which Faraday lacked and the lack of which had driven Faraday to the conception of the field. Maxwell took the results of Faraday and formulated them in the precise language of the calculus; in doing so he opened the way to the full potential of the field theory. He took the arithmetic and empirical laws of Faraday as his starting point. These laws were essentially descriptions of two experiments, Faraday's induction of an electric field by the motion of a magnetic field and Oersted's (Rowland's †) demonstration that a changing electric field was accompanied by a magnetic field. From these experiments, Maxwell induced a set of relationships called the equations of the field. Faraday had been obliged to represent his results by pictures, by drawings of the geometry of the field. Maxwell was to express this geometry in analytic form. The lines of force of Faraday became force *vectors* in Maxwell's theory. The field about a magnet which Faraday was obliged to map out carefully, using button com-

---

* A coil of wire in a circuit, which is surrounded by a magnetic field of the same structure as the field about a bar magnet.

† Rowland's experiment was actually performed in 1878 so that Maxwell was assuming the very important idea that a current of electricity was a motion of charges and therefore a *changing* electric field.

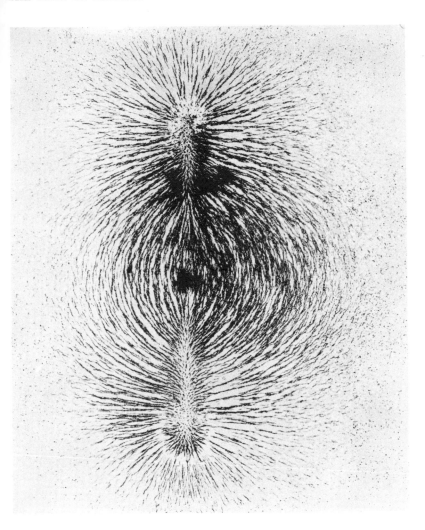

Fig. 36. *Magnetic field about a bar magnet.*

passes or iron filings, was generalized by Maxwell who considered the behavior of the field itself, independently of magnets, wires, compasses, etc. In Faraday's induced law, a bar magnet moving up through a coil (Figure 37) is accompanied by an electric field coiling around the line of motion in the sense of a right-handed screw. But the bar magnet is

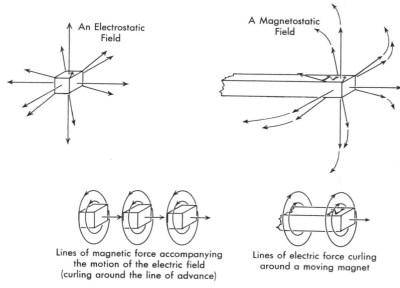

An Electrostatic Field

A Magnetostatic Field

Lines of magnetic force accompanying the motion of the electric field (curling around the line of advance)

Lines of electric force curling around a moving magnet

Fig. 37. *The two pillars of the field theory.*

not essential to the experiment. The identical result is obtained by replacing the magnet by a solenoid moving up through the coil. It is the motion of the *field* which counts, and not its origin. The field itself is the reality which Maxwell's equations were to describe. In Faraday's experiment, the coil through which the magnet moves was essential for the detection of the field. But even without the coil the electric field still curls around the line of advance of the solenoid or the moving magnet in the sense of a right-handed screw. If instead of a coil, a cylinder of copper is used, the electric field will be detected in that. If nothing is used, the field does not cease any more than the cow disappears when no one is there to observe it. Further, the size of the detecting coil or cylinder is equally irrelevant. The strength of the induced electric field depends on the strength of the magnet (or solenoid) and on how fast it moves—that is, on the rate of change of the magnetic field. Maxwell's equations connect the changes in the magnetic and electric fields centering on a point. Since all real magnets and real electric circuits are some arrangement of single points, it is possible to go mathematically, by summing the effects of many points, from Maxwell's single ideal point to the entire electromagnetic field. Faraday's experiment could be expressed by an equation showing that the curl of the electric field about a point is proportional to the change of the magnetic field through that point. Oersted's experiment could be expressed by an equation showing that the curl of the magnetic field about a point is proportional to the change of the electric field through that point. For Maxwell, the magnet was an enormous number of moving points, each a center of magnetic force, each surrounded by a curling electric field. These results, Maxwell wrote,

> . . . give rise to an independent method of electrical measurement founded on . . . electrostatic effects. The relation between the units employed in the two methods is shewn to depend on what I have called the "electric elasticity" of the medium, and to be a velocity which has been experimentally determined by MM. Weber and Kohlrausch.

Maxwell thought of all space as pervaded by a material medium. When a glass jar was evacuated the ponderable matter, air within the jar, was removed, but a material ether remained to transmit light and heat. The ether was capable of receiving and storing up energy of two kinds:

> . . . "actual energy" depending on the motion of its parts, and "potential" energy, consisting of the work which the medium will do in recovering from displacement in virtue of its elasticity
>
> The propagation of undulations [waves] consists in the continual transformation of one of these forms of energy into the other alternately.

When subject to an electric or magnetic force, the material of the ether was put into a state of polarization: a "state of constraint in which opposite extremities are oppositely electrified, and from which the body tends to relieve itself as soon as the disturbing force is removed." When a conducting medium like metal or a solution of salts was subject to an electric force, the opposite ends of the metal were at opposite polarities immediately and the salts or water was torn apart into oppositely charged elements. A nonconducting body such as glass or the all-pervading ether offered high resistance to this separation of positive and negative charges and the resulting flow of current. These nonconducting media were then electrically and magnetically "stiff." On being displaced by a momentary force, they rebounded with great speed. The greater the resistance of the medium, the greater the speed. The greatest possible velocity was that in the evacuated jar containing nothing but ether.

Maxwell's equations are a complete description of the electromagnetic field. From these, by the operations of mathematics, we can derive the experimental results of Faraday and Oersted and Rowland, or of Coulomb, or indeed of any other of the electricians of the nineteenth century. Maxwell's equations of the field are the summary of all the results of the sciences of electricity and magnetism in their most complete

and most general form. They stand at the head of a new theory
of the electromagnetic field, just as the universal law of gravitation stood at the head of Newtonian theory. Newton had
spoken of his method as proceeding from the phenomena to
the forces and from these deducing new phenomena to be
compared with nature. In Maxwell's theory, the method is the
same. From his induced law, Newton was able to deduce the
original phenomena. From the equations of the field, Maxwell
was able to recover by deduction the complete description of
the experimental results of previous investigators including the
result of Rowland's experiment, which was not to be performed for another sixteen years. Beyond that, the induced
general law of gravitation could, by the operations of mathematics, yield new and hitherto unsuspected deductions, which
could be tested by comparison with nature. The most important deduction to be drawn from Maxwell's equations was the
idea of electromagnetic waves. The highly elastic, incompressi-
ble ether was like a piece of spring steel. Subject to a displac-
ing force, it would rebound on the removal of the force. Energy
would be stored in the field in the form of kinetic and potential
energy and the alternations between the two would be regular
and periodic as in the motion of a spring or pendulum or the
vibrations of a tuning fork.

An electric field centered on a point extends to the boundaries of the universe. If the point is disturbed and the field is
moved, a magnetic field springs up and out from the disturbance. The spreading of the magnetic field must in turn be
accompanied by an electric field, which in turn must be accompanied by a magnetic field and so on. Imagine a point that
is alternately charged and discharged. Surrounding the point,
the electrical field comprising all space must curl first in one
sense and then in the opposite sense. Every point of space is
affected and becomes itself a center of disturbance. As the

electric field curls first one way and then in reverse a magnetic field comprising all space springs up to curl, first in one sense and then, as the electrical field is reversed, in the opposite sense, around each point on each curling line of force in a plane at right angles to the line. Electromagnetic waves originate at the site of an electrical or magnetic disturbance and propagate themselves to the ends of the universe. The velocity of the waves is determined by the stiffness constants of the medium and in vacuum is computed to be c, the constant of proportionality in the equations of the field. The value of c is 300,000 kilometers per second or 186,000 miles per second, the velocity of light.

From this, Maxwell drew a second deduction. Light itself was electromagnetic waves. Earlier experiments of Faraday and Henry had suggested this and were now explained by this unexpected conclusion of Maxwell's. The whole of the science of optics, hitherto a separate and unrelated branch of physics, was now subsumed under the heading of the electromagnetic theory. The radiation, refraction, reflection, dispersion, interference, polarization, and indeed every optical phenomenon then known could be deduced directly from the equations of Maxwell.

The two deductions show that the field concept is not simply an intellectual crutch or a happy idea which leads one by analogy to important results—the kind of idea which the scientist terms "heuristic." The field concept is a completely self-sufficient scheme for the organization of reality. It is an alternative to mechanism. It attempts a total description of reality.

> We remember how it was in mechanics [wrote Einstein and Infeld]. By knowing the position and velocity of a particle at one single instant, by knowing the acting forces, the whole future path of the particle could be foreseen. In Maxwell's theory, if we know the field at one

instant only, we can deduce from the equations of the theory how the whole field will change in space and time. Maxwell's equations enable us to follow the history of the field, just as the mechanical equations enabled us to follow the history of material particles.

Maxwell had discovered electromagnetic waves by deduction from his equations. It remained for experiment to generate and detect these waves and in this way confirm the theory of the electromagnetic field. Heinrich Hertz, a German physicist and student of Helmholtz's, designed the apparatus. Hertz devised a crude spark gap across which an electrical charge could be oscillated rapidly. The rapidly alternating spark would be an emitter of electromagnetic waves. But since these must spread out in all directions their detection requires extremely sensitive apparatus (Figure 38). Hertz made use of the phenomenon of wave interference in order to amplify the incoming wave to detect it. He placed a loop of wire in the path of the wave. The alternations of the field would induce an alternating current in the wire. This would be extremely weak but of the same frequency of vibration as the frequency of vibration of the spark emitter. The piling up of electrical oscillations all of the same frequency would cause *resonance*. The occasional accident of a wine glass shattered by the sound of a violin is an example of the same phenomenon. If the frequency of vibration of the glass is exactly matched by the incoming frequency of the violin note, each separate vibration of the air will reinforce the already vibrating glass and the amplitude of vibration increases until the strength of the glass is exceeded. When Hertz's loop was tuned to the frequency of the transmitter it would resonate, and this was detected by observing a feeble spark across a gap in the loop. Hertz's experiments confirmed in every particular the predictions of the Faraday-Maxwell theory.

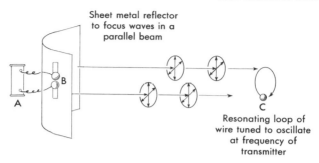

Fig. 38. *Hertz's apparatus for the generation and detection of electromagnetic waves.* A is a high-frequency induction coil (source of rapidly alternating current). B is a spark gap placed at the focus of the reflector. The gap at B is adjusted to match the coil at A so that the spark discharge at B is continuous. This is equivalent to a rapid and repetitive change of the electric field at B. The accompanying rapid and repetitive changes in the magnetic field at B and the consequent rapid and repetitive changes in the electric field, etc., are propagated as electromagnetic waves focused in a parallel beam by a sheet metal reflector. The periodic oscillations of the magnetic field at C induce an alternating current of electricity in a loop of conducting wire. By adjusting the size of the loop so that the oscillation of the current within the loop is in phase with the incoming vibrations of the electromagnetic field, a spark discharge appears at C.

In 1896 a 22-year-old student, Guglielmo Marconi, built a more elaborate transmitter-receiver with which he could send signals by varying the length of time of emission of the waves. A long pulse of waves was a dash and a short pulse was a dot. Using the telegraphic code, Marconi sent messages. In 1899 his wireless telegraphy bridged the English Channel. In 1901 he sent and received messages across the Atlantic. By the time of World War I it was possible to modify the waves as they were emitted, in the pattern of sound waves, making wireless telephony possible. By 1939, careful modification of the signals could cause a glow in selected parts of a plate coated with fluorescent crystals and so television was born.

With the experimental confirmation of deductions from the equations of the field, the theory of the electromagnetic field was established. The new concept was of a continuum; the field. All space was the scene of the field, and not merely the points where test particles were located. Particles themselves had disappeared to be replaced by point centers of force. The laws of mechanics had governed the behavior of particles in space. The equations of the field described the structure of space. The laws of mechanics may be compared to a description of the trains in a freight yard. The equations of the field may be compared to a map of the tracks. The structure of the field and its changes in time and distance govern the behavior of the particles, which in the field theory are point centers of force. The structure of the field leads to the idea of electromagnetic waves. But the field theory for Maxwell and his great contemporary, Lord Kelvin, was not a pure field concept. Maxwell thought of the field as made of particles of ether and with Kelvin still prisoner of mechanism, he defined the elastic properties of this ethereal substance.

> I never satisfy myself until I can make a mechanical model of a thing [wrote Kelvin]. If I can make a mechanical model, I understand it. As long as I cannot make a mechanical model all the way through I cannot understand, and that is why I cannot get the electromagnetic theory of light.

Accordingly, Maxwell and Kelvin attempted to visualize machines in their laboratory, elaborate mock-ups that would duplicate the mechanism by which electromagnetic waves were transferred. Huygens' old model of tiny spheres of ether was unsatisfactory because electromagnetic waves were transverse and not longitudinal vibrations. Maxwell conceived of an ether constructed of tubes of flow carrying Faraday's lines of force. These were rotating rapidly and therefore had a tendency to contract (as the rotating earth contracts at the poles). Since they were all to rotate in the same sense, he introduced ball bearings between them. These he was able to identify with particles of electricity. If the ball bearings start to flow across the axes of the tubes, they will set the tubes to rotating. Maxwell thought of this as a model of the curling magnetic field induced by the motion of an electric field. Kelvin and Maxwell were mechanists to the end, and space as they knew it was a congeries of tiny machines, rotating tubes or gyroscopic tops. Like backsliding cannibals who have come to the mission church of the field theory on Sundays, they succumbed on Mondays to the lure of mechanism. Faraday wrote to Maxwell, "I was at first almost frightened when I saw such mathematical force made to bear upon the subject, and then wondered to see that the subject stood it so well." Yet Faraday's concept of the field was the purest. Faraday understood as his successors did not that the field was constructed of forces and not of matter, whether ponderable or imponderable, and indeed that matter itself, in the terms of the field theory, was simply the site of abrupt changes in the intensity of the field. The lump of matter was a thickened portion of the field.

The old mechanical view would have reduced all phenomena to particles and the void. This mechanism was a mechanism of idea. It was a human mental construct. It was not obtained as a necessary consequence of observation or experiment. It was not empirical. Rather, it explained the empirical observations of the world—such measurements for example as Boyle and Hooke had made before 1661. Boyle's law that the product of the pressure and volume of a gas was constant was determined empirically.

Boyle found his law without recourse to *atoms*. Atoms and their behavior were an explanation which he attached to his law. The concept of the field and electromagnetic waves may dispense with the idea of particles and the void without fear of coming into contradiction with truth. Boyle's law still holds; indeed every empirical result once accurate must always be accurate. The hypotheses which Newton had scorned have been upset but the mathematical descriptions within the *Principia* and the *Optics* are still intact and accurate.

The field theory deals with the same phenomena as mechanism, but it discards mechanism completely. Even the basic concept of materialism, of matter itself, is implicitly discarded. But in discarding mechanism and questioning materialism the scientist is not adopting mysticism. He is not idealist enough to think that the sum of existence and reality is comprised in the mind. Outside the mind there still remains the world of phenomena. Our apprehension of this world is of the mind but the standard against which we must continually match our ideas is still external. Mechanist or field theorist, the scientist still sees his task as the investigation of phenomena in time and space. Nor is the scientist simply the intelligent spectator of facts external to himself. R. G. Collingwood wrote of the historian Toynbee, ". . . he fails to see that the historian is an integral element in the process of history itself, reviving in himself the experiences of which he achieves historical knowledge."

The scientist is an integral element in the process of science, for science is not the catalogue of the facts of things as they are which so many unimaginative people would have it. Faraday is the integral element in the concept of the field as Roger Boscovich through his nonmaterialistic preconceptions was the integral element in the concept of the point center of force. The field, like the atom, is a mental construct, the product of idea into experience. Above and beyond the minds and ideas of men lies the totality, of which the totality of human experience forms a minute part.

17. Classical and Nonclassical Science

THERE ARE MANY PEOPLES TODAY WHO ARE
IGNORANT OF THE CAUSE OF ECLIPSES OF THE
MOON, AND IT HAS ONLY RECENTLY BEEN
DEMONSTRATED AMONG OURSELVES. THE
DAY WILL COME WHEN TIME AND HUMAN
DILIGENCE WILL CLEAR UP PROBLEMS WHICH
ARE NOW OBSCURE. WE DIVIDE THE FEW
YEARS OF OUR LIVES UNEQUALLY BETWEEN
STUDY AND VICE . . . WE IMAGINE OUR-
SELVES INITIATED IN THE SECRETS OF NA-
TURE; WE ARE STANDING ON THE THRESHOLD
OF HER TEMPLE.

SENECA, *ca.* A.D. 30

THE GENTLEMEN of the turn of the century in Europe or
America had reason to congratulate themselves. The world had

never before imagined such a volume of civilization. The oldest enemies of mankind appeared defeated or on the verge of defeat. Medicine had entered upon the first fantastic successes of the germ theory of disease and the postponement of death was a reality. Agriculture with the aids of farm machinery, genetically guided breeding programs, and agricultural chemistry promised an end to material want. Fast trains and steamships had annihilated distance. The poles would be reached. Submarines had penetrated the sea; the first airplanes were in trial. The miracles of telegraphy and telephony and the wireless were at hand. Electrical machinery promised advances at least as great as those which had accompanied the introduction of steam. Within his own lifetime, the cultivated European had witnessed the advent of refrigerated food, electric lighting, mechanical transportation, and synthetic cloth. Morally, the world had not stood still. Slavery had disappeared from its last European and American locales. Constitutional government was almost universal. The Spanish-American and the Boer Wars were not marked by that prodigious volume of suffering and hatred that had characterized the great destructive conflicts of the past. Religious tolerance was widespread and the Russian pogroms of 1905 caused a wave of shock and loathing all over the world.

Of course, the world was not yet perfect. Just beneath the surface were the dislocations which were to find expression in the World War of 1914 and its subsequent horrors. But the complacency of the first generation to taste the fruits of technology was understandable. The triumph of human reason foreseen in the eighteenth century, the certainty of progress, the benevolence of the Deity and the goodness of man were, if not actually demonstrated, about to be. Science itself, that temple of the human mind, seemed about to conclude its task and complete its book. The principles of atomistic chemistry, the regularities of the periodic table, appeared incontrovertible. Armed with these, even the least imaginative of men in industrial laboratories and schoolrooms were subjecting the complexity of the material world to analysis and achieving momentous discoveries at every turn. The foundation science of Newtonian mechanics had spread so widely in the public consciousness as to come to coincide with common sense. Where once the physics of Aristotle, the idea that a moving body would continue to move only so long as a force was exerted, had been obvious, three hundred years had displaced this with the Galilean principle of inertia. Though the evidences of the senses still showed the sun rising in the east and setting in the west, in 1900 schoolchildren accepted without questioning the highly abstract notion of Copernicus. The completely mysterious force of gravity was explained no better in 1900 than it had been in 1687, but by 1900 it had become a part of common sense. The eclipses which divided the world into the superstitious and the nonsuperstitious in 168 B.C. were accepted as natural phenomena all over Europe and America. The commonsense mechanism that was the *Principia* had proliferated into an enormously complex and precise science. Part of this was applied to the multiple motions of random aggregates of particles and became the kinetic-molecular theory. The study of work, heat, and energy had been subsumed under the simple assertions of the laws of thermodynamics and these in turn had been shown as the necessary consequences of the assumptions of mechanics by the union of thermodynamics and the kinetic-molecular theory in the subject of statistical mechanics. Electricity and magnetism, at first so inconceivably mysterious, had been reduced to orderly phenomena, capable of direct interpretation. Franklin had applied a yardstick to them and divested them of their supernatural powers. Coulomb had comprehended them in the inverse square language of mechanism. Oersted had found them stubborn, with an apparent behavior of their own, but the spreading meshes of the field theory had caught them again. With Maxwell's development of the electromagnetic field theory and the subsequent discovery and utilization of radio waves, classical science had reached a pinnacle. It could hardly be doubted that these ideas, these systems of atomistic chemistry, mechanics, thermodynamics, the kinetic-molecular theory, and the theory of the electromagnetic field were absolute truth. There were difficulties, it was true, and these were well known. The scientists of the latter nineteenth century were not so arrogant as to assume that they knew everything. But in their triumph it is perhaps forgivable that they assumed that the missing pieces would fit the puzzle as they had thus far arranged it; that the contradictions would be resolved within the terms of the classical science they knew. They had made the fundamental error of confusing the permanent validity of their experiments with the permanent validity of their interpretation of those experiments. The basic assumption of experimental science is this; if under conditions *entirely* described by A, effects described by B occur once, then conditions A will again be followed by effects B whenever and wherever conditions A may come about. But let us modify conditions A to conditions A' by changing the time, or the temperature, or the air pressure, or whatever, and the scientific law written for conditions A may no longer hold. The classical physicists induced too widely. They extended the results of their observations too far into regions and conditions too widely distinct from those under which they had made their observations. They asserted that the laws governing planets must also govern particles so small that 10^{23} might be found in one gram; that the laws governing the temperatures of the laboratory furnace would also govern the temperatures of the space between the stars. When Kelvin applied the thermodynamics of a coal furnace to the sun and deduced from this a brief lifespan for the earth, he extended his induced laws of thermodynamics that had been obtained under one set of conditions A to conditions A'. They did not apply. Nor in applying the results of classical physics to the nonclassical science of geology was he justified, any more than the eighteenth-century musicians were justified in believing that their results were the reward for faithful adherence to the laws of aesthetics.

The nineteenth century had shown in the development of geological science that the principles and assumptions of physics were not universally applicable: that a separate discipline of history in science was possible. The historical science of geology and its most significant development, evolution, had sharply checked the positivism of the age. Not all physicists and not all geologists and biologists were aware of this. In the swell of positivistic thinking that accompanied the successes of nineteenth-century science, the myth of scientific absolutism had grown up. The science of the latter nineteenth century was absolute truth. The discarded theories of the past, Aristotelian physics, Ptolemaic cosmology, phlogiston, caloric, represented error, pure and simple. The scientist in 1900 conceded the possibility of error to show that he had retained the open mind of an impartial Baconian but in his heart, he did not anticipate it. It would be difficult to exaggerate the confidence with which the classical physicist faced the world. Mechanics, atomistic chemistry, thermodynamics, electromagnetic theory were triumphs too impressive for anyone to doubt their ultimate and absolute truth. Not only had the deductions stemming from these fields been found in experiment and applied usefully, but the mathematical body of classical theory led to exact and specific numerical predictions. Experiment had confirmed these in instance after instance. To question an edifice of this magnitude on the basis of minor discrepancies seemed sheer perversity.

If we were suddenly transplanted into the world of only fifty years ago [wrote Edmund Gosse in 1907], we should be startled and even horror-stricken by the wretchedness to which the step backwards would reintroduce us. . . . Can our thoughts embrace the mitigation of human torment which the application of chloroform alone has caused? . . . Everywhere, in the whole system of human life, improvements, alleviations, ingenious appliances and humane inventions are being introduced to lessen the great burden of suffering.

With hindsight, we are wiser. The twentieth century was not yet the millennium. The discrepancies of classical science were not minor but overwhelming. Already by 1900 the fundamental departures from classical predictions had been found whose resolution would topple the edifice. By 1915 not one of the fields of mechanics, atomistic chemistry, thermodynamics, or electromagnetic theory rested on the same bases as it had in 1900. A revolution had occurred in physics. The illogicalities and minor discrepancies of the latter nineteenth century had inspired a series of profound investigations into the fundamentals and philosophy of science. What is this knowledge? What is its relationship to truth? How do we know that we know? These are questions of epistemology, the theory of knowledge. Such questions, Einstein wrote, arouse ". . . an almost irresistible feeling of aversion . . . in people who are inexperienced in epistemological analysis and who are unaware of the precarious nature of theoretical thinking in the fields with which they are familiar."

At the moment of greatest triumph at the turn of the century then, classical science was attacked from within and without. The nineteenth century was less the age of reason than it was the romantic age. The basic idea of reason itself had come under attack. The fundamental character of man which the eighteenth century had asserted was good the nineteenth century questioned. The problem of evil had been reintroduced, in large part through the influence of Freudian psychology. On close inspection, the psychologists reported that man was prey to his physiological urges and that the rational side of the human mind was simply a subordinate tool for the fulfillment of desire. Moreover, physiological drives themselves were insufficient to account for such phenomena as suicide, and psychologists discussed the concept of a basic urge to destruction. Between the urge to destruction and the urge to satisfy physiological needs, rational man in the image of Newton as envisioned in the age of reason had been forgotten.

The attack from within science was more serious. It centered on the basic notions of mechanism. Ernst Mach, physicist at Prague and Vienna, challenged the basic idea of mechanism, that all natural effects were the work of the tiny machines of nature; that the unraveling of this fine structure of nature was the primary task of science. Science was neither truth nor reality, Mach asserted, but a system of ideas for the organization of phenomena. Scientific laws did not exist in nature but in the minds of men. They were devices for human comprehension and as devices they were neither true nor false, but rather good or bad. A good scientific law was one which was economical in that it bound the largest number of diverse phenomena into a single expression. A better scientific law would be a simpler and more comprehensive expression. Mechanism and mechanical models were cumbersome and mutually contradictory. Besides they were hypothetical and like Newton, Mach fiercely rejected hypotheses. In this he was joined by Duhem, Ostwald, and Mayer.

> One single number has more real and permanent value than an expensive library of hypotheses [wrote Mayer]; the attempt to penetrate by hypotheses to the inner recesses of the world order is of a piece with the efforts of the alchemists.

In place of the hypothetical science of the microscopic, Mach asserted the claims of the abstract science of the macroscopic, of thermodynamics, that purest temple of the human mind, its innermost recess unsullied by the hint of model.

But thermodynamics itself was shaking. Not only were Kelvin's applications of the law of conservation of energy in serious conflict with the historical structure of geology and evolution; the discovery of radioactivity by Becquerel in 1896 and of radium by the Curies in 1900 were direct denials of this most fundamental axiom of all science. Even the second law had been challenged. According to statistical mechanical theory, the concept of the universal increase of entropy was a probable rather than an absolute law. It is true that this was not yet a serious challenge. Mechanics provided the means for calculation of the behavior of one particle. The behavior of two particles was more complex and if the particles were assumed to exert forces upon each other, an exact solution of the three-body problem had not yet been achieved. But in principle the problem was soluble for any finite number of particles including the 10^{23} particles of laboratory samples. If statistics and probabilities were introduced, it did not imply a necessary uncertainty or indeterminacy, but merely a convenient method of calculation. The idea of probability, of chance, of random distribution and of luck had been introduced into science but solely as a temporary expedient; science reserved the right to discard these unscientific ideas and perform the 10^{23} calculations at any time that the probabilistic interpretation became embarrassing.

Certain minor inconveniences also plagued science. The amount of light produced by heating matter to incandescence was calculated nicely by classical theory but the distribution of light among the colors of the spectrum was not. Kinetic-molecular assumptions enabled one to calculate the energy in matter at ordinary temperatures, but not at very high or very low temperatures. Atomistic chemistry had achieved great practical successes in predicting the compounding of the elements, but the nature of the chemical bond was largely a mystery. Theory based largely on the empirically determined periodic table predicted the combination of hydrogen and oxygen to form water but theory had nothing to say about the temperature at which the combination occurred or the energy involved in the combination.

The electromagnetic theory of light offered the major difficulties. The mysterious ether stubbornly eluded all experimental traps. The basic ideas of mechanics itself, of matter, of space, and of time were involved. Discussions of continuity and discontinuity, of freedom and necessity were resurrected and did not fail to arouse the aversion with which men of common sense always and everywhere greet philosophical problems. It did not seem possible to challenge atomism without challenging rayon and gasoline, or to challenge mechanics without challenging airplanes. Science had hardened into dogma. Thousands of servitors in universities, laboratories, even a few in government agencies, pursued their labors with the frequent sweet taste of success as undismayed by the criticisms from within as by the romantic and petulant attack from without. Rather than battle over ideas, they concentrated on "facts" and perpetuated the myth of scientific autonomy. Religion and science were placed in separate compartments. History, apart from a positivistic scissors and paste rearrangement of "facts," did not exist, and all philosophy was metaphysics to be dumped in the box with religion marked "For Sundays Only." But knowledge, any knowledge, swallowed unquestioningly and without the active participation of its recipient, is dead knowledge. Science is a process, a searching, and it is not the end which is significant but the means, not the destination but the journey. Knowledge, trapped and stuffed, stands in the way of the thinker. There is no scientific knowledge; there is only scientific research.

> What do you say of the leading philosophers here [wrote Galileo to Kepler] to whom I have offered a thousand times of my own accord to show my studies, but who with the lazy obstinacy of a serpent who has eaten his fill have never consented to look at the planets, or moon, or telescope?

Productivity had become confused with creativity. The development that had burst upon the world in the seventeenth century with Galileo and Kepler had reached its apex and its end. Man had emerged from the cocoon of space and time of medieval cosmology and in three hundred years had acquired a sense of his place in space and time. Now in the twentieth century a revolution in thought at least as profound as that begun by Copernicus and Newton is in progress. Space and time themselves have been rocked. The most sacred assumptions of knowledge and rationality, the axioms of Euclid, have been modified. The breath of Pythagoras coming down the long corridor of the centuries may even be lost. The search for order at the turn of the century led into strange pathways and even to one which offers at the end not the pure figure of order but the grinning face of chaos. Perhaps it would have been better to have stopped the world at the turn of the century when gentlemen wore muttonchop whiskers and the Emperor Franz Joseph presided over the waltzes of Johann Strauss. Or perhaps it would have been better to have stopped the world still one stage earlier when Leonardo da Vinci cast the great statue of the Sforza and Lorenzo the Magnificent ruled Florence at the center of a tidy and benign universe. It is idle to speculate on what might have been. The genii have emerged from the bottle and the world we live in is the result. To stop the process of inquiry is to die the death of the intellect and whether the world is better now or worse than it was then, we still live who would have died, stifled in the morass of our own encyclopaedias.

18. The Theory of Relativity

I. ABSOLUTE, TRUE, AND MATHEMATICAL
TIME, OF ITSELF, AND FROM ITS OWN NA-
TURE, FLOWS EQUABLY AND WITHOUT RELA-
TION TO ANYTHING EXTERNAL, AND BY AN-
OTHER NAME IS CALLED DURATION: RELATIVE,
APPARENT, AND COMMON TIME, IS SOME SEN-
SIBLE AND EXTERNAL . . . MEASURE OF DU-
RATION BY THE MEANS OF MOTION, . . .
SUCH AS AN HOUR, A DAY, A MONTH, A YEAR.
II. ABSOLUTE SPACE, IN ITS OWN NATURE,
WITHOUT RELATION TO ANYTHING EXTERNAL,
REMAINS ALWAYS SIMILAR AND IMMOVA-
BLE. . . .

NEWTON, *Principia*

ALBERT A. MICHELSON, a graduate of the Naval Academy
at Annapolis, reported in 1887 on the failure of his attempt to

measure the earth's motion; a failure which in effect unraveled all the results of science back to the time of Copernicus. Michelson's first try had been made in an underground laboratory at Potsdam, Germany. He had failed to detect any evidence of the earth's motion through the ether by comparing the velocity of light in the direction of the earth's motion and other directions. Encouraged by Lord Rayleigh, Michelson on his return to the Case School at Cleveland enlisted the aid of Edward W. Morley, a professor of chemistry at Western Reserve, and the two repeated the experiment with elaborate refinements of detail. They could detect no difference between the velocity of light in the direction of the earth's motion and any other direction. The experiment implied that the earth was motionless in space. Yet the whole of classical physics seemed to demand a difference in the two velocities. *Eppur se muove!*

The problem was that of the mysterious ether, the medium which did the waving when light waves traveled through otherwise empty space. Maxwell's electromagnetic theory of light had been amply confirmed by the experiments of Hertz and others. The diverse fields of electricity, magnetism, optics, and even thermodynamics could all be included under the simple assumptions of Maxwell's theory. Light consisted of electromagnetic waves. Since light reached the earth from distant stars, space must be permeated by a waving ethereal medium. Since the motions of the earth and the planets show no signs of braking or friction, the earth cannot drag the ether with it or disturb the ether in any way as it sails through it on its passage around the sun. The other planets too must pass without friction through a fixed, calm, ether sea. If not, the light coming to us from a planet rushing toward us would be faster than the light from a planet rushing away from us, just as a bullet fired ahead of a moving plane travels faster than a bullet fired behind a moving plane. If the light from a distant planet varied in its speed, Kepler's laws would not appear to hold, and Newtonian mechanics would not work. Since Newtonian mechanics does work and measurements of the speed of light coming from distant planets and stars give a consistent value, there can be no drag of the ether by bodies moving through it. The ether must be fixed to the framework of space itself. But what was this framework?

When Copernicus set the earth in motion and displaced man from his position at center of the universe, the sun became the fixed hub about which the planets could revolve. Before Copernicus, the velocity of a ship on the earth could be easily measured. But after Copernicus, the measurement was understood to be relative. The earth itself, rotating on its axis and revolving about the sun, was in motion. To find the true velocity of the ship would require adding the velocity of the earth about the sun. By the end of the nineteenth century, however, it was clear that the fixed stars and the sun were not themselves fixed. The sun and all its satellites are in rapid motion through the galaxy. Taught by Copernicus to regard the earth as moving and the stars as fixed, what were we to regard as fixed, now that the astronomers had found even the stars in motion? The ether sea seemed to be the answer, its fixity guaranteed by the fixed rate of travel of light waves coming to us from all the universe. In the fifteenth century a sailor out of sight of land had nothing with which to locate himself on the endless surface of the sea. One of Columbus' methods of navigation had been to throw over a log and measure its drift behind the ship to tell how fast the ship itself moved through the sea. In the latter nineteenth century, the astronomers reported us adrift in an infinite sea of ether. Michelson and Morley proposed to cast over a log. The Dutch theoretical physicist, Hendrik Lorentz, who was responsible for many of the later developments of Maxwell's theory, had appealed for just such an experiment.

. . . one would do well, in my opinion, not to be guided in a question as important as this, by considerations of the degree of probability or of simplicity, of one or another hypothesis, but to address oneself to experiment to determine the state whether of rest or of movement, in which the ether finds itself with respect to the surface of the earth.

Michelson's method was beautifully simple. He split a beam of light into two parts, sending one out at right angles to the other and reflecting both back to a common focus. If either had gained as much as a fraction of a wave length (about one hundred thousandth of a centimeter), the two beams would interfere. Michelson and Morley made repeated measurements at all hours of the day and during different seasons of the year so that all possible motions of the earth through the ether would be observed. The results were definite and negative. There was no difference in the velocity of light in the direction of the earth's motion. The velocity of light was always constant.* It was as if a man swimming in a swift flowing river found that he could swim as fast upstream as in any other direction. Michelson and Morley had failed to detect the violent rush of ether wind across the earth. Light spread out in all directions exactly as though the earth was at rest.

It appears [concluded Michelson and Morley] . . . reasonably certain that if there be any relative motion between the earth and the luminiferous aether, it must be small; quite small enough entirely to refute Fresnel's explanation. . . . Stokes has given a theory . . . but Lorentz shows that these conditions are incompatible. Lorentz then proposes a modification which combines some ideas of Stokes and Fresnel. . . . If now it were

* Light is slowed down in passing through transparent media, glass, water etc., including air, but the slowing down of light in air is very slight. In referring to the velocity of light as c, vacuum is intended.

> legitimate to conclude from the present work that the
> aether is at rest with regard to the earth's surface, . . .
> according to Lorentz . . . his own theory also fails.

With the word *fails,* the momentous paper describing the
Michelson-Morley experiment concludes. The violent wind of
ether blowing across the surface of the moving earth was un-
detectable. The hypothesis of the calm ether sea would not
stand in the light of experiment. All efforts to detect the motion
of the earth through the ether had failed.

If opaque matter such as the earth did not move through
the ether, then it dragged the ether with it. True, astronomical
observations indicated that this did not happen. The last possible loophole, the slight chance that some other unknown cause
acted in astronomical phenomena which did not affect the
problem of light and ether, was closed by a direct experiment
of Oliver Lodge in England in 1893. Lodge set heavy wheels
in rapid motion and measured the velocity of light in the
vicinity of the wheels. The rapidly rotating wheels did not
affect the ether in the slightest. The dilemma was complete.
Michelson and Morley had reasoned that if they were carrying a
headlight pointing into the ether ahead of them, the velocity
of the light measured aboard the moving earth would be decreased. It was not. Lodge had reasoned that if one stood
beside the moving earth and measured the velocity of the light
carried within the moving ether, it would be increased by the
velocity of the ether-earth train. It was not. A logical impasse
had been reached.

Repeated experiments with ingenious variations confirmed
the impasse. Not only did the velocity of light stubbornly
refuse to change with motion through the ether; electrical and
magnetic forces themselves refused to change in the slightest
in acknowledgment of the ether wind. Experiment says that we
do not rush through an ether sea. Experiment says that we do

not carry the ether with us on our trip through space. Classical physics led directly and inexorably to the choice between the calm ether sea and the ether sea thrown into turbulence by the passage of matter. Either the ether interacted with matter or it did not. A thing, said Aristotle, is either A or not A.

G. F. Fitzgerald (1851–1901), a theoretical physicist of the University of Dublin, was discussing the Michelson-Morley result with Lodge and suddenly remarked that it could be explained if Michelson and Morley's measuring rods were distorted by a very slight amount. In fact, this must be the answer. Michelson and Morley's apparatus must itself shrink in the direction of the earth's motion by an amount exactly enough to compensate for the ether wind. This was not too fantastic an idea. The atomic theory by this time postulated that the atoms making up all solid matter, including Michelson and Morley's apparatus, were held together by electrical forces. In moving against the ether wind, these moving charges would give rise to magnetic effects which would contract them. It was not at all unreasonable to suppose that the magnitude of these effects would be determined by the relative velocity of the earth and the ether. A yardstick would contract very slightly as it turned to the direction of the earth's motion. This contraction would be invisible since the stick would continue to read one yard and all other scales with which it might be compared must themselves contract in exactly the same proportion. This contraction, the *Fitzgerald contraction*, would never have been noticed or detected at all if it had not been for the Michelson-Morley experiments. In the direction of the earth's motion, Fitzgerald asserted, the velocity of light with respect to the earth was really $c - v$. But the apparatus itself had been shortened in exactly the same proportion. Michelson and Morley had been, unbeknownst to themselves, measuring their track with a short measure. Their distance had really been proportional to $c - v$. They measured it instead as proportional to c.

But the consequences of the Fitzgerald contraction are discouraging. If all our instruments must contract in exactly the proportion necessary to cause our experiments to fail, how shall we continue to experiment? The principle of helplessness that is implied here was expressed by Lorentz. It was as if all nature was in a conspiracy to conceal from us our true velocity through the ether. The principle of Lorentz asserted that the contractions of matter were in such proportion that no experiment, however made, could determine our true velocity through the ether. It has the ring of Galileo's principle of relativity. No experiment made *restricted to the earth* could ever detect our motion about the sun. But Galileo had not closed the door. His observations of Venus and the satellites of Jupiter revealed the motion that the principle of inertia prevented us from detecting in earth-bound experiment. The Lorentz principle was one of total surrender. With gloomy efficiency, Lorentz calculated precisely the contractions in length which would be necessary to accomplish this masking effect. The contracted distance $c - v$ must be in the same proportion to the true distance c as the contracted length of the measuring rod l' is to the true length l. Setting up this proportion, Lorentz and Fitzgerald obtained a factor β which could be multiplied by any length l to determine the amount that a rod of length l would measure when traveling at the velocity v through the ether.*

* To be mathematically precise, the Lorentz-Fitzgerald factor is obtained from the proportionate squares of the quantities specified above.

$$\frac{c^2 - v^2}{c^2} = \frac{(l')^2}{l^2}$$

$$\left(\sqrt{1 - \frac{v^2}{c^2}} \right) l = l'; \text{ as defined above, } \beta = \sqrt{1 - \frac{v^2}{c^2}}$$

Not only would the length of all material substance be con-tracted in the amount β, but, as Fitzgerald's Dublin colleague, Larmor, pointed out, clocks being material systems, would like-wise be affected. To maintain the conspiratical illusion of no relative velocity between the surface of the earth and ether, moving clocks would be slowed down in the amount β. Lo-rentz's careful development of the mathematical consequences of his principle resulted in the exact expressions for the kind and degree of the contractions which were necessary to explain the Michelson-Morley experiment, and all possible experiments aimed at "determining the state, whether of rest or of move-ment, in which the ether finds itself with respect to the surface of the earth."

This was the state of affairs at the turn of the century. Every effort to detect the ether had failed completely. It neither in-teracted with matter nor did it *not* interact with matter. The whirling tubes and ball bearings, Kelvin's gyroscopes, Maxwell's resistances, all these seemed to display themselves in only one capacity, in the transmission of light. The ether which Newton calculated to be 490 billion times as elastic as air was completely imponderable. In transparent media like glass, the ether interacted to slow down the passage of light waves. But the transparent glass, water, air, etc., of the planets rushed through the ether without the slightest frictional resist-ance or drag. Here was action without a corresponding re-action. For Kepler's laws to hold, for Newtonian mechanics to have any significance, it was absolutely necessary that the ether have no effect on opaque matter—on the earth, in short—but only on the light which it transported. To test this null effect, Michelson and Morley had been at great pains. They had failed in every effort to detect the motion of the earth through the nonresisting ether. They could only turn back on the other horn of the dilemma and insist that the earth dragged ether with it.

Lorentz had put forth his principle as Fitzgerald had suggested his contraction, with no intentions of presiding over the dissolution of the scientific empire. Insofar as his principle closed the door to future ideas, Lorentz could hardly have accepted it. The inexorable processes of logic led directly to certain conclusions, but over and against the processes of logic and of reason stood the bits of glass and brass of Galileo's *perspicillum*. The dilemma of science was not a new one. Once before, Kepler had stood between his certain knowledge of the accuracy of Tycho Brahe's observations and his equally certain confidence in the Pythagorean ideal, and resolved his conflict by the construction of his *laws*. The revolution in physics that broke in the early twentieth century can only be compared with the revolution in thought brought about by the work of Galileo, Kepler, and Newton.

The crisis was first resolved through the efforts of Albert Einstein (1879–1956). Born in Germany of middle-class Jewish parents, Einstein passed his youth in Switzerland studying physics at the Zurich Polytechnic. He apparently made too little of an impression on his superiors to be offered a teaching or research position. For more than a year, the only work that Einstein could obtain was that of a private tutor. Through the efforts of friends he obtained a minor post as a junior clerk in the Swiss patent office at Bern, and there in 1905 at the age of 26 young Einstein published three major papers in the now historic 17th volume of the *Annalen der Physik*. One of them, a 30-page article entitled, "On the electrodynamics of moving bodies," founded the theory of relativity.

Einstein suggested that the major difficulty was with the concept of the elusive ether. The ether was conceived in the intellect and if no connection could be found between the conception and the world of nature, it should be discarded. Einstein proposed instead that a theory uniting electromagnetics (electrodynamics) and mechanics start with the results of experiment rather than that experiments be conducted to fit a preconceived theory. There were enough experiments in this area for the time being, and these had always led to the same answer; the velocity of light was a constant (c) regardless of the motion of the observer or of the source. With the peculiar insight which Kepler had displayed before in realizing that the results of Tychonian observations were to be accepted as they stood in the form of an ellipse, rather than that the futile attempt to constrain them to the form of the perfect circle continue, Einstein proposed that this experimental result be made the first postulate of a new theory. The second postulate of the new theory which Einstein proposed was an extension of the principle that no mechanical experiments confined to a body in uniform motion could detect that motion. Einstein asserted that no experiments whatsoever, mechanical or optical (electrodynamic), confined to a body in uniform motion, could detect such motion. The failures of the Michelson-Morley and Lodge experiments were the postulate of the new theory. The equations of Lorentz were the mathematics of the new theory.*

The implications of the special theory of relativity were in such outrageous opposition to common sense as to appear pure paradox. A delighted press could revel in the absurdity of yard-sticks that shrank and clocks that quickened, depending on one's point of view. Not since Shadwell had lampooned Boyle in *The Virtuoso* nor since Swift had mocked the mathematicians of Laputa had such an opportunity appeared to confirm the solid prejudices of men of common sense against dreamers.

---

* Previously it had been taken for granted that the velocity of light in the Michelson-Morley experiment would be c-v, or that the velocity of a system in uniform motion measured relative to another system in uniform motion would be simply the difference between their absolute velocities—the so-called classical transformation. The Lorentz-Einstein transformation (the equations of Lorentz) is an algebraic bridge enabling the computation of relative velocities, etc., as between systems in uniform motion in such a way as to preserve the constant velocity of light and the invariance of the laws of electrodynamics.

The Lorentz-Einstein transformation purported to calculate changes in mass, length, and time, according to the relative motions of systems. A yard was larger or smaller, an hour longer or shorter, a pound greater or lesser, depending on one's relative motion. But all human experience showed that length and distance were fixed and absolute values. All chemistry was based on the principle of Lavoisier, the law of conservation of mass, and if masses were not fixed, then what of the principle of Newton and all celestial mechanics? Ever since the first Babylonian calendar, man's sense of the fixed, immutable flow of time had been developing. If an hour was not an hour, how could railroads work, or telegraphs? What meaning could be attached to the statement that an eclipse of the moon would occur at a given date, or that Julius Caesar had fallen on a certain day?

The apparently paradoxical conclusions of the theory of relativity are not to be understood in the usual sense, which is that of reconciling them to the great fund of common experience which we ordinarily accept as truth. Common sense tells us that a yard is always a yard, that an hour is always an hour, that one and one must equal two. All the ordinary experience of the human race has gone into these truths which we feel intuitively are absolute. But the Michelson-Morley and Lodge experiments and all the confirming experimentation to which these have given rise are new and extraordinary experiences. We learn from them that length, mass, and time are absolutes on only one level of experience. On the deeper level which will include the new kind of experience of highly refined experiment, common sense is shown as only an approximation, incapable of dealing with the new level of reality. The two postulates of the special theory of relativity are a deeper truth. If we accept them, the apparently paradoxical conclusions follow directly by simple deduction. Einstein showed that nothing could move faster than light without violating the postulate of the constant velocity of light; similarly, length and time could not be fixed; yardsticks and clocks must vary in reading from system to system in such a way and to such a degree that the velocity of light measured with these yardsticks and clocks will always be c. Repeated experiment had always found it so; Einstein postulated that experiment would always find it so in the future. Railroad men could set their Hamiltons, commuters could make their trains, astronomers keep their celestial rendezvous without fear of error because the relativistic corrections for systems in these slow mechanical motions were so small. Only as velocities approach the speed of light do the corrections become appreciable.* Ordinary mechanics had served so well and so long because not until the era of the Michelson-Morley experiments had any measurements been made with enough refinement to detect the minute discrepancies of the relativity theory.

Just one year before Einstein's paper, at the 1904 International Congress of Arts and Sciences, Henri Poincaré had remarked:

> Perhaps . . . we should construct a whole new mechanics, that we only succeed in catching a glimpse of, where inertia increasing with the velocity, the velocity of light would become an impassable limit.
> The ordinary mechanics, more simple, would remain a first approximation, since it would be true for velocities

---

* Let t' represent the duration of an event measured on a system moving with velocity v relative to the reference system; t is the duration of the same event measured on the reference system. Then $\left(\sqrt{1 - \dfrac{v^2}{c^2}}\right)t = t'$; [therefore for velocity v very much smaller than c, $v << c$]; $\dfrac{v^2}{c^2} \sim 0$; $\sqrt{1 - \dfrac{v^2}{c^2}} \sim 1$; and $t = t'$.

not too great, so that one would still find the old dynamics under the new.

Lorentz had anticipated Einstein in the concept of relativistic
time. The idea of the conversion of energy into mass had also
been suggested by experiments with electrons and speculation
on the pressure of light. Both now followed neatly from the two
assumptions of Einstein. If energy was added to a moving body
to accelerate it, the energy normally remained constant, appearing as the increased kinetic energy of the moving body. But
bodies approaching the upper limit of velocity, c, offered increasing resistance to further acceleration. This increase in
inertia was increase in mass. The work of acceleration was
transformed into extra mass in the proportion of the now famous
$E = mc^2$. Instead of the principles of conservation of energy
and conservation of mass, relativity theory proposed a single
principle of conservation of mass-energy.

The twenty-six-year-old Einstein became famous overnight.
Theoretical physicists in general accepted the new ideas and
called upon the experimentalists to devise methods of proving
them. Experimental physicists in general dismissed the theory.
It was not particularly easy to have a twenty-six-year-old clerk
in the Swiss Patent office explain the meaning of experiments
on which one had labored for years. Michelson went to his
grave in 1931 unwilling to concede that all of relativity was
not simply an elaborate screen of words designed to capture
the credit of discovery as it had already appropriated the substance of discovery from those who had the wit and the skill
to subject nature to the absolute question. It was not simply
the subject of relativity. Einstein had, in the same volume of
the *Annalen der Physik,* extended the tentatively projected
quantum theory of Max Planck to cover the phenomenon of
photoelectricity. Philip Lenard, the Nobel Prize physicist whose
experimental results were thus explained, conceived an impla-

cable hatred of Einstein which he came to extend to all Jews and to all theoretical physics. Honors and appointments now fell to Einstein and a share of the extravagant publicity which then attended the romantic figure of the student-revolutionary, Marie Curie. Einstein was immediately appointed to the Physics faculty at Bern. In 1909, he became Associate Professor of Physics at the University of Zurich. At the age of 29, he was a full Professor at the University of Prague, then full Professor at Zurich. At 34, he was elected to the Prussian Academy of Sciences and invited to Berlin.

Meanwhile, attempts to confirm the consequences of the theory of relativity were made. The equivalence of mass and energy which had already appeared in the increasing inertia of an accelerated electron suggested that energy itself must be ponderable. The old caloric theorists who had looked for a difference in weight between hot bodies and cold bodies had not been entirely wide of the mark. Hot bodies do have greater mass than cold bodies, but the difference in mass is extraordinarily small. The mass associated with energy E is equal to E divided by the velocity of light squared. No ordinary balance could detect such a difference, but Einstein proposed (1911) to use the solar system itself. If energy is ponderable, then the light from distant stars passing close to the enormous mass of the sun should be attracted to the sun and the beam of light should be bent toward the sun, just as an approaching comet. The force of gravity acting between the sun and light Einstein calculated would be very slight, but sufficient to deflect a beam just grazing the sun by 0.83 seconds of arc. If the light from a distant star was bent, the star would appear to have changed position relative to the rest of the sky. In particular, a photograph taken at the moment of the starlight grazing the sun would show the star as displaced slightly from the position it would occupy on a photograph taken of the

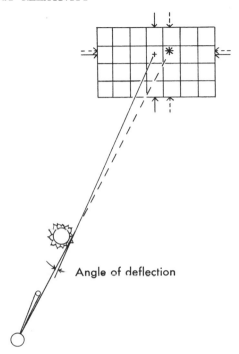

Fig. 39. *Deflection of light rays passing the sun.*

same portion of the sky at a different time of year. In 1919 and again in 1922, expeditions were sent out to photograph the sky behind the solar eclipse.

> It was my good fortune to be present at the meeting of the Royal Society in London [wrote Whitehead] when the Astronomer Royal for England announced that the photographic plates of the famous eclipse . . . had verified the prediction of Einstein that rays of light are bent as they pass in the neighborhood of the sun . . . in the background [hung] the picture of Newton to remind us that the greatest of scientific generalizations was now,

> after more than two centuries, to receive its first modi-
> fication . . . a great adventure in thought had at length
> come safe to shore.

These verifications in experience of the deductions made from the postulates were sufficient to establish the claims of the special theory of relativity. Even the variance of time, the single concept most in contradiction to common sense, could be confirmed.

There is a story that shortly after the initial presentation of his theory, Einstein was addressed at a public meeting by a conservative German physicist, deeply offended by the challenge to physical orthodoxy. Did the new theory really assert that the apparent slowing down of a clock on a moving system marked a difference in the rate of passage of time on that system? If so, would all timekeeping devices, all physical and chemical processes, slow down in the same proportion? The answer was yes to both questions. Then, the questioner persisted, if twins were born on earth and one of them were immediately whisked away on a space ship while the other remained here on earth, and the traveling twin returned after a time, he would find the twin on earth grown old while he had himself preserved his youth. Einstein is said to have thought a moment and then to have replied that this was indeed so. This is the famous paradox of the twins. It has had in itself a long history. Beginning with the philosopher Henri Bergson, who was willing to accept the theory of relativity but denied that this was a consequence of it, the paradox was most recently challenged by the astronomer and philosopher of science, Herbert Dingle, who in 1956 asserted that "the special theory of relativity is very imperfectly understood even by mathematical physicists of high distinction." If the paradox were true, we can imagine a host of delightful possibilities. The crewmen on a space ship need only deposit some advance portion of their pay at compound interest in a bank to return after the passage of long years, hardly aged at all, to find themselves wealthy and their children grown to be their contemporaries. The defeated politician can return at the end of a brief voyage to find his rival's term up and a new campaign in prospect. That most romantic of situations, the unseasonable love of an older person for a younger, can be resolved into banal conclusion. A voyage of carefully computed duration will adjust the lovers' ages.

The paradox of the twins, like the paradoxes of Zeno, is a searching challenge to orthodoxy and common sense. Einstein argued that the processes of aging are physical and chemical and therefore represent a timing mechanism like that of the clock. The modification of the timing of the clock did not depend on the kind of clock, whether pendulum-actuated or spring-controlled, or even a radioactive clock. The modification of timing, as Larmor had pointed out, was necessary to maintain the conspiracy of nature to conceal our true motion with respect to the ether. If the traveling twin aged at the same rate as the twin at rest, then it would be possible to use the rate of aging of the traveling twin to measure the velocity of light as less than (c) with respect to the twin. The Lorentz-Einstein transformation would not hold. The postulate of the constant velocity of light would be false. But the postulate of the constant velocity of light regardless of the motion of the observer or of the source was an induction that had been drawn from repeated and careful experiments. In asserting this postulate as a fundamental law of nature, Einstein expressed his confidence that it must hold in all its consequences. Therefore it must apply to the case of the twins, and the age of the traveling twin (t') must be to the age of the stay-at-home twin (t), as β is to 1.

Experimental verification of the paradox of the twins would

appear to be a long way off [*] but the particle accelerator offered a directly parallel case. Some of the nuclear particles with which modern physics is concerned have a definite rate of disintegration. One of these, the meson, is observed at the end of a certain period of time to be transformed into other kinds of particles. If mesons are placed in a particle accelerator, they are in a position comparable to the traveling twin. Their rate of aging should be slower (to a stationary observer) as their velocity is increased. Experiments to test this point were performed successfully in 1941. Again in 1956, after Professor Dingle's objection that public acceptance of the paradox of the twins would have undesirable consequences, Professor Frank S. Crawford of the University of California pointed out that the half-life of particles called mu mesons traveling from the upper atmosphere to the earth at high velocities is fifteen times as long as the half life of the same particles at rest. The objection by Bergson and Dingle that the paradox was mathematical illusion is invalid. The consequences of the theory of relativity are part of physical reality. The theory is rigid and it must stand or fall in the light of the experimental test of its conclusions. We are not permitted to accept some of the equations and say that these ideas are translatable into physical terms which we will find in experiment and observation and at the same time to reject others of the same equations and say that these are mathematical illusion which we will not find in experiment and observation. The postulates of the constant velocity of light and the invariance of the laws of physics for systems in uniform motion require that time be relative. A. d'Abro wrote:

> . . . a theory of mathematical physics is not one of pure
> mathematics. Its aim and its *raison d'être* are not solely
> to construct the rational scheme of some possible world,
> but to construct that particular rational scheme of the

[*] Cf. p. 331.

particular real world in which we live and breathe. It is for this reason that a theory of mathematical physics, in contradiction to one of pure mathematics, is constantly subjected to the control of experiment.

The great importance of Einstein's work and the basic reason for the excitement that spread from the pages of the *Annalen der Physik* to debating halls and the public press was the radical revolution in our concepts of time and space and motion which the theory demanded. In 1908, at the 80th assembly of German natural scientists and physicians, Hermann Minkowski, Professor at Gottingen, formulated the new image of the world which had been "discovered by Lorentz and further revealed by Einstein," and called for a return to the Pythagorean ". . . idea of a pre-established harmony between pure mathematics and physics." The world of events was not the familiar three-dimensional world of length, breadth, and height, proceeding along a smoothly flowing river of time. The three spatial dimensions were profoundly linked with the dimension of time by their mutual conspiracy to preserve the constant velocity of light. "Space by itself," Minkowski wrote, "and time by itself sink into the shadow and only a kind of union of the two retains self-dependence." Space, empty and absolute, a kind of box without walls in which to fit the universe, is simply an idea, a human concept like number. "If number is really a product of our mind," Karl Friedrich Gauss had written a century before, "space has also a *reality beyond* our mind of which we cannot fully foreordain the laws *a priori*."

The union of space-time which Minkowski envisioned was not simply the empty box within which the drama of the universe was played. Space-time acts upon matter and is in turn acted upon by matter. What in Lorentz' imagery had been a conspiracy upon the part of nature, in Minkowski's theory was the fundamental property of the world. The action of space-time on matter was not simply illusion designed to give us variable readings on the yardsticks and clocks with which we locate events. The action necessary to change our observations is real and physical. The dials which move, the displaced photographic images of stars are tangible. On a darker note, the great bomb at Hiroshima would have been impossible in the empty world of Newtonian space drifting serenely down the river of time.

In the new world in which we find ourselves, ". . . space by itself and time by itself are doomed to fade away into mere shadows. . . ." To locate a point in space or an event in time was as incomplete as to specify the location of a city by its longitude alone and ignore its latitude. In this world there are no points in space or events in time but only point-events in space-time. The world in which we live is the continuum of all possible point-events. Distances or times in this world are only relative. The interval separating one point-event from another is called the Einsteinian interval. No two events can occur simultaneously in an absolute sense because what is simultaneous for one observer will be separated in time for another. Simultaneity is a familiar part of the ghost story. At exactly the moment of a soldier's death on a distant battlefield, his ghost appears at his wife's bedside. The time of the event is the same for both soldier and wife. The distance between the two events is fixed. But the real world of soldiers and of soldiers' wives is not the world of classical physics. There is no absolute true length.

The relative distance between two events must be variable in such a way and by such a degree that the velocity of light measured with this length as a yardstick will be c for all observers. To be completely fanciful, we may conceive that a physicist located midway between the soldier and his wife sends a beam of light in both directions and by its reflection back to him sees both deathbed and ghost simultaneously. Imagine that the line joining the simultaneous events runs from east to west and that an outside observer stationed off the earth observes the physicist's beam illuminating the deathbed to the west and the ghost to the east. When the earth is rushing past him from east to west, the observer will see the light beam illuminate the ghost scene which is rushing toward the moving beam before he sees the deathbed which is rushing away from the moving beam. Thus, the events which are simultaneous to the physicist, occur in sequence to the outside observer. From his point of view, the ghost has been premature! The same two events which are simultaneous for one observer occur with a separation in time for another observer. Simultaneity in an absolute sense does not exist, even as uniform motion, in an absolute sense, does not exist. Minkowski described the world of space-time and showed that all the results of the theory of Einstein and Lorentz could be derived from a single fundamental postulate.

> The substance at any world-point may always, with the appropriate determination of space and time, be looked upon as at rest.

The world-point (point-event) could no longer be specified by three numbers standing for the three coordinates of familiar Cartesian space and a fourth number for a unidimensional time. The three spatial coordinates and the fourth time coordinate were linked together in an equation expressing the fundamental interaction of space-time with matter—the maintenance of the constancy of the velocity of light.* The world in which we are

---

* In classical physics, two events are separated in space by a distance measured in units, $ds^2 = dx^2 + dy^2 + dz^2$, and in time by an interval measured in units, dt^2.

In space-time, two point-events are separated by an interval measured in units, $ds^2 = dx^2 + dy^2 + dz^2 - c^2dt^2$.

born and die is the four-dimensional continuum of space-time, in which every event is also a point. A succession of point-events locates a line through space-time, the so-called *world-line*. It is the life path of a material point in space-time. By referring to the space vs. time graphs of Galileo's experiments (Figures 13, 14) we can see the difference between uniform and accelerated motion. The life path of a particle in uniform motion is a straight line. The life path of accelerated motion is a curve through space-time.

Minkowski died shortly after the Congress at which he formulated the new image of the world. Einstein meanwhile, profoundly influenced by Minkowski's work, was developing his ideas on the deflection of starlight in the sun's gravitational field. In two major respects he could not consider the new mechanics as complete. It applied the principle of relativity only to systems in uniform motion. Accelerated motion was still absolute: that is, the laws of physics for systems in accelerated motion were different from those for systems in uniform motion. But uniform motion was a fiction. No system existed of itself, independent of the action of external forces. The universal force of gravitation, for one, joins all bodies in the universe. Universal gravitation itself was completely mysterious. Its discoverer, Newton, had rejected the idea of a force acting instantaneously across empty space.

A general theory of relativity would apply to all systems, the accelerated as well as those in uniform motion. Its equations would be laws of nature which were the same for all systems, and it would substitute for the mysterious force of Newtonian gravitation the interaction of matter with the space-time field.

Einstein began by considering the geometry of the four-dimensional space-time continuum. He showed first that this geometry was not that of Euclid. Imagine a circle at rest with respect to one coordinate system and rotating with respect to another. The equator of the earth is an example. Measured on earth, the ratio of the circumference of the circle to its diameter is π. But with respect to the sun, the circumference is moving rapidly and the circumference measured with respect to the sun contracts. The diameter is unchanged. The ratio of the circumference of the circle to its diameter is no longer π. The foundation postulates of Euclid's geometry are upset, and with them the whole body of the thirteen books of theorems.

Euclidean geometry is based upon five postulates: a straight line may be drawn between any two points; a finite straight line may be continuously extended; a circle may be constructed; and all right angles are equal. The fifth postulate is of a different order from the first four. It may be expressed thus: through a point not on a given line, one and only one line may be drawn parallel to a given line. Euclid actually came to this theorem in I, 27. Unable to prove it, he assumed it as a postulate.

Expressed in another way (parallel lines meet at infinity) it offers an obvious difficulty. Either parallel lines are everywhere equidistant or they approach at infinity. As early as 1733, Geronimo Saccheri, a Jesuit father of Milan, undertook to vindicate Euclid "from every flaw," by an exploration of the consequences of this difficulty. In this, Saccheri succeeded in showing that the difficulty extended to the notions of a straight line and indeed to the whole foundation of geometry. The philosopher Kant, in the nineteenth century, took Euclidean geometry as an example of absolute truth. Like Pythagoras before him with the number series, Kant, whose philosophy was one of absolutes, could seize upon plane geometry as that proof, which had elsewhere eluded reason, of the existence of the Absolute. Aquinas had taken the continuous motion of the sphere of the fixed stars as the first proof of the existence of God, but from this position the system of Copernicus and the Galilean principle had driven his successors. Kant was to fare no better. Almost contemporaneous with Kant's philosophy of the Universal Absolute, an obscure Russian, Nicolai Lobachevski, in 1826 realized the impossibility of proving the absolute truth of the parallel axiom and assumed the contrary. Through a point an infinite number of lines may be drawn in a plane, none of which intersect a given line in the same plane. With the four original postulates and the new postulate, Lobachevski constructed a simple "imaginary geometry." All the theorems and propositions of this Lobachevskian geometry were generalizations, of which the particular cases were the corresponding theorems of Euclid. Almost coincidentally the Hungarian, Johann Bolyai, made the same assumption and developed the same generalized geometry. Karl Friedrich Gauss, the greatest of mathematicians, had already worked on a generalized geometry. Gauss made a series of attempts to discover whether the geometry of the world was Euclidean, or whether it corresponded instead to one of the new geometries, which he called non-Euclidean. All his experiments seemed to prove that the world of space in which we find ourselves is truly Euclidean. It was for this reason that Gauss had never published his early speculations on non-Euclidean geometries. Gauss was not a formalist and mathematics was not for him a game with complex rules. It was a fundamentally serious pursuit, and its aim was the comprehension in human terms, that is, in terms of number and form and order, of reality. If reality was Euclidean, then non-Euclidean geometry was without purpose and Gauss abandoned it.

Bernard Riemann in 1854 developed a non-Euclidean geometry using a generalized form of the calculus of vectors called *Tensor Calculus*. The fifth postulate, which he inserted in place of the parallel axiom, was that through a point no *line* could be drawn on a surface not intersecting a given *line*. The spaces so defined were boundless but finite. The geometry

of a sphere is an example. The familiar lines of longitude illustrate the postulate. If two ships proceed on a parallel course,
i.e., due north, they will meet at the pole.

The non-Euclidean geometries make redefinition of a straight
line necessary. This idea, like that of the parallels, is not a priori
reality beyond the mind. A straight line, as Saccheri determined, was intimately bound with Euclidean geometry. If the
parallel axiom is replaced, the definition of the straight line is
changed. We might attempt to define it in terms of measurement. A straight line is the path of a light ray. But in that case,
how will we interpret the deflection of a light ray grazing the
sun? These difficulties can be avoided if the definition of a
straight line is itself variant so that it may depend on the kind
of geometry with which it is employed. Let a straight line in
the common sense be called a *geodesic* and defined as the least
interval between two points. Then a geodesic in the geometry
of the parallel axiom (Euclidean) is our former straight line,
but a geodesic in non-Euclidean geometry is a curve. On the
surface of a sphere like the earth, geodesics are the intersecting
curves of the Riemannian postulate.

In this light, Einstein considered a graph such as Figure
14. The body whose life path was a straight line in *space*
alone followed a curve through *space-time*. Furthermore, it
could be shown that the curve through space-time of Figure
14 is the *least interval* between the two points. Freely falling
bodies trace out geodesics through space-time. The structure of
the gravitational field in space could be mapped by freely
falling bodies. The structure of the gravitational field in space-
time could be mapped by the same bodies. Matter determines
the gravitational field, hence matter determines the nature of
the least paths through space-time. The geodesics in space-time
are curved in the vicinity of matter, less curved far from matter,
and straight or Euclidean in the regions of empty space where

there is no matter at all. As early as 1679, Hooke had shown that the Keplerian ellipse was the natural path of a freely falling body, as today's earth satellites released high above the earth follow elliptical orbits. The ellipses are geodesics through space-time. They reveal the curvature of the field about a body. The paths of planets, comets, and meteors are geodesics through Riemannian space-time.

Newton had described these paths as a balance between the centrifugal force of rotational motion and gravitational force Newton's mechanics was a mathematics of particles and forces. But it was equally possible to describe the curvature of space-time, to write the equations of the gravitational field. Einstein conceives of a billiard table with slopes carved into the surface leading down into the pockets. A ball placed on the table starts to move toward one of the pockets with uniformly accelerated velocity. We explain this by the geometry of the table and say that the surface is curved. But an equally valid description of the phenomenon would assert that the pockets are the centers of a mysterious inverse square force attracting the balls.

We have to come to the problem of gravitation from the second point of view and have placed a mysterious inverse square force at the center of every element of matter. We have described the sun as the center of such a mysterious force But it is equally valid to describe the sun as a center about which space-time is warped. It is a step from a mechanistic view to a field theory. In electromagnetics, the step from the Coulomb forces to the equations of the electromagnetic field began the era of modern physics. The electromagnetic field theory concentrated on the field of force about a charge in motion. The changing field was a complex curling described by Maxwell's equations. Similarly, Einstein's equations of the gravitational field describe a complex curl in the four-dimen sional space-time continuum about a material point. They describe not the actors but the stage; not the free-willed inhabitants but the deterministic environment. In the graph of Figure 14, nothing was said about the mass. It could have weighed one pound or ten pounds or ten million pounds. It must follow the same path through space-time—the least interval between the two world-points of the start and the finish. It is therefore sufficient to describe the field in full confidence that the structure of the field will determine its history.

There is a story that Einstein was walking on the street one day, when he chanced to see a man fall from the roof of a house. What was the frame of reference for the falling observer? Einstein imagines an elevator at the top of a tall shaft that has broken its cable and falls freely to the ground. A physicist, caught in the elevator, at once sees the possibility of testing this frame of reference. Removing weights, pendula, balls, etc., from his pocket, he proceeds with the roster of elementary physical experiments. The ball dropped from his hand remains in midair. If it is pushed, it travels in a straight line until it strikes the wall of the elevator. The system is truly inertial! This idealized experiment which Einstein had

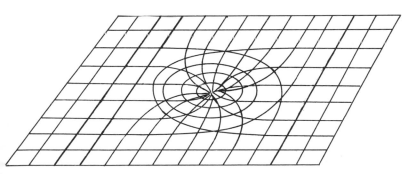

Fig. 40. *Paths of moving bodies in the vicinity of a warp in the surface of space.*

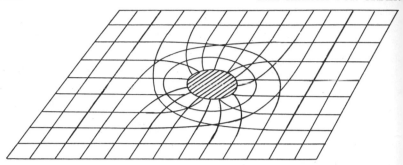

Fig. 41. *Paths of moving bodies in the vicinity of an inverse square center of force.*

not considered realizable was recently performed. *The New York Times* for March 30, 1957, describes an Air Force flight, made expressly to investigate the inertial field:

> Dr. Siegfried J. Gerathewohl tossed a kitten into the air and the bewildered animal floated for several seconds, feet up.
>
> . . . The silver jet serves as a laboratory for the two men. A notebook with pages of mathematical formulas, the kitten, and the golf ball are their only equipment.
>
> "Weightlessness," Dr. Gerathewohl explains, "occurs when an object travels in a circular path around the earth at such velocity that its centrifugal force balances the pull of gravity. . . ."

For Einstein there is a simpler explanation. There is only one force, the force of gravitation. When the elevator is at rest, the physicist finds that objects, a kitten, a golf ball, drop to the floor. When he finds, however, that the kitten floats in the air, feet up, and the golf ball remains in the air where he places it, he asserts that the gravitational field has vanished. To an outside observer, a second and opposite force, that of the acceleration of the freely falling elevator, has exactly counter-balanced the force of gravitation. To Einstein, the exact mathematical equivalence of acceleration and gravitation is not simply coincidence but an observational fact of the greatest importance. The two are one and the same. Einstein postulates that no experiment whatever will be able to distinguish between them. This, the famous postulate of equivalence, banishes absolute motion to the limbo where absolute time and absolute space have already been consigned. The difference between inertial or uniform motion and accelerated or nonuniform motion is now destroyed. Inertial motion is motion in the absence of a gravitational field or motion under conditions where certain values of the field functions are zero. Like the moving charge whose motion changes the electromagnetic field, the moving mass changes the gravitational field. But the field description is invariant. The space-time continuum from the point of view of the man falling from the house top is the same as the space-time continuum from the point of view of the observer on the street. For both, certain values of the field along the geodesic which is the life path of the falling man are zero.

Einstein announced the postulate of equivalence in 1911 and by 1915 he had published the general theory of relativity. There were at first few deductions from the theory which could be experimentally tested. One of these was a revision of Newton's law of gravitation. In 1911, Einstein had computed the deflection of a ray of light grazing the sun to be 0.83 seconds of arc. The special theory of relativity had furnished him with the relativistic mass of the light and he computed the deflection, inserting this mass in Newton's inverse square law. But after 1915 he corrected this value to 1.7 seconds. The observations of the deflections made in the eclipses of 1919 and 1922 confirmed not only the fact of the deflection and thereby the theory of relativistic mass but also the amount of deflection, and thereby the mathematical laws of the general theory. As an-

other consequence deduced from the new general law of gravitation, Einstein was able to account for the rotation of the
orbit of Mercury. The astronomer Leverrier, who had predicted
the planet Neptune, had discovered that the axes of the orbit
of Mercury rotate about the sun at the rate of forty-three
seconds per century. Newton in Book III, Theorem XIV of the
Principia had proved that the planetary orbits are fixed and
immovable and Leverrier's observation of a slight but definite
contradiction to Theorem XIV had been until then a flaw in
the otherwise secure pattern. The rotation of forty-three seconds per century would make the actual path of the planet
Mercury a rosette about the sun, making a complete rotation
once every three million years. Though slight, the effect was
there and could no more be ignored than could Kepler's famous
eight seconds of arc. Either the universe including Mercury
was governed by law and determined or it was chaotic and
probabilistic, and the order of nature was only an approximate
thing. If one surrendered forty-three seconds of arc now, it was
not this miniscule departure that was conceded but the whole
principle of causation and determinism. Attempts to patch this
defect included the postulation of a new planet, *Vulcan*, within
Mercury's orbit, but this planet, designed to explain the pertur-
bation of the Mercurian orbit, has no other properties such as
visibility or gravitational effects on bodies other than Mercury.
The relativistic law of gravitation, however, contradicts Newton's theorem of stability of planetary axes. The geodesic
through space-time about a center of force is not a fixed Keplerian ellipse but a rosette. Upon calculation, Einstein found that
the rotation of the orbit according to the relativistic equations
was exactly forty-three seconds per century. With increasing
distance the effect for all planets beyond Mercury was too small
to be measured. Much later, unexpected confirmation of the
general theory's law of gravitation came from the philosoph-

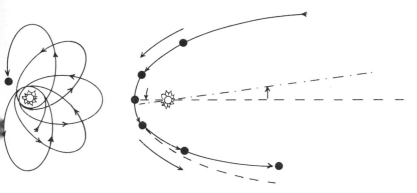

Fig. 12. *The rosette traced by the planet Mercury revolving about the sun.* The major axis of the ellipse of the Mercurian orbit rotates about the sun because as Mercury approaches the sun its velocity increases (according to Kepler's Second Law). Its mass must increase correspondingly (from the special theory of relativity) and the force drawing it to the sun is stronger than that which would be calculated for a body with a constant mass. As Mercury goes into aphelion, its velocity slacks off with a corresponding weakening of the solar attraction.

ically antithetical quantum theory. The atom was pictured as a nucleus of positive charge about which negatively charged particles revolved, held by the inverse square Coulomb force. The paths of the electrons were at first computed as Keplerian ellipses but with increasing refinement of observations the mechanics that had been displaced from the solar system was pursued into the realm of the nuclear atom. Fine effects were found, which indicated that the electrons too described rosettes through the space-time continuum about the center of force.

Einstein himself considered that the fact that he could, from his field equations, derive Newton's law of attraction and the motion of the perihelion of Mercury was convincing proof that the general theory was correct. He had previously deduced, from a consideration of the gravitational effect on light, that the frequency of vibration of light waves would be reduced by the attraction of gravitation. Since a change in frequency meant a change in color, the light from heavy stars would show a shift toward the red or low frequency side of the spectrum as compared with light on earth. In particular, the light from any incandescent gas passed through a diffraction grating was a line spectrum characteristic of the gas. The component waves making up the light were not of all possible frequencies (continuous spectrum) but appeared rather as sharp lines on the spectrum analysis plate, each representing a definite frequency. Einstein calculated in the same paper in which he first proposed the deflection of starlight grazing the sun that the number of waves per second of any line of the spectrum of any element reaching us in sunlight would be two millionths less than the value for the same line measured on the earth. The later revision of the law of gravitation predicted that the shift in frequency to the red end of the spectrum, known as the red shift or Einstein shift, would be twice as great or about four parts per million. From 1923 to 1928, careful measurements of the solar spectrum confirmed the Einstein shift for lines of iron, titanium, and cyanogen on the surface of the sun. The dwarf companion of Sirius is the center of a gravitational field vastly stronger than the solar field, and the red shift has been found to be correspondingly greater.

These measurements of the red shift are an experimental verification of the major points of the theory of relativity. They resolve the paradox of the twins. Although it is impossible for the Air Force at the present to jet a twin into space, the twin is not absolutely necessary. He serves, in fact, simply as a dramatic kind of clock to record the passage of time. A mechanical clock would accomplish this purpose at least as well, and an electrodynamic clock is of far greater accuracy than either. Although we are not able to ship an electrodynamic clock into space,* this turns out to be unnecessary, since every star is such a clock. The postulate of equivalence, therefore, which may have occurred to Einstein with the sight of a man falling from a roof, entails the equivalence of mass and energy previously derived from the special theory.

The practical results of the general theory are not immediately spectacular. We obtain Newton's law, which we had already known, and we account for the rotation of the orbit of Mercury to a second approximation, a motion of which we had already been aware. The deflection of a ray of starlight grazing the sun, which the special theory had already predicted qualitatively, the general theory accounts for quantitatively. The red shift neatly if somewhat uselessly confirms the entire relativistic edifice and promises an arrest of the aging processes of twins, which Professor Dingle fears is of michievous tendency. But it is not as an entry in an inventor's contest that the theory of relativity is to be considered. Newton's theory of universal gravitation, Copernicus' revised cosmology, the *Discorsi* of Galileo, did not immediately nor directly increase the world's wealth. They were instead landmarks in the intellectual growth of the race, victories in the conflict with chaos and the search for order. In the long journey from the cave to the world of law, to the idea of "a pre-established harmony between pure mathematics and physics," the theory of relativity is a step of almost conclusive power. It banishes from physics that occult force of gravity which Newton would not defend, reaching

* Since the original preparation of this manuscript the acceleration of missile technology has turned major portions of the theory of relativity into experimental science. In *The New York Times* for Sunday, July 5, 1959, a project is described which will place an atomic clock (maser clock) in a satellite designed to test separately the slowing down of time with increase in velocity predicted by the special theory and the change in time with change in gravity predicted by the general theory.

instantaneously across the equally occult idea of void. It re-
places these by a continuous field in space-time acting on, and
being acted upon, by matter. It joins the dual concepts of
matter and energy as it had joined those of gravitation and
acceleration. It rids us of absolutes, of ethers, and of the last
vestiges of that parochialism which Copernicus first overthrew
A theory in the grand manner, it touches of earthly physics and
the cosmology of the universe. It is deterministic, and it is rigid
Instead of the positions of particles and their momenta, an
intelligence requires only the gravitational field to calculate
the whole of the past and the whole of the future. The equations
of the field are the equations of the space-time continuum con
necting the here-now by the infinitesimal steps of the tensor
calculus with the there-then.

Most significantly, the theory of relativity effectively divorce
physics from a priori philosophical constraints. Incorporating
the new geometries, the theory must forever remain a stum
bling block to the idealist. At its heart lies Gauss's assertion tha
space has also a reality beyond our mind of which we canno
fully ordain the laws a priori. The mechanist can derive little
comfort from this, however. In the equations of the gravita
tional field, in the four dimensions of space-time, in the pro
found and completely abstract reasoning of the theory of
relativity, there are no references to machines, no images of
machines, no models, even of the mathematical kind. Particle
and void alike have vanished and with them the inverse squar
forces. Not Kelvin himself could model the principle of the
constant velocity of light. Gone are the tubes and their bal
bearings, the gyroscopes, the elastic strings, the ether marbles
They have not been replaced by better images. The physicis
has not left his wife for another love but for a purer concept
He has recovered the continuum from which he had been
banished since the long-ago time of Zeno. He can say agai

with Pythagoras in that springtime of our civilization that he has found a preordained harmony between pure mathematics and the world.

Not only mechanism but the far more durable doctrine of materialism must bow to the exclusion of the a priori philosophical constraint. Materialism in a world in which mass is relative and takes on such values as will preserve the constancy of the velocity of light is no longer materialism. The principle of Lavoisier is shattered and with it the whole of chemistry loses its logical base. In a science of variant length and time and mass, the crude assertions of matter and void cannot be accepted as guides for future experiment and investigation. Matter is not conserved. The concepts of matter and substance lose all meaning. In the light of other branches of modern science, we can describe matter as a kind of electromagnetic condensation. We retain the concept of mass, as we retain length and time, but with the equivalence of matter and motion in mind. With materialism, mechanism, idealism, and realism gone, we free ourselves at last from the intellectual conflicts that attended the death of scholasticism and the Renaissance. We can turn again with Bacon to the fertile soil of experience.

The ghosts of positivism and operationalism, more recent and more sophisticated doctrine, will not so easily down. Yet in the light of the rise of the theory of relativity is the view of the scientist as simply the spectator of facts external to himself an adequate or even an accurate explanation for the collection of papers, experiments, and ideas that we refer to today as the concept of the red shift? The operationalist, a latter-day sensationalist, would limit knowledge to the description of operations (measurements) and their results. Would he then describe the Michelson-Morley apparatus and would that be the theory of relativity? And could the operationalist account for the Michelson-Morley experiment in the first place except as a terrible mistake? It is true that relativity is all theory and that in a certain sense we can *know* only the reports of our senses, aided and abetted by the galvanometers and interferometers of our ingenuity. The operationalist wishes to save himself from the embarrassment of error. He shuns the brilliant generalizations of an Einstein. He undergoes a metamorphism in reverse like the queen ant, which having soared high above the swarm on its nuptial flight returns to earth, its wings to atrophy, its future function fixed.

The theory of relativity is not the end of science. It is a way station on an infinite railroad. It is not true, but it is not false. It is a theoretical construction to enable us to find our way through the labyrinthine maze of the world of our senses. In its light, we can see much farther than Newton, farther than Faraday, Maxwell, and Michelson. By this intellectual comprehension of our world, tentative though it may be, we distinguish ourselves from the naked savages huddled about the campfire from which we sprang. We are not the helpless prisoners of a brief, mortal coil. In this act, this reduction of the chaos about us, we master our environment. We reassert the dignity of man. We distinguish ourselves from the brute in the one way in which it is possible to make a distinction. But if our age is the age of science, it is also the age of the anti-intellectual. In prisons and camps, in the great mass movements, the twentieth century has seen ample evidence of our kinship with the brute deliberately and premeditatedly manufactured. This is the worst of which man is capable. In the profundity of thought and conception, in the unity and precision of the idea which marks the great world-systems of thought, we have a glimpse of the best. The power of the mind is not constrained. In the act of creation the limitations of mortality are transcended

19. The Fall of Causality

THIS EVENT HAS MADE MORE NOISE THAN
THE PRECEDING, AND IT IS IN ALL THE
MEMOIRS.

POINCARÉ, 1904

AS RELATIVITY arose out of the problems of motion and of cause and of effect, to answer again the old questions of the persistence of planetary motion and the nature of fall, so the quantum theory rose out of the old argument of the continuum and discontinuity. The quantum theory asserts that nature is discrete in all respects. Atoms are particles of matter. Quanta are particles of energy. This reasoning, which had appeared first in the concept of the electron, was now extended to all energy.

It was not a conscious innovation. Max Planck, Professor at

Berlin and a thermodynamicist of note, was working on the
relationship between the energy and the frequency of radiation
emitted by solids. It had been known for half a century that
a solid such as a piece of iron would begin to glow red at
about 525°C., and with increase in temperature add one after
the other the colors of the spectrum until it eventually reached
a white heat. Remarkably enough, the colors (frequencies)

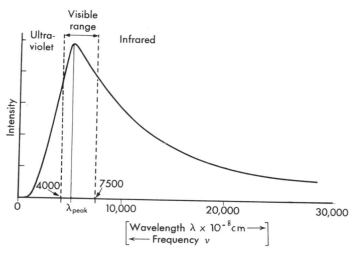

Fig. 43. *Black body emission curve*. Distribution of
intensity of light emitted by a solid at 6000° Kelvin.

change at the same temperature for all kinds of solids. This
independence of chemical composition is always the surest sign
that a fundamental principle is involved. Maxwell theory had
explained light as electromagnetic waves and Hertz had demonstrated that long electromagnetic waves were generated by the
mechanical oscillations of an electric spark. It was confidently
assumed that the shorter electromagnetic waves of the visible
spectrum must be generated by some sort of natural electric
oscillator proportionately smaller and of higher frequency than
that of Hertz. In 1900, J. W. Strutt, Lord Rayleigh, derived a

law for the distribution of energy in a large assembly of natural oscillators. He assumed that a natural oscillator, like a violin string or an organ pipe, could vibrate with an infinite number of possible frequencies—all the possible harmonics of a fundamental note with wave lengths of 1, ½, ⅓, ¼, . . . times the wave length of the fundamental.

Heat energy would set the natural oscillators in a solid to vibrating and so emitting light. Since the wave lengths are infinitely divisible, there are infinitely many ways of vibration at the short end of the electromagnetic spectrum beyond the violet. On the average, all these ways of vibration should share equally in the energy. Accordingly, Rayleigh's Law shows that

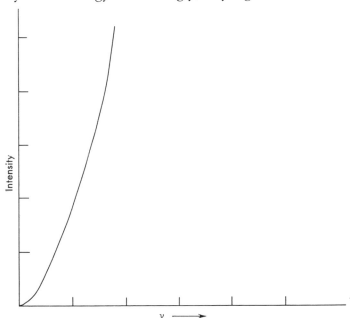

Fig. 44. *Rayleigh's law for the distribution of spectral intensity* based on the principle of the equipartition of energy—the ultraviolet catastrophe.

an ideal radiator or "black body" (which is approximated by any solid) would convert all the energy that falls upon it to very short wave radiation. Solid bodies would accept the energy of the universe in all its forms and transform it to ultraviolet light. This disastrous turn of events is known as the ultraviolet catastrophe.

Since we are spared the ultraviolet catastrophe, the principles from which Rayleigh deduced this consequence were in doubt. Max Planck, then forty-two and at the height of a successful career in thermodynamics, first modified Rayleigh's law and emerged with an equation that fitted the experimentally determined curves. But thermodynamic reasoning led to Rayleigh's law and Planck's modification, although successful in fitting reality, was at first simply an exercise in analytic geometry—in fitting an equation to an empirical curve.

At that point, Planck recognized that he could obtain his law by challenging the classical assumption that energy is shared equally among all the vibrators. He proposed instead that the vibrators are not free to take on any possible value of energy, but only amounts of energy per vibration of multiples of a fundamental unit, h. Planck's radiation law * expresses the most

* $E/v = h, 2h, 3h, \ldots nh, \ldots$; v is frequency.
$E = nhv$

In order to account for the skew-type curve which fits experimentally the distribution of the intensity (energy) throughout the spectrum, it is necessary to assume that it is a statistical distribution curve of the same type as the frequency distribution curves for the velocities of particles in a gas. In the statistical analysis of a gas, the frequency or proportion of particles was plotted on the vertical axis against the velocity (which is related to the energy) on the horizontal axis. In the black-body emission curves, the intensity of emitted light can be related to the proportion of oscillators excited to a given frequency. The variable plotted along the horizontal axis, the frequency of the emitted light, must therefore, following the analogy, be related to the energy. In its simplest form, make the assumption that the energy of a particle is proportional to the frequency, $E = hv$. The black-body emission spectrum becomes simply the most probable distribution of particles plotted against their energies. In accordance with the theory of probabilities, this should be a skewed curve. Raising the

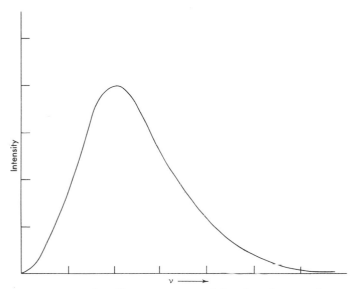

Fig. 45. *Planck's quantum model.* The theoretical curve fits the experimentally determined curve with precision.

probable distribution of the energy assuming that it can only be absorbed or radiated out in discrete packets called quanta, of value proportional to the frequency.

He had solved the radiation problem, but only by assuming an atomicity to energy and by introducing a discontinuity to

---

temperature of the black body displaces the hump of the curve to the right exactly as in the analogous situation in the Maxwell-Boltzmann analysis of molecular velocities. This is not surprising since Planck designed the theory to fit the observations.

In the assumption of the proportionality of energy to frequency there is the implied assumption of *particles*. But what are these particles? They are not the molecular oscillators of classical theory for these were free to oscillate with any frequency and would on the average share equally in the energy. Planck's radical assumption is that the energy itself can only be absorbed or emitted in units. The quanta of energy must be distributed among the oscillators, which interact among themselves in such a way as to reach a state of maximum probability—the state described by the skew curve appropriate to the temperature.

natural processes. ". . . contemporary physicists did not at
once comprehend the importance of the revolution that had just
been accomplished," Louis de Broglie commented.

> The hypothesis of Planck without doubt must have
> seemed to them an ingenious means of improving the
> theory of an interesting but, all in all, a particular phe-
> nomenon, and not a brilliant idea destined to upset all
> the classical conceptions of physics.

Then in 1905 in the same volume of the *Annalen der Physik*
in which he had laid the spectre of the absolute, Einstein extended the concept of discontinuity from the natural vibrators
to light itself. The great Hertz and later his successor and
protégé, Philip Lenard, had observed that light falling on a
metal plate discharged a stream of electrons, the more light the
more electrons, the higher the frequency of the light the
greater the energy of the outgoing electrons. Einstein explained
this on the assumption that light itself was a stream of particles
called *photons* with energies proportional to the frequency of
the light. The photons striking the plate dislodged the electrons

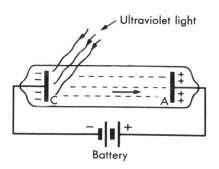

Fig. 46. When ultraviolet light falls on a
negatively charged electrode in an evacuated quartz tube, a photoelectric current is
set up in the gap between the electrodes.

much as a spray of bullets striking a bed of stones would dislodge some of the stones.

Aware of the mischievous tendencies of this idea, Einstein called his paper "a heuristic point of view." It was a disclaimer, a protest in advance that this at any rate must not be taken literally, but simply as a temporarily useful model. Planck himself objected that his original idea had merely imposed restrictions on the hypothetical oscillators, which were presumably mechanical systems and therefore quite possibly subject to limitations. But Einstein was extending this limitation on the

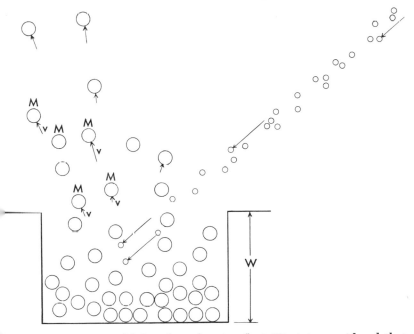

Fig. 47. *Einstein model for photoelectric effect.* Einstein considered that the energy of the incoming photons was in packets of value $h\upsilon$ and was entirely transferred to electrons in the metal in the form of work W to get the electron out of the metal, and kinetic energy $\frac{1}{2} mv^2$. The diagram is a crude mechanical analogy.

the part of the vibrators to energy itself. The wave theory of
light was threatened. And the discontinuity that Planck had
introduced to avoid the ultraviolet catastrophe had reappeared
in a totally unrelated context. With the greatest reluctance, scientists were forced to the recognition of this seeming discontinuity in natural process.

Again in 1906, Einstein demonstrated his virtuosity by still
another extension of the quantum idea. Francis Bacon's ancient
supposition that heat was nothing but a motion of the parts of
bodies had flowered in the kinetic-molecular theory. By considering the vibration of the particles of a solid, it had been
deduced that solids could absorb heat at the rate of 6 calories
per gram molecular weight per degree. Experiment confirmed
this at ordinary temperatures but showed a rapid falling off
from this value at extremely low temperatures. As the temperature of a solid was lowered past a threshold value, fewer
and fewer of its component particles seemed able to vibrate.
Einstein explained this by assuming that the particles of a

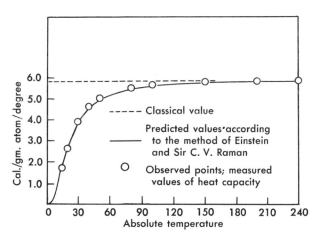

Fig. 48. *The heat capacity of lead.*

solid all vibrated with a certain fixed frequency. The minimum energy that the vibrating particle could absorb was a single vibration quantum called a *phonon*. A particle could absorb only integral multiples of a phonon, 1, 2, 3, etc., of energy hv, $2hv$, $3hv$, . . . At low temperatures there was less energy available than enough to provide at least one phonon per particle and therefore not all the particles could vibrate and the capacity of the solid to accept heat was reduced.

It was no longer possible to ignore the quantum theory or to regard it as confined to unimportant areas of science. In three entirely different and unrelated areas, Planck's radical assumptions of discrete states of energy, of the proportionality of energy to frequency, and of the emission or absorption of energy in grains, had explained results that directly contradicted fundamental principles of classical physics. It could neither be coincidence nor insignificant that the same number h appeared in the context of black-body radiation, the photoelectric effect, and heat capacities. The experimental results of these three fields, until then separate and unrelated, could be derived from the single set of assumptions of Planck. The new quantum theory was now seen to be a fundamental insight into the nature of energy itself. From 1907 on, it appeared in more and more force as the most generally fruitful concept of the century.

THE QUANTUM ATOM

The union of the quantum and atomic theories was the foundation of that tremendous burst of physical science which we see around us today. At the turn of the century, it had already become clear that the atom was not the hard, round, unchanging particle of the Greeks. Atoms had been observed to give off electrons and helium ions and other rays, and were no longer to be regarded as the least units of matter, but as consisting of or containing these other, smaller things. The original Greek atom was a philosophical atom unlinked to the equally philosophical chemistry of the four elements, earth, air, fire, and water. The seventeenth-century atom, a tiny machine of hooks or fleeces and springs, unchanging, unwearing, was the first atom with properties, and therefore the first atom on which a chemistry could rest. Dalton's atom arose out of the numerical identities of the combining weights and, coupled with the kinetic-molecular theory, had promised a total science of matter. By 1911, with the discovery of X-ray diffraction, the atoms were classified, their properties known and sorted, their sizes, weights, and chemical affinities tabulated. Yet as they had become more and more real in our science, they had lost one by one their absolute characteristics. They were no longer the least units of matter; they had parts. They were no longer hard, round, and unchanging, as the study of radium showed, and in the light of the theory of special relativity, their masses and sizes were no longer to be regarded with confidence. The idea that the atom had parts grew out of the research in the passage of electricity through gases. J. J. Thomson, who was born in 1856 and lived on into the electronic era, made the first estimates of the masses of subatomic particles making up the rays that appeared in gas discharge tubes.

"Some with Goldstein, Hertz, or Lenard, think that this phenomenon, like light, results from vibrations of the ether, or even that it is light of short wave length," wrote Jean Perrin in 1895.

> We then easily see that these rays might have a straight trajectory, excite phosphorescence, and act upon photographic plates.
> Others with Crookes or J. J. Thomson, think that these

rays are formed of matter negatively charged and moving with great velocity. We then can easily understand their mechanical properties and also the way they bend in a magnetic field.

Thomson found that the electric particles had a mass about 1/1000th that of the hydrogen atom.

> At first there were very few who believed in the existence of these bodies smaller than atoms. I was even told long afterwards by a distinguished physicist who had been present at my lecture at the Royal Institution that he thought I had been "pulling their legs."

Thomson designed an atom consisting of a sphere of positive electricity holding together electrons very much like the seeds in a pumpkin. When electrons were torn from the atom by cathode rays, the spheres were left with a net positive charge, and therefore drifted in the electric field as positive rays.

At the same time as Thomson's speculations, the integrity of the atom was under attack from the spectacular new discoveries of radioactivity. These began with the invisible X-radiation of Wilhelm Roentgen in 1895 and the discovery of radioactivity by Becquerel in 1896. Becquerel's discovery was seized upon by Marie Curie, who was looking for a suitable topic for her doctor's thesis. The announcement of the new elements, polonium and radium, by the attractive Polish revolutionary student [*] recently rescued from semistarvation in her garret on the Left Bank foreshadowed the dramatic events of our own immediate past—the political upheavals in Europe, the refugee scientists, the race with Nazi Germany, and the destruction of Hiroshima.

Pierre Curie's measurements of the energy spontaneously emitted by radium were a direct contradiction to the principle of conservation of energy. Ernest Rutherford (1871–1937), a

[*] As one of three authors with P. Curie and G. Bremont.

New Zealander of great energy and enthusiasm, and Frederick Soddy made an even more direct attack on materialism itself. They identified some of the radiation called α-rays given off by uranium as helium (lacking its electrons), and proposed a theory of the transmutation of these elements one into the other. Using the steady rate of conversion of uranium to helium as a kind of clock, Rutherford made new calculations of the age of the earth, multiplying Kelvin's previous estimates of about twenty million years by nearly one hundred.

"I came into the room which was half dark, and presently spotted Lord Kelvin in the audience and realized that I was in for trouble, . . ." wrote Rutherford of his appearance at a London meeting on the age of the earth.

> To my relief Kelvin fell fast asleep, but as I came to the important point, I saw the old boy sit up, open an eye and cock a baleful glance at me!

In 1906 at the meetings of the British Association for the Advancement of Science, Kelvin launched a frontal attack on the new doctrines of energy and the transmutation of matter. He was eighty-two. He fought through the pages of the London *Times* and the halls of the British Association a valiant battle in defense of the principles of conservation—the energy principle which his century had regarded with the theory of evolution as the underlying foundation of existence. It was the death of Kelvin in 1907 and not the shot at Sarajevo in 1914 that brought an end to the comfortable world of the nineteenth century.

Rutherford's model of the atom was conceived after experiments which showed that a thin foil of gold only a few atoms thick would scatter a beam of α-particles.

". . . I remember two or three days later Geiger coming to me in great excitement and saying, 'We have been able to get some of the particles coming backwards, . .'" Rutherford wrote of these experiments.

> It was almost as incredible as if you fired a 15-inch shell at a piece of tissue paper and it came back and hit you. . . . When I made calculations I saw that it was impossible to get anything of that order of magnitude unless you took a system in which the greater part of the mass of the atom was concentrated in a minute nucleus. It was then that I had the idea of an atom with a minute massive center carrying a charge.

Rutherford proposed a planetary model of the atom with the electrons moving in regular orbits about a positively charged nucleus containing most of the mass of the atom. This model was both in agreement with and an explanation of the empirical data of chemistry. As more and more detailed experiments confirmed the Rutherford atom, and in particular as it became clear that all chemical reactions could be explained in terms of the number of the orbital electrons, it could not be doubted that here at last was the model of the atom and the key to the interpretation of the host of results which had crowded up to the door of the twentieth century. All chemistry could be taken as experimental verification, if more were needed. The Rutherford atom was a model reconciling the laws of chemical reaction, Faraday's experiments on electrolysis, the newly discovered phenomenon of radioactivity, and the emerging results of X-ray crystallography. The warnings of those who like Lavoisier had sought to model chemistry on mathematical laws and rejected the inferences of particle numbers from the recurrence of various constants in their equations were totally forgotten in this triumph of unbridled mechanism. Hypothesis had piled on hypothesis, oblivious of the example of Newton, oblivious of the abolition of the ether and with it the fundamentals of absolute space and time on which this mechanism

RUTHERFORD'S PLANETARY ATOM, 1911

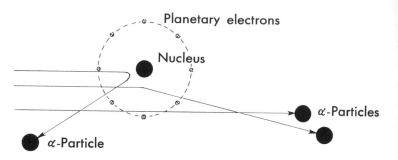

RUTHERFORD'S ATOMIC MODEL OF A METAL FOIL

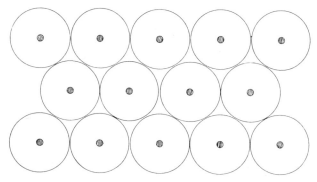

Fig. 49. The deflection of heavy α-particles in crossing thin gold foils could only be explained by assuming that the mass and positive charge of each atom was concentrated in a spot at the center. The greatest part of the atomic volume was empty space.

rested. The enormity of the achievement, the relating of the laws of planetary motions to the atom, the subsuming of all that welter of chemical observation and experiment, made for a veritable orgy of mechanism. The purity of the Pythagorean vision seemed lost forever.

But there was a discordant note in all this rejoicing. One

field of classical physics at least had not been bidden to the feast. Electromagnetic theory stood outside the gates, and like some Old Testament prophet recalled the revelers to the eternal verities. The electrons revolving about the positively charged nucleus were just those moving electrical charges in just those rapid motions which the equations of the electromagnetic field theory described. The motion of charge should be accompanied by the emission of electromagnetic radiation. However, if the electron is to lose energy in radiation, how is it kept from spiraling in toward the nucleus? And if the atom in a stable state is not to emit electromagnetic radiation—and most atoms do not unless excited—then the electron cannot move in the positive field surrounding the nucleus. But in that case, what is to keep it from falling into the positive nucleus like a meteor into the sun? The electron must revolve about the nucleus to generate the centrifugal force to counterbalance the attraction of the nucleus. But if it moves, it emits radiation and so moves less and less, and the atom collapses. And if it does not move, the atom still collapses. The objection to the perpetual motion of the electron was the same that had been made to Copernicus' motion of the earth. Where was the force to maintain the motion of the earth? Where was the energy to maintain the motion of the negative electron in a positive field? The prime mover could not, surely, be expected to attend individually to all electrons in all atoms.

The light that atoms actually do emit was, by the 1870's, carefully described. When any gaseous element is excited to incandescence, the light given off is limited to certain sharply defined frequencies characteristic of the element, called line spectra. The line spectrum for hydrogen (Figure 50) is the simplest. In 1885, a Swiss physicist at Basel, Jacob Balmer, found a formula relating the wavelength of the bright red, green, blue, and violet hydrogen lines to the inverse squares of the numbers

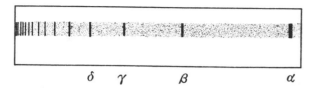

Fig. 50. *The line spectrum of hydrogen.*

3, 4, 5, and 6. A relationship of such simplicity was obviously a clue to a fundamental harmony. The formula held with remarkable consistency, but Balmer chose to see it the other way around, and congratulated the spectrographers for their accuracy.

Balmer's sense of numerical relationship impelled him to postulate a whole series of formulas based on the squares of two integers n' and n''. By 1924, four series of lines corresponding to his formulas had been described by spectrographers.

It was the quantum theory which provided an interpretation of these results. Niels Bohr, a young Danish scientist who had visited Thomson's laboratory and then joined Rutherford at Manchester, proposed that the electron within the atom was quantized; that is, that it could neither absorb nor emit radiation except in Planck's discrete grains. Bohr's hydrogen atom was a planetary model like Rutherford's but whereas a planet may be at any distance from the sun, the quantum restriction limited the electron of the Bohr atom to discrete orbits r, $4r$, $9r$, . . . from the nucleus. The motions of electrons in their stable orbits were not governed by Maxwell theory. Energy was radiated or absorbed only when an electron jumped from one orbit to another, and the difference in energy between any two orbits was a quantum of radiation, $h\nu$. Starting with the single quantum assumption, Bohr was able to derive Balmer's formulae for the wave-lengths of the lines of the hydrogen

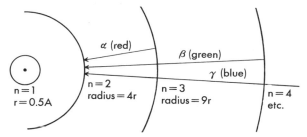

Fig. 51. *The Bohr atom (hydrogen)*. The energy lost by electrons falling from high energy outer orbits to the lower energy $n = 2$ orbit, is emitted as quanta of radiation in the visible or Balmer spectrum (photons). The fall of electrons to the still lower $n = 1$ orbit is accompanied by the emission of higher energy ultra-violet photons. The discrete lines of the hydrogen spectrum are explained by the assumption of discrete levels between which electrons can exchange energy.

spectrum. The past developments of classical physics were seen as an approximation, effective enough in dealing with matter on an ordinary scale and energy in gross amounts where the smallness of the quantum would effectively conceal the fundamental discontinuity. The atomic theory could be neg-lected and most of its results obtained as Boyle's law was obtained, empirically, without the crutch of hypothesis. But the quantum theory led to precise results and to the prediction of phenomena of which classical theory had no inkling. The Bohr atom was the beginning of a quantitative theory of chem-istry. The miniscule oscillators of Planck were now found and the Bohr theory explained in great detail the mechanism of atomic absorption and emission of radiation. A fluorescent solid, for example, is a solid which emits light in the visible range on being exposed to invisible ultraviolet light. The high-frequency ultraviolet light knocks electrons in the solid from low energy inner states to high energy outer states. The electrons are then free to cascade down the energy staircase, dropping from level to level and emitting light of the frequencies associated with these energy transitions.

Bohr also marked the appearance of a new generation of scientists. Although he was only twenty-eight in 1913 when his paper appeared, making him six years younger than Einstein, he was twenty-seven years younger than Planck. There appeared to be a dividing line in basic philosophy and attitude between the scientists who reached their productive years before and after 1913. The new young men (most of them were in their twenties and early thirties at the times of their greatest productivity) concentrated on theoretical and mathematical methods for the exact explanation of the phenomena. They strove continually to free themselves of philosophic preconceptions. Again and again, they found experience in contradiction with deterministic theories in such ways and to such degrees that they came eventually to regard the theory of relativity itself as of a piece with classical physics. De Broglie writes:

> . . . the theory of relativity, while pushing them to their extreme consequences, retains the guiding ideas of the old physics. Thus it can be said that, despite the so-new and almost revolutionary character of the Einsteinian conceptions, the theory of relativity is in some ways the culmination of classical physics.

For the older scientists, the turn which physics had taken was a displeasing one. Planck, who had begun the mischief, for a long time would not accept the photons of Einstein's 1905 paper, until, after Bohr had obtained the same equation in another context, and after Millikan had confirmed experimentally the predictions of the paper and again Compton had identified the X-ray photons, Planck was obliged to concede to his own hypothesis. As for Einstein, "I always regarded these ideas as temporary," he said, "I never thought that others would take them so much more seriously than I did."

Except for the arbitrariness of Planck's assumption of discontinuity and the particle-wave duality of light, the logical deficiencies of the new theory were not at first apparent, and it was characteristic of the new men that they were concerned with experience in preference to logic. Like Kepler abandoning the imperfect circle for the perfect ellipse, they were willing to forego the luxury of metaphysics. The mathematical deficiencies of the new theory concerned them more than the logical. Bohr had described a kind of Copernican atom with electron orbits as circles. But Kepler's laws of motion must hold for a particle in an inverse square force field. The electron must move in an orbit characterized not by one number r, but by two numbers, corresponding to the major and minor axes of the elliptical path. In 1916 the German physicist Sommerfeld pointed out that the mechanics of Kepler and Newton were predicated on absolute space, which had been replaced by the four-dimensional space-time continuum of relativity. The path of an electron was not a stationary ellipse but an ellipse rotating about the nucleus in a rosette according to the predictions of the general theory of relativity. Relativistic mechanics yielded two values for each of the hydrogen wavelengths and these were found to correspond to a previously unexplained split of the hydrogen lines.

With the theory of Sommerfeld, final and complete like that of Einstein's relativity, the older quantum theory of the Bohr atom had reached the end of the line. It was not the ultimate atom. "The scheme of spectral terms established by Sommerfeld, although more complete than that of Bohr, is not yet as rich as that whose existence is proven by spectroscopic experiments." The wave-particle duality remained. To the arbitrariness of the original quantum assumptions Bohr had added the idea of the stability of the moving electron in its orbit, thus directly contradicting electromagnetic theory. Yet at the same time electromagnetic theory was brought in as needed, and the quantum theory spoke freely of frequencies and wavelengths when it was convenient, or photons and corpuscles when it came to a gap, like a fluid orator who manages in one and the same sentence to be on both sides of the fence.

There was a solution to the dilemma, much in the spirit of Einstein's postulate of the constant velocity of light. Prince Louis de Broglie (1892–   ) in his doctoral dissertation formalized the duality by elevating it to the rank of first principle. De Broglie combined Einstein's expression for the dependency of the energy of a particle upon its mass and velocity with Planck's expression for the dependency of the energy upon frequency. As a result, it appeared that every particle must be associated with a wave;[*] an idea complementing the earlier ascription of a corpuscular character to energy. These de Broglie waves or matter waves are an aspect of matter not readily apparent for particles of appreciable mass such as a dust grain. The discontinuities of the quantum theory are negligible in such cases and ordinary classical mechanics will describe the behavior of the particle with precision. But for particles of very small mass the associated wavelength will be appreciable and the mechanics of waves will apply as well as that of particles. The electron is such a small particle and must therefore exhibit the properties of waves.

In 1925, Davisson and Germer of the Bell Telephone Laboratories obtained a peculiar variation in the pattern of the reflections of a beam of electrons from a nickel surface. This was explained as the alternate cancellation and reinforcement of the de Broglie waves associated with the electrons. Repeated

[*] Of length $\lambda = \dfrac{h}{mv}$; mv is the momentum of the particle.

experiments showed that the electron beam could be diffracted in the same way as the X-ray beam and the light beam, and that the measured wavelengths and velocities confirmed the equation of de Broglie. Since then, molecular beams of hydrogen and helium have also been diffracted in ingenious experiments. The de Broglie thesis introduced a kind of principle of equivalence: if a phenomenon is susceptible to mechanical interpretation, it can be explained by a wave interpretation of equal validity, and vice versa. No experiment can distinguish between the two.

Proceeding from de Broglie's idea, Erwin Schrödinger began by considering the electron waves about the atomic nucleus. The requirement of Bohr that the electron is stable in one of a discrete sequence of orbits is interpreted as the requirement that the electron wave must fit the orbit. The stability of the electron in the orbit is associated with the stability of a stationary or standing wave fitting the atom exactly as the standing wave in an organ pipe. Instead of particles in motion, Schrödinger pictured a continuous cloud of negative electricity about the nucleus, a kind of three-dimensional wave system with crests coinciding with the old Bohr orbits. Schrödinger used the calculus of vectors to set up a function describing the electron cloud—the famous ψ function. From the ψ function the amplitude of the wave at any point may be found and this may be considered as a kind of density of the electron. This developing theory of wave mechanics led to important corrections of the earlier values for the energy levels and explained the packets of energy absorbed or emitted by atomic systems as the differences between the energies of the standing waves.

Working independently of Schrödinger, who, with de Broglie, took Einstein's photon theory as a starting point, and directly under the influence of Bohr, Werner Heisenberg (1901–   ) formulated a purely mathematical mechanics, which Schröd-

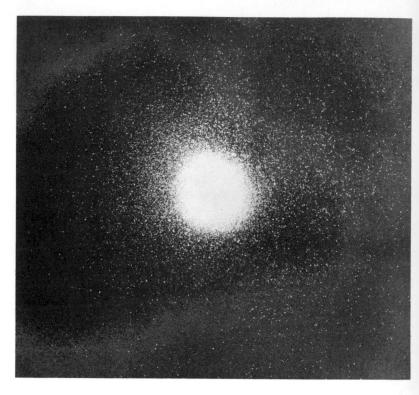

Fig. 52. *The hydrogen electron in the 1s state.* A picture of an electron. Actually the shadowgraph of iron filings on a glass plate. In the light of wave-mechanics, the electron is represented by a probability distribution function giving the probability of finding the electron in an element of volume at a given distance from the nucleus. Alternatively, the picture may be considered as a statistical summary of the electron positions in a very large number of hydrogen atoms, or again, as the charge density per unit volume. Photographic infelicities apart, the distribution of iron filings dropped from a few feet above a point target is mathematically parallel. The picture is a pun (to borrow from Norbert Wiener) but a useful and instructive pun. Compare with photographs of globular star clusters.

inger was able to show was an equivalent expression of wave mechanics. Heisenberg writes that his education, like that of any well-educated German in the early twentieth century, rested firmly on the traditional and the humane studies, and in particular the classics. This austerity of mind was profoundly shocked by an early textbook of physics which fell into his hands and represented the linkage of atoms by hooks and eyes. The crude mechanism of the conception repelled Heisenberg. It was in the best spirit of the Pythagorean tradition, therefore, that he founded the extension of the quantum theory which became known as quantum mechanics. Heisenberg took an idea of Born's, that the concept of wave and the concept of particle were the gross concepts of objects on the scale of the everyday world. What reason was there to assume that these gross concepts must fit the submicroscopic world within the atom? Our models, Heisenberg asserted, were too crude. We were attempting to push the validity of various induced laws into regions too far from those for which the laws had been formulated. What do we really know about the photon or the electron? We have only the mathematical formulation of certain observations and measurements. It was on the basis of these that Heisenberg drew up a purely mathematical theory. Certain metaphysical preconceptions, he asserted, had long been difficulties in the way of this purely mathematical approach. For one thing, it had always been assumed that a particle was completely determinate, that its position and velocity at any time could be found. If we had resorted to statistical equations, it was as a convenience, a simplification which we could forgo at any time, and laboriously treat a system of particles with all their interactions, one by one. But the particle as Born pointed out is not completely determined. The basic contradiction between wave and particle aspects of matter and energy was paralleled by the basic contradiction between the determinism of the initial Schrödinger formulation and the in-determinism of the Heisenberg mechanics. "Bohr has declared outright that there is an incomprehensible irrational factor in physical events," wrote Max Born. To reconcile the wave-par-ticle duality, Max Born proposed to interpret the de Broglie waves, the "matter waves" as they were called, as expressions for the probable situation of the particle. Experiments, the line spectra on which wave mechanics were based, dealt after all with enormous numbers of atoms. The electron cloud of Schrö-dinger (Figure 52) was by this interpretation simply the statis-tical summary of all the locations of all the electrons. Where the cloud was thick, most of the electrons were concentrated. Or, interpreting the cloud for one atom, the density of the cloud expressed the probability of the situation of the electron. Where the cloud was thick, that is, where the amplitude of the wave function was high, was the most probable location of the electron. The amplitude of the ψ wave at a point was the prob-ability of finding the electron at that point.

By an extension of this interpretation, the light waves of Huygens and Young are simply probability waves. In the dif-fraction of light, the blackening of a film at one spot indicates that the amplitude of the wave reaches a maximum at that spot and therefore the number of photons to reach that spot is great-est. All determinism vanishes. If a single photon approaches two fine holes close together in front of a screen, it is impossible in principle and not merely in practice to predict so simple a matter as where on the screen it will land. Classical theory in-ferred the existence and motions of the molecules of a gas from the movements of pollen grains visible under the microscope. It assigned the characteristics of the gross visible world to the inferred submicroscopic world of the molecules. With the in-sight into this new level of existence provided by the quantum theory, we find that the classical inferences fail. And even the fundamental principle of causality fails. Events in the world within the atom do not happen in response to due and sufficient cause.

The fall of a card in the gross world of visible specimens is not purely chance. In theory, we could analyze precisely the various movements that went into shuffling, the exact forces involved in the touch of the dealer's hand. We treat the fall of a card as purely a chance phenomenon to avoid the fantastically difficult problem of the mechanics of shuffling a deck. In principle we recognize that the fall must be governed by due and sufficient cause. But the movements of the electron and by extension all particles are only probabilities. The natural law that prevails on the level of classical physics is simply an expression of the probabilities that prevail on this deeper, more fundamental level of experience.

NUCLEAR PARTICLES

In 1919 Rutherford had demonstrated again the apparently inexhaustible complexity of nature by causing artificial radioactivity in nitrogen bombarded with α-particles. The subsequent development of particle accelerators, in which beams of high-speed particles could be concentrated upon matter, led to the splitting of nuclei and the study of the particle fragments produced in this kind of collision. The positively charged nucleus of the ordinary hydrogen atom was the first known of these particles. It was given the name of *proton*. A neutral particle (neither positive nor negative) with the mass of a proton (atomic weight 1) consisting of a combined proton-electron, was proposed by Rutherford, and found and named *neutron* by Chadwick (1932). The *neutrino* postulated by Wolfgang Pauli in 1931 to conserve energy in the β discharge of electrons was not actually detected until 1956. The *positron* was pro-

posed by Paul Dirac to account for certain mathematical difficulties, and identified by Anderson in 1932. The *meson* was
suggested by Yukawa in 1935 and subdivided into a series or
family of mesons, π mesons, μ mesons, π° mesons, etc.

Again, as in the nineteenth century, information of all sorts
has been accumulating, much of it puzzling, much of it confusing. Instead of the hard round unchanging spheres of the
early atomists, instead of the simple atom constructed out of
one, or two, or even three or four elementary particles, the
structure of the atom itself is proving a complex tangle. The
mathematical methods of approach to this complexity are generally subsumed under the single heading of the *quantum field
theory*. Quantum *field* theory is not *a* theory of elementary particles but many closely related mathematical formulations,
none of which at the present moment can be said to be complete. All of them are attempts to bring into an orderly formulation the ever-increasing number of particles.

Quantum field theory began in 1928 with the efforts of Dirac
who treated Schrödinger's wave equations, much as Einstein
had treated the electromagnetic wave theory of Maxwell. Dirac
set the ψ waves in four-dimensional space-time and wrote the
general relativistic mechanics of the field. In this, Dirac may
be said to have closed the development of the quantum and
wave mechanics, even as he extended it into new regions. The
older quantum mechanics "was restricted to problems in which
the numbers of particles remained constant, and their velocities
were low enough for a nonrelativistic approximation. . . ."
The new quantum field theory had the transmutations between
particles to consider: the decay of mesons into photons, into
electrons, into neutral particles, etc. The Japanese physicist
Umezawa distinguishes physical theories by the scale of the
phenomena to which they apply—nebulas and heavenly bodies,
matter on the laboratory scale, atoms, nuclei, and the elemen-

tary particles. The laws of Newtonian mechanics (and relativistic mechanics) apply to matter on the laboratory scale. The laws of quantum mechanics are valid for atoms and atomic aggregates. The quantum field theory is the attempt to codify the laws of the truly elementary particles, those which have no structure at all.

In 1900, the minor problem of black-body radiation had been resolved by Planck's hypothesis of quanta. Einstein's extension of this to explain the photoelectric effect showed that Planck's tentative hypothesis of a fundamental discontinuity in energy was linked to the basic problem of light, and that the electromagnetic wave theory of light was by no means final. Again in 1907, Einstein showed that the discontinuity in energy was linked to the discontinuity in matter, in extending the quantum theory to calculate the specific heats of solids. Then in 1913 Bohr had shown that from the assumptions of Planck a structure of the atom could be derived which could be related to the highly precise experimental science of spectroscopy. From the Bohr atom grew the two fields of wave and quantum mechanics, the first an exploitation of the wave-particle duality which had appeared in the theory of the photon, the second an attempted return to the Newtonian avoidance of hypothesis. Both were equivalent. Both revealed the probabilistic nature of the quantum theory. Unlike the classical statistics of the kinetic-molecular theory, the quantum statistics were more than a convenience. They were in fact the deepest expression of these phenomena, the particles. Like the hydra of mythology, the electron cannot be trapped to stay and perform for us. If we stop it, it transforms to other, more elusive particles. The mesons become electrons; the neutrons, protons. Our touch is the touch of death in this world of the smaller than small; our senses, refined by all the complex instrumentation of technology are, *in principle* and not simply in practice, too coarse.

These particles are not real particles in the sense that grains of dust or marbles or tennis balls are real particles. These particles are instead constructs, ideas, schemes for the organization in mathematical law of a tangle of experimental complexity. They elude the sight and the touch as any idea must elude the sight and touch. Entropy was such an idea, immaterial, invisible, and intangible and at the same time without appeal to our intuition. The lines of force of Faraday's fields were similarly ideas. The particles of the quantum and the quantum field theory have no more (and no less) reality than entropy, lines of force, or the ratio of the circumference of a wheel to its diameter. Therefore, the assertion of uncertainty in principle is not something which we can hope to overcome with future developments of superior instruments. The uncertainty, the indeterminacy of the wave-quantum mechanics is inherent in the idea. And the idea, unlike a metaphysical idea, is not susceptible to mere redefinition. Idealism offers no escape. These ideas are not the product of mind reacting on mind. They are the product of mind reacting on the world of experience. They are not found in nature; they are instead our attempts at organization of the chaos in nature. The scientist is not the spectator of facts external to himself, the detached observer of a cryptogram set by other hands, the passive photographic plate on which theories of relativity and probability are inscribed. The scientist is the creator of his own order of reality. Out of the idea of the conservation of energy, Pauli proposed the neutrino —a particle without mass, without charge, but with just enough angular momentum to make up for a slight amount missing during the decay of a neutron into a proton and an electron. Such a particle, it was calculated, must go through 50 light years of solid lead on the average before colliding with a nucleus. It was, twenty-five years after its creation, finally detected by a most ingenious experiment, but in the meantime this idea, this difference between energies on a nuclear balance sheet, had entered firmly into the quantum field theory, had led to the theory of mesons, and in innumerable ways displayed its importance in the nuclear scheme of things. In a sense, all particles are in the position of the neutrino before 1956. Dials register, engines turn, thermometers and gauges rise or fall. A bomb explodes or a streak appears on a photographic plate or in a cloud chamber. These are the events of one level of experience. The neutrino, the proton, the electron, etc., are of a different level of reality. The dials, the engines, the bombs, the photographic marks—these are the stuff of observation and the scientist is the observer and recorder of these. The neutrino, entropy, π, the space-time continuum are not simply the stuff of the world. They are in Einstein's words free creations of the human mind. They encompass the observations, growing out of these and in turn predicting new observations, but they are not simply new words for the observations or new groupings of these. It would have been correct to describe Pauli's neutrino in 1931 as simply a name assigned to a difference appearing in an equation and hence, a gap in two readings of a dial. But even neglecting the superstructure of theory erected upon that frail but fertile base, how would such a categorization of the neutrino explain the experiment twenty-five years later using five hundred photomultipliers, ten or twelve tons of scintillator liquid, and a powerful nuclear reactor? The followers of Bohr and Heisenberg, the "Copenhagen School," have dismissed the objections of Planck and Einstein and their followers to an indeterministic physics. These are for them metaphysical questions, with which they can have no concern. For them, the direction of physics is controlled inexorably by the pattern of experimentation. They cannot change this without falsifying their results. What Oppenheimer has called the hope of order recedes further and further from them with every fresh discovery. The world of events, the world of nature is indeterminate. The behavior of the particle is uncertain and therefore the behavior of the atom is an uncertainty. The behavior of the atom can be predicted only to a degree of probability. The behavior of an aggregate of atoms is therefore only a probability, and not a certainty. And it is no use saying that the degree of uncertainty is too small to effect events on the ordinary scale, for the notion of determinism is similarly based on the fundamental determinism of the individual molecules, multiplied many times to become the world of nature. Is the world of events then a chaos, a jungle, devoid of law, devoid of order, with only the simulated order of statistics, the laws of chance, which are not really laws at all? "I cannot believe," Einstein said, "that God plays dice with the world." For Heisenberg, determinism and indeterminism must arise out of a physics, and not the other way around.

20. Science in Mid-Twentieth Century

FOR TWENTY-FIVE YEARS, ALMOST ALL PHYS-
ICISTS HAVE ALIGNED THEMSELVES WITH THE
PURELY PROBABILISTIC INTERPRETATION OF
BOHR AND HEISENBERG. THERE ARE HOWEVER
SEVERAL NOTABLE EXCEPTIONS, SCIENTISTS
AS FAMOUS AS EINSTEIN AND SCHRÖDINGER
WHO HAVE ALWAYS REFUSED TO ACCEPT IT
AND HAVE ATTACKED IT WITH DAMAGING
OBJECTIONS.

DE BROGLIE, 1953

THE THEORY of relativity was determinist and continuist.
From the equations of the field, a complete structure of the
field could be derived. If the field is known here and now, the
equations of the field enable us to know the field an infinitesi-

mal distance away and an infinitesimal time from now. By the summation of these steps, we can determine the whole of the space-time field and recover that certainty which Laplace had claimed for mechanics. If an intelligence was armed with the complete set of equations of the field, the whole of the past, the whole of the future of the particles making up a man or even mankind would be known. As the Newtonian astronomer could predict by the perturbations in the orbit of Uranus that a new planet, Neptune, would be found, as a system of planets with their mutual interactions present a more complex but still perfectly soluble problem, so any system of particles, however large, however complex, is conceivably determined in natural law. Relativity does not deal with particles and their interactions, but rather with the gravitational field. Not the charges and the masses but the field of force that makes up the space between them is the ultimate reality. There are not particles and void, there is only the field, invisible, intangible, immaterial, and universal.

But relativity is not yet a pure field theory. There are still two realities in relativist theory, matter and field. The equations of the field stop abruptly at the surfaces of material particles. Such surfaces form a kind of discontinuity, a kind of hole in the field—a region not governed in its entirety by the same natural laws. The philosophical objections of Boscovich to a Newtonian atom, hard, round, impenetrable, and perpetual had proved to be sound. The atom was not hard, it could be penetrated, it could be split, it could be abraded of its parts as easily as in electrolysis, it could be stripped of its electrons. It was not round; it had parts and the organic chemist could logically claim for certain atoms the shape of a tetrahedron. The atoms were not perpetual; some of them were engaged in a constant spontaneous transmutation, emitting of their own accord helium nuclei, electrons, and energy of other sorts. Boscovich (and Faraday) had thought of the atom as a point center of force, having no dimensions, no shape, no parts, but simply a point focus of an infinite field of force. This was too simple. The field of Faraday did not extend uniformly to a single point representing the center of an atom. Instead, fields such as Fara-

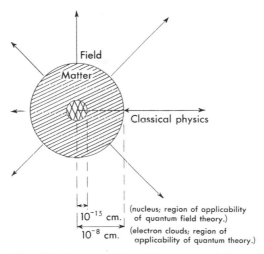

Fig. 53. *Boscovich's point center of force revisited.* The diagram is not to scale. The nucleus is actually only one millionth the size of the atom. The boundaries between the atom and the classical field, and between the zone of the electron clouds and the nucleus are not sharply defined.

day's and their development at the hands of Maxwell, Lorentz, and Einstein stopped at the surface of matter. Beneath that surface lay another world, another science, another mathematics. The boundaries of the universe did not lie beyond the stars but within the smallest grains of matter. Here at the border of the atom was a frontier, an iron curtain of the understanding. Outside this boundary (the surface separating matter from field) the universe is deterministic and natural law prevails. Within the boundary the uncertainty principle governs. Individuality is lost. We cannot distinguish one electron from another. The only order that we can find is the order of the bell curve and the uniformity of statistics in which all individuality is surrendered. There are still laws, but they are the laws of chance. There are still equations, but they are the equations of statistics. It is natural law that prevails but natural law without purpose, without plan, without aim. "Without the belief in the inner harmony of our world," wrote Einstein, "there could be no science." Is this the inner harmony of the dice game? Is the face at the end of the long corridor we have been following since the first cave man fashioned the first tool the face of chaos? Are we now being dispossessed as Adam and Eve were dispossessed from Eden, as the world of the Renaissance was dispossessed from the center of the tidy little egg of space and time in which mankind had so long been nurtured? Are we now being sent from the world of inner harmony on the last step to the world of blind fate? Has the search for order failed?

There are still two universes and two sciences, the universe of field and the universe of matter. The first is described by our traditional science (which must now include relativity); the second by the science of quanta. Although they are now separate sciences, both agree that they represent two aspects of one and the same fundamental universe. There are too many connections between them for mere coincidence. The matter and charge of the one is the origin of the field of the other. Just as Kepler's laws describing the gross universe are applied within the atom to the motion of the electron, so general relativity applied to wave mechanics, yielded a new and productive insight to the world within the atom. The theorists of the quantum field are concerned with the minute universe within the atom. Boscovich's center of force is not a simple point but rather a large and complex array of point centers of force. The points within the atom, the truly fundamental particles without internal structure of any kind, the electrons, neutrons, mesons, etc., are the true "atoms" of Boscovich. Because of their regrettable tendency to transmute one into the other, and their extraordinary fragility, which makes their detection forever uncertain, the task of the quantum field theorists is far more difficult than was Einstein's. But there is the hope that this problem too will prove soluble and a complete description of the quantum fields will be possible. From a few simple and well-verified assumptions, the entire complex structure of the universe within the atom will be deduced. This theory the group beginning with Bohr, Heisenberg, Born, Pauli, and Dirac would assert must ultimately govern the larger universe of traditional science, as the fields of the larger universe must be referred in the last analysis to the matter and charge of the lesser.

Einstein spent the final years of his life in attempting the same synthesis in reverse. His aim was to create a unified field theory, a theory of the total field, in which as in the idea of Boscovich there would be not two realities, matter and the field, but only one, the field. General relativity treats of two kinds of fields, the gravitational and the electromagnetic. Gravitational effects do not, however, enter into quantum fields. They are far too small compared with the enormous electromagnetic forces within the atom. Einstein's unified field theory would treat of but one field. In that field the surface separating matter from nonmatter would be a surface of abrupt change in field values as the interface between oil and water could be taken as a surface along which the value of mass per unit volume changed abruptly. Present theory describes a particle moving in a field. A unified theory would speak of the particle as a region of exceptionally high values of the field. The motion of the particle in the field would become the fluctuation of the field itself, as the region of high value changed its position. With the unified field theory we recover that determinism and continuity from which the arbitrary postulates of the quantum theory had appeared to bar us. The wave-particle duality, enthroned by de Broglie as a first principle, now vanishes. The particle is a region of certain values of the field. The wave is a fluctuation of certain values of the field. Knowing the structure of the field, the whole of the past and future evolution of the field is fixed.

The unified field theory must be so constructed that from its initial assumptions we should be able to recover on the one hand the full mathematics of the general theory of relativity, and on the other hand the equations of the quantum field theory. This is an impressive requirement. It is not to assert the impossible, however. The assumptions of the unified theory need not yield all the empirical formulas of quantum theory, any more than from Newton's law, once found, the system of planets must ensue. But from Newton's law, once found, the relationships governing the motions of those planets in the world could be determined. From Newton's first assumptions applied to the phenomena of Kepler's laws the inverse square law was induced. From the inverse square law in turn the phenomena of Kepler's laws could be derived. The motion of a planet of the size and distance from the sun of Mars could be deduced. But the existence of a planet at this point could not be determined solely by deduction from Newton's inverse square law. If the planet's path is disturbed, the law will enable us to locate the disturbance. And given once only the position and momentum of the planet (including its environment), the law enables us to predict its future path and determine its past history. In the same way, Boyle's law is an empirical law and cannot be deduced solely from the first and second laws of thermodynamics. It is a phenomenological law and once we have it, regardless of how we obtained it, whether by guess, experiment, or vision, the laws of thermodynamics enable us to utilize it to predict the behavior of gases in situations completely removed from those of present experience. Similarly, the unified field theory need not yield the whole of experimental nuclear physics. What we require from it instead is the unified system of natural law into which the chiefly empirical phenomena of nuclear physics must fit. Einstein had several times approached this unified field theory and toward the end of his life he announced that he had found it. But unfortunately, he could not think of a way to test it. The equations exist. "The derivation, from the equations, of conclusions which can be confronted with experience will require painstaking efforts and probably new mathematical methods," he wrote. We have no way of comparing the world of ideas with the world of reality and until this is done the equations remain an exercise in the higher mathematics. Meanwhile, spurred by government subsidy and the uneasy feeling of a race against time, a flood of empirical data accumulates, a flood so vast that in our country alone it has been estimated that the full time efforts of nearly all the people capable of understanding them would be required simply to decide which of these results can safely be made public. Would it be fair to apply Lavoisier's caustic characterization of the work of Priestley as "a web of experiments almost uninterrupted by any kind of reasoning"?

One further attempt to recover determinism has been made along slightly different lines by de Broglie who, starting after his first publication on the wave-particle duality, attempted to cast wave mechanics in a form which would subsume the particle as a mathemetical singularity* in one type of solution of the wave equations.

---

* Somewhat analogous to the hole in the continuous line of the rational numbers occupied by the irrational number π.

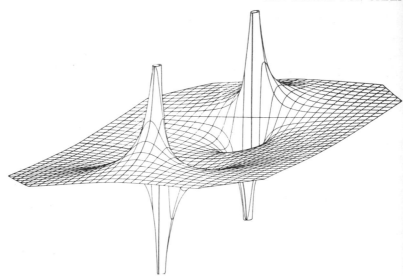

Fig. 54. Singularities of the field.

Both the particle and the wave phenomena associated with it would be described by a real wave with a moving singularity. The ψ wave of Schrödinger would be a nonphysical wave, a mathematical parallel related to the real, the physical wave. The probability of finding the corpuscles at a point would be equal to the square of the amplitude of the ψ wave, but in diffraction experiments it would be the other, the real wave that would diffract. De Broglie's theory would be in essence an electromagnetic field theory within the bounding shell of the atom. It would treat not of several realities—particles and the field—but of one reality, the field in which particles appear as singularities in the equations of waves.

There are definite analogies between de Broglie's work starting from the field of quanta and Einstein's starting from gravitational fields. The two are *philosophically* alike. Both offer the hope of an ultimate resolution of the present duality.

We are left in the position of the men of the Renaissance. Competing views of the organization of reality bid for our attention. Then, Francis Bacon would promise an *experimentum crucis*, a key experiment which would distinguish between the true and the false, such as the experiment which Newton suggested to Hooke to prove the rotation of the earth, or the diffraction experiment for Thomas Young—a proof of the wave as against the corpuscular theory of light. But we can today hope for no crucial experiment which will irrevocably decide between truth and falsehood. The general theory has shown that we may with confidence regard the earth as fixed and the universe as rotating about us. Our physics can be cast into the form appropriate for any frame of reference. The photoelectric effect has shown that diffraction did not prove finally and irrevocably the wave nature of light. We cannot hope that somewhere at this moment an experiment is being performed which will decide for us this Ptolemaic-Copernican dilemma. We must in the last analysis decide on the same basis as Kepler and Galileo chose for, and Tycho Brahe against, Copernicus. The image in our minds of the form of natural law, whether of order of one kind or order of another, is our only basis for choice.

SCIENCE AND TRUTH

Our science is not a collection of laws and facts, however accurate or however confirmed in observation and experience. It is not truth strewn about the fields of reality for us to pick and store in a cabinet of curios for some future museum of Ashmole's. It is not the bookkeeper's paradise of the operationalists. The theories we propound are ways of organizing our experience and we recognize their lack of finality. But if we are not seekers after truth in a metaphysical sense, we are nonetheless concerned with truth. There is a scientific ethic and the scientist who violates it ceases to be a scientist. He cannot falsify his results. The geometry of Lobachevski twists the triangles of Euclid out of shape, but within the geometry of Euclid the angles of a triangle must sum to 180°; within the geometry of Lobachevski, the web of geodesics must swell and shrink to lawful music. Between positivism and realism, between causality and chance, the scientist may find latitude in which to maneuver, but between one reading of a dial and another, between black and white, between explosion and nonexplosion, there is no choice.

Science is after all the use of the creative imagination, but it differs from the arts in one major way. It is self-corrective. All the ideas of science, the good, the bad, the wild and the mild, are sooner or later subject to test. An authoritarian scientist can impose his discipline and his ideas on an entire generation—but there will be another generation and other experiments. Nature lies open to all. The Copernican theory smoldered underground for fifty years before the flames of Bruno's pyre broke out. Cuvier demolished the arguments of Lamarck and St. Hilaire but Darwin and evolution won out nevertheless. This is the meaning of science and this is its purpose—to negate the book-burnings, to destroy the Inquisition, to establish the fundamental dignity of man.

Ours is an age of politics: ". . . those passions termed political owing to which men rise up against other men, the chief of which are racial passions, class passions, and national passions." In the early twenties in Berlin, societies were formed to combat relativity. Some German scientists, notably Lenard and Stark, became Nazis and to the ordinary criteria of physical theory they brought the artificial criteria of race, nation, and political reliability. In 1776 Benjamin Franklin, acting as director of naval affairs, had issued an order to all ships of war under the authority of the rebellious colonies to assist in every possi-

ble way and under no circumstances to interfere with the expedition of H.M.S. *Resolution* under the command of Captain
Cook. By the 1920's, Einstein, who had suffered indignities in
Germany as a Jew, had to be spirited through a mob in Paris
that would tolerate no German. The curious claim of "Soviet"
science was raised, as if an electron can have nationality and
citizenship to be taxed and drafted like any other national asset.
In Russia, scientific questions were put to vote to be decided
"democratically" like any other questions. The decision of the
Russian leadership to press their geneticists to adopt the
Lysenko theory of inheritance of acquired characteristics destroyed Russian science in this field. The biologist Vavilov died
in a prison camp. J. Robert Oppenheimer had successfully led
the research that had placed in the arsenal of the United States
the most powerful weapon in history. The announcement in
Congress that despite the clear assurance of his loyalty he was
to be suspended from further contact with the nuclear research
he had guided for ten years was received by a standing ova-
tion.

We wish to exploit science, to milk it of the plastics and the
hydrogen bombs. Like Gregory setting astronomers to work on
reform of the calendar, we have a clear idea in mind of the
results we wish. But the tools we must employ to satisfy our
material wants are men, and exceptional men. Gregory got his
calendar reform, but his successors inherited the Copernican
theory as well. There is a kind of second-rate thinker who will
guarantee to produce only the results required—who will not
stray like Newton into forbidden paths of Unitarian theology,
whose thoughts have never pushed beyond the limits of orthodoxy. These are the thinkers of a static society. They will never
account for a doctrine of evolution, a theory of relativity, a concept of universal law. They are safe and they are competent,
but they are dull. They form the legion of the slide rule, the

white-coated multitude. Their productivity fills the skies with jets and the home with gadgets. They are the new scholastics, their dogma a jelly of conformity, oozing from the universities and the laboratories, flowing into the societies and the technical journals, drowning out question and answer alike. These men will never give us security. These men are the most dangerous of all. They are the illusion but not the stuff of which civilization is made. It is the free mind, the free thought that determines the future.

In the sixteenth century the Spanish Empire circled the globe. The armored troops of Spain, the gold of the Indies, the fleets of floating castles bristling with cannon, the hardened cutthroats that in Peru alone slaughtered 30 million people, that captured the Aztec Empire, the silks, the gems, the slaves all vanished in a generation, swept away by the power of the free mind in Holland and England. This is the ultimate weapon, this is the intercontinental ballistic missile with hydrogen warhead.

The idea of the power of the mind, of the force of truth, is the most difficult idea of all. We see it demonstrated again and again, but with our hands on the gag in the mouths of our enemies we seldom believe it. The full power, clerical and secular, of the authority of the seventeenth century could not suppress Galileo, and the exercise of that power only served to advertise the pernicious doctrine. The full power of the modern totalitarian state could not establish the inheritance of acquired characteristics.

All this means essentially that science is intimately connected with the values which our society and our world respect. There is a basic contradiction between tyranny and science. The contradiction is in this: that the fruits of science essential to the continuation of any kind of civilization rest on the activities of the free mind, freely thinking, freely creating. The free mind can be destroyed, individually as in the case of Bruno, collectively as in the case of modern Germany, but it thereupon ceases to create. Technology is limited to the exploitation of the science already won. As it presses beyond these limits it treads on the stuff of creativity and merges into science. The men, the societies which embark upon creative thinking pass into regions where the censor and policeman cannot follow. This is the dilemma of the tyrant. If he calls back the march of thought, if he reigns in the free mind with his laws of history, he must renounce all hope of the laws of nature. The paradox is in the relationship of the fruit to the tree. The press, the radio, the weapons, the abundant food, the *technology* are indispensable to the modern state. But behind them and before them, inseparably intertwined with them, is the free mind. The penalty for checking it is not only the loss of freedom, it is the loss of civilization.

SCIENCE AND HISTORY

When Kelvin asserted the supremacy of thermodynamic reasoning over geological observation he was in fact returning to the scholastic method. No reasoning, no logic can take precedence over the mute evidences of the bits of glass and brass, the broken stones, the flick of a needle on a dial, of which experience consists. Kelvin's thermodynamics was corrected in time, but the principle remains. There is a validity to history apart from and independent of physics and chemistry. Even as all history must unfold in nature and to that extent within the framework of natural law, all nature must evolve in the framework of history. These are not separate subjects nor are they one or the other. They are mutually interdependent aspects of our thoughts. Without science thought is trivial. Without history it is lifeless.

The nineteenth-century battle over evolution did more than simply establish the mutual interdependence of science and history although this was one important aspect of Darwinian evolution. It pointed to a profound unity in nature. The particular passions of race, the private hatreds that flared in the United States over the issues of slavery were not by coincidence, in opposition to Darwinism. Nor was it by coincidence that the rigid mechanism of the early nineteenth century rejected in its entirety the evolution of species. The theory of evolution was a historical idea, not a law of nature. Its validity was to be tested by other criteria than those of mechanics. It affirmed the unity of mankind and the subordination of those passions and hatreds of the particular man to the universal man. The Biblical account of Adam and Eve was just such an account of the origins of humanity. Darwinism did not contradict it. It reaffirmed it, and reaffirmed, beyond the unity of mankind, the unity of all living things, of all life. There is a Garden of Eden. It is the universe we inhabit. There is a unity to mankind, to life, to all of nature. It is the inner harmony which Minkowski sought between pure mathematics and physics. It is the reverence for life of which Schweitzer writes, and which he glimpses in the music of Bach.

Suggestions for Further Reading

Chapters 1, 2, and 3

ARMITAGE, ANGUS, *The World of Copernicus*, New York: New American Library, 1951.

DE SANTILLANA, GIORGIO (transl.), Galileo Galilei, *A Dialogue on the Great World Systems*, Chicago: Chicago University Press, 1953, with *Appendix* by William Stahlman.

FRAZER, SIR JAMES G., *The Golden Bough*, abr., New York: Macmillan, 1935.

HOOKE, ROBERT, *Micrographia*, London: Martyn and Allestry, 1665.

KOYRÉ, ALEXANDRE, *From the Closed World to the Infinite Universe*, Baltimore: Johns Hopkins University Press, 1957.

JOWETT, B. (transl.), Plato, *The Republic*, in *The Dialogues of Plato*, 5v., Oxford: Clarendon, 1875.

SARTON, GEORGE, *A History of Science*, Cambridge: Harvard University Press, 1952.

SINGER, CHARLES, *A Short History of Science*, Oxford: Clarendon, 1941.

WHITEHEAD, A. N., *Science and the Modern World*, New York: New American Library, 1945.

——, *The Aims of Education*, New York: New American Library, 1953.

WHITEHEAD, A. N., *An Introduction to Mathematics,* London: Oxford, 1948.

WICKSTEED, H., and CORNFORD, F. M. (transl.), "Zeno," in Aristotle, *Physics VI,* 9, London: Heinemann, 1929–35.

Chapters 4 and 5

CAJORI, F., "The History of Zeno's Arguments on Motion," *American Mathematical Monthly XXII,* 1, 1915.

CREW, H., and DE SALVIO, A. (transl.), "Galileo Galilei," *Dialogues Concerning Two New Sciences,* New York: Macmillan, 1914.

DE SANTILLANA, G. (1953), *op. cit.*

———, *The Crime of Galileo,* Chicago: Chicago University Press, 1955.

DRAKE, STILLMAN (transl.), *Discoveries and Opinions of Galileo,* New York: Doubleday, 1957.

HOLTON, GERALD, *Introduction to Concepts and Theories in Physical Science,* Cambridge: Addison-Wesley, 1953.

KEPLER, JOHANN, *Harmonices Mundi Libri V, 1619,* in *Opera Omnia V* (Ch. Frisch, ed.), Frankofurti a.m.: Heyder and Zimmer, 1864.

MASON, S. F., *Main Currents of Scientific Thought,* New York: Schuman, 1953.

MILLIKAN, R. A., ROLLER, D., and WATSON, C. W., *Mechanics, Molecular Physics, Heat and Sound,* Boston: Ginn, 1937.

PLUTARCHUS, *The Lives of the Noble Grecians and Romans,* DRYDEN, J. (transl.), New York: Modern Library, 1932.

SINGER, CHARLES (1941), *op. cit.*

Chapter 6

AUBREY, JOHN (Powell, A., ed.), *Brief Lives and Other Selected Writings,* New York: Scribner's, 1949.

BALL, W. W. ROUSE, *A Short Account of the History of Mathematics,* London: Macmillan, 1912.

CAJORI, FLORIAN, *A History of Mathematics,* New York: Macmillan, 1919.

D' ABRO, A., *The Evolution of Scientific Thought,* New York: Dover, 1950.

———, *The Rise of the New Physics,* I, New York: Dover, 1951.

DESCARTES, RENÉ (HALDANE, E. S., and Ross, G. R. T., transl.), *Philosophical Works,* New York: Dover, 1955.

EUCLIDES (HEATH, T., transl.), *Elements*, in *Great Books, 11*, Chicago: Encyclopaedia Britannica, 1955.
PIGGOTT, S., *William Stukeley, 1687–1765*, Toronto: Oxford, 1950.

Chapters 7, 8, 9, and 10

AGASSIZ, L., "Professor Agassiz on the Origin of Species," *American Journal of Science*, Ser. 2., *30*, 1860.
ARCHIMEDES, *Works* (TALIAFERRO, R. C., transl.), in *Great Books, 11*, Chicago: Encyclopaedia Britannica, 1955.
BACON, FRANCIS, *The New Atlantis* (1627), in *Great Books, 30*, Chicago: Encyclopaedia Britannica, 1955.
BERINGER, C. C. *Geschichte der Geologie und des Geologisches Weltbildes*, Stuttgart: Ferdinand Enke, 1954.
BURY, J. B., *The Idea of Progress*, London: Macmillan, 1924.
CASSON, STANLEY, *The Discovery of Man*, New York: Harper & Brothers, 1939.
COLLINGWOOD, R. G., *The Idea of History*, New York: Oxford, 1956.
DARWIN, CHARLES, *On the Origin of Species by Means of Natural Selection*, London: John Murray, 1859.
EINSTEIN, A., and INFELD, L., *The Evolution of Physics*, New York: Simon and Schuster, 1954.
'ESPINASSE, M., *Robert Hooke*, Berkeley: Univ. of California Press, 1956.
GEIKIE, A., *The Founders of Geology*, London: Macmillan, 1897.
GRAY, ASA, "Review of Darwin's Theory on the Origin of Species by Means of Natural Selection," *American Journal of Science*, Ser. 2, *29*, 1860.
GUERLAC, H., "Joseph Black and Fixed Air," *Isis*, 48, 2, 152, 1957.
HOLTON, G. (1953), *op. cit.*
HUBERT, RENÉ, "Auguste Comte," *Encyclopedia of the Social Sciences, IV*, 1942.
KEPLER, JOHANN, *Strena seu de nive sexangula*, Frankfurt: 1611.
KOYRÉ, ALEXANDRE, "An Unpublished Letter of Robert Hooke to Isaac Newton," *Isis*, 43, 4, 134, 1952.
LECOMTE DU NOÜY, PIERRE, *Human Destiny*, New York: Longmans, Green, 1947.
LURIE, EDWARD, "Louis Agassiz and the Races of Man," *Isis*, 45, 3, 141, 1954.

LYELL, CHARLES, *Principles of Geology*, 3v. London: Murray, 1830–33.

MASON, S. F. (1953), *op. cit.*

MOORE, RUTH, *The Earth We Live On*, New York: Knopf, 1956.

NASH, L. K., *The Atomic-Molecular Theory*, Cambridge: Harvard Univ. Press, 1950.

NEWTON, I. (1686); MOTTE, A. (transl.), 1729; CAJORI, F. rev., *Philosophiae naturalis principia mathematica*, Berkeley: Univ. of California Press, 1934.

RONGE, GRETE, *Atom und Element vor zweienhalb Jahrtausenden*, Limburg/Lahn: Limburger, 1950.

SARTON, G. (1952), *op. cit.*

SINGER, CHARLES, *et al.*, *A History of Technology, I, II,* and *III,* New York: Oxford, 1954, 1956, 1957.

STENO, NICOLAUS, *De solido intra solidum naturaliter contento dissertationis prodromus*, Florence: 1669.

WINTER, J. G. (transl.), New York: Macmillan, 1916.

STIMSON, D., *Scientists and Amateurs*, New York: Schuman, 1948.

VAN DE KAMP, PETER, "The Nearest Stars," *American Scientist, 42,* 4, 1954.

VAN MELSEN, A. G. (KOREN, H. J., transl.), *From Atomos to Atom*, Pittsburgh: Duquesne Press, 1952.

WALD, GEORGE, "The Origin of Life," *Scientific American, 191,* 2, 4, 1954.

Chapters 11, 12, 13, and 14

COHEN, I. B., "Roemer and the First Determination of the Velocity of Light (1676)," *Isis, 31,* 84, 2, 1940.

————, *Franklin and Newton*, Philadelphia: American Philosophical Society, 1956.

COULOMB, C., Extracts, 1785, in MAGIE, *vide infra*.

DU FAY, C. F. DE C., The Two-Fluid Theory of Electricity, 1734," in MAGIE, *vide infra*.

DUHEM, PIERRE (WIENER, P. P., transl.), *The Aim and Structure of Physical Theory*, Princeton: Princeton Univ. Press, 1954.

EINSTEIN, A., "On the Generalized Theory," *Scientific American, 182,* 4, 1950.

EINSTEIN, A. and INFELD, L. (1954), *op. cit.*

GALVANI, L. G., Extracts in MAGIE, *vide infra*, 1791.
GIBBS, J. W., *The Scientific Papers*, New York: Longmans, Green, 1906.
GILBERT, WILLIAM, *De magnete magneticisque corporibus et de magno magnete tellure physiologia nova*, 1600, in MAGIE, *vide infra*.
GUERLAC, HENRY, *Selected Readings in the History of Science, I, II*. (Ithaca, 1953).
HOLTON, G. (1953), *op. cit.*
HOOKE, ROBERT, *Lampas*, London: Martyn, 1677.
HUYGENS, C., *Treatise on Light* (THOMPSON, S. P., transl.) in *Great Books*, 34, Chicago: Encyclopaedia Britannica, 1955.
KELVIN, WILLIAM THOMSON, LORD, "Dynamical Theory of Heat, 1848–1852," in MAGIE, *vide infra*.
MAGIE, W. F., *A Source Book in Physics*, New York: McGraw-Hill, 1935.
MASON, S. F. (1953), *op. cit.*
NEWTON, I., *Opticks, 1704*, New York: McGraw-Hill, 1931.
OERSTED, J. C., "Experiments on the Effect of a Current of Electricity on the Magnetic Needle," *Annals of Philosophy, XVI*, 1820, in GUERLAC, *op. cit.*
PERRIN, JEAN (HAMMICK, D., transl.), *Atoms*, New York: 1923, in GUERLAC, *op. cit.*
ROWLAND, H. A., "On the Magnetic Effect of Electric Convection," *American Journal of Science*, 3, 15, 1878, in MAGIE, *op. cit.*
VOLTA, A., "The Voltaic Pile, 1800," in MAGIE, *op. cit.*
VOLTAIRE, M. A. DE, *Siècle de Louis XIV, II*, Paris: Flammarion, 1934.
VON MUSSCHENBROEK, P., "The Leyden Jar," correspondence with NOLLET, J. A., in MAGIE, *op. cit.*
WOLF, A., *A History of Science, Technology, and Philosophy in the 18th Century*, New York: Macmillan, 1939.

Chapters 15 and 16

BOLTZMANN, L., "Entropy and Probability, 1877," extracts in MAGIE, *op. cit.*
D'ABRO, A. (1950), *op. cit.*
DUFF, A. W., ed., *Physics*, 8th ed., Philadelphia: Blakiston, 1946.

DUHEM, P. (1954), *op. cit.*

FARADAY, MICHAEL, "The Nature of Matter," *Phil. Mag.*, 24, 1844, extracts in GUERLAC, *op. cit.*

HENRY, JOSEPH, "On the Production of Current and Sparks of Electricity from Magnetism," *American Journal of Science*, 22, 1832, extract in MAGIE, *op. cit.*

HERTZ, H., *Electric Waves* (JONES, D. E., transl. 1900), extracts in GUERLAC, *op. cit.*

KONDO, H., "Michael Faraday," *Scientific American*, 189, 4, 1953.

LEVINSON, H. C., *The Science of Chance*, New York: Rinehart, 1950.

MASON, S. F. (1953), *op. cit.*

MAXWELL, J. C., "Illustrations of the Dynamical Theory of Gases," *Phil. Mag. 4*, 19, 1860. Extracts in MAGIE, *op. cit.*

——————, "A Dynamical Theory of the Electromagnetic Field," *Phil. Trans. 155*, 1865, Extract in Magie, *op. cit.*

ORE, OYSTEIN, *Cardano, the Gambling Scholar*, Princeton: Princeton Univ. Press, 1953.

WILSON, M., "Joseph Henry," *Scientific American*, 191, 1, 1954.

Chapters 17 and 18

BROWN, R., "On the General Existence of Active Molecules in Organic and Inorganic Bodies, 1827," extracts in MAGIE, *op. cit.*, cf. GUERLAC, *op. cit.*

CAJORI, F. (1919), *op. cit.*

D'ABRO, A. (1950), *op. cit.*

DINGLE, H., quoted in "Science and the Citizen," *Scientific American*, 195, 12, 1956, and 196, 3, 1957.

EINSTEIN, A., "I. On the Electrodynamics of Moving Bodies," "II. Does the Inertia of a Body Depend upon Its Energy Content?" *Annalen der Physik*, 17, 1905.

——————, "On the Influence of Gravitation on the Propagation of Light," *Ann. d. Phys. 35*, 1911.

——————, "The Foundation of the General Theory of Relativity," *Ann. d. Phys.*, 49, 1916. PERRET, W., and JEFFREY, G. B. (transl.) in *The Principle of Relativity*, New York: Dover, 1956.

——————, and INFELD, L. (1954), *op. cit.*

FRANK, P., *Einstein, His Life and Times* (ROSEN, G., transl.), New York: Knopf, 1947.

Gosse, E., *Father and Son*, New York: Scribner's, 1907.

Holton, G. (1953), *op. cit.*

Infeld, L., *Albert Einstein*, New York: Scribner's, 1950.

Michelson, A. A., and Morley, E. W., "The Michelson-Morley Experiment," *Phil. Mag.* 5, 1887. Extract in Magie, *op. cit.*

Minkowski, H., "Space and Time," 80th Assembly German scientists, Cologne, 1908, in *The Principle of Relativity, op. cit.*

Poincaré, H., "Principles of Mathematical Physics" (Halstead, G. B., transl.), *The Monist*, 1905; reprinted in *The Scientific Monthly*, 82, 4, 1956.

Reichinstein, D., *Albert Einstein*, London: Edward Goldston, 1934.

Whitehead, A. N. (1945), *op. cit.*

Whittaker, E., "G. F. Fitzgerald," *Scientific American*, 189, 5, 1953.

Chapters 19 and 20

Balmer, J. J., "The Hydrogen Spectral Series," *Annalen der Physik und Chemie*, 25, 1885; in Magie, *op. cit.*

Benda, Julien, *The Betrayal of the Intellectuals* (Read, H., transl.), Boston: Beacon, 1956.

Bohr, Niels, "On the Constitution of Atoms and Molecules," *Philosophical Magazine*, Ser. 6, 26, 151, 1913.

Born, M., Jordan, P., and Heisenberg, W., "On Quantum Mechanics II," *Zeits. f. Physik* 35, 1926.

Bronowski, J., "Science and Human Values," *The Nation*, 183, 26, Dec. 1956.

De Broglie, L., "Quantum Theory," *Ann. de Physique* 3, 22, 1925.

———, *The Revolution in Physics* (transl. Niemeyer, R. W.), New York: Noonday, 1953.

Cottrell, A. H., *Theoretical Structural Metallurgy*, London: Edward Arnold, 1948.

Curie, Eve, *Madame Curie* (transl. Sheean, V.), Garden City, N. Y.: Doubleday, 1938.

Davisson, C., and Germer, L. H., "Diffraction of Electrons by a Crystal of Nickel," *Physical Review*, 30, 1927.

Dirac, P. A. M., "The Fundamental Equations of Quantum Mechanics," *Proc. Roy. Soc.*, 109, (1925).

Einstein, A., "A Heuristic Point of View Regarding the Emission and Conversion of Light," *Annalen der Physik, 17*, 1905.

EINSTEIN, A., "On the Theory of the Emission and Absorption of Light," *Annalen der Physik, 20,* 1906.

———, "Planck's Theory of Radiation and the Theory of Specific Heat," *Annalen der Physik, 22,* 1907.

GEIGER, H., and MARSDEN, E., "On a Diffuse Reflection of the α-Particles," *Proc. Roy. Soc. 82,* 1909.

GOUDSMIT, S., *Alsos,* New York: H. Schuman, 1947.

HEISENBERG, W., "The Quantum Theoretical Interpretation of Kinematic and Mechanical Equations," *Zeits f. Physik 33,* (1925).

———, "Atoms With Hooks and Eyes," *Atlantic, 199,* Mar. 1957.

HUME-ROTHERY, W., *Electrons, Atoms, Metals and Alloys,* New York: Philosophical Library, 1955.

MARGENAU, H., *The Nature of Physical Reality,* New York: McGraw-Hill, 1950.

MORRISON, P., "The Neutrino," *Sci. Am. 194,* 1, Jan. 1956.

PERRIN, J., "Nouvelles Proprietes Des Rayons Cathodiques," *Comptes Rendus, 121,* 1895. Extract in MAGIE, *op. cit.*

PLANCK, M., "On the Law of Distribution of Energy in the Normal Spectrum," *Annalen der Physik, 4,* 1901.

ROENTGEN, W. K., "On a New Kind of Rays," *Sitz. der Wurz. Phys. —Med. Ges.,* Dec. 1895.

RUTHERFORD, E., "The Scattering of α and β Particles by Matter and the Structure of the Atom," *Phil. Mag. XXI,* 1911.

SCHRODINGER, E., "An Undulatory Theory of the Mechanics of Atoms and Molecules," *Phys. Rev. 28,* 1926.

THOMSON, J. J., "Thomson's Discovery of the Electron," 1937, in GUERLAC, *op. cit.*

UMEZAWA, H., *Quantum Field Theory,* New York: Interscience, 1956.

WELLS, A. F., *Structural Inorganic Chemistry,* Oxford: Oxford, 1945.

Index